Introduction to Nuclear Safety

Principles and Applications

Paul F Coley

WHITTLES PUBLISHING

Published by
Whittles Publishing Ltd.,
Dunbeath,
Caithness, KW6 6EG,
Scotland, UK
www.whittlespublishing.com

Printed and bound by CPI Group (UK) Ltd, Croydon, CR0 4YY

To Rebecca, Thomas and Xavier

Contents

Preface

This book is intended to be an introductory and accessible working text for engineering or applied physics/science undergraduates studying the field of nuclear power generation and/or nuclear waste management. It is also written for those working in the industry, particularly recent entrants into the field of nuclear safety or the wider nuclear industry. This is not only restricted to safety assessors but all who interface with the safety case such as engineers and operators.

Within the United Kingdom (UK), each nuclear site licensee has its own way of undertaking nuclear safety, though there are many similarities across them. I have tried to steer a middle-of-the-road approach to the various methodologies used in the industry. Armed with the knowledge presented in this book, an individual should have a good grounding for the application of nuclear safety in the manner required for the industry sector.

For those lucky to be working directly for a nuclear site licensee or a good well-equipped consultancy, there are structured training programmes. However, for the wider consulting industry, it is sometimes a matter of pot luck as to the quality of training. Some of it will be formal, but much of the training is 'on-the-job' with little structured training in the basics. Therefore, any learning is within the context of project delivery timescales and costs. This is not an ideal start for a career in the industry. In my view, it may also lead to an inferior project delivery if those tasked with producing safety documentation do not fully understand the wider picture.

The idea for the book emerged after many years in a contracting career. I recognised that there is little accessible and relevant 'off-the-shelf' introductory text in the libraries and academic bookshops. There are industry guidance documents for specific aspects, but nothing consolidated and available for the general industry working population. I therefore wrote this book to provide a consolidated introduction to the subject, being keen to impart knowledge and experience in the written form. The intent was to write the sort of book I would have found useful at the start of my career where there were a large number of unknown unknowns. I have, therefore, tried to provide a sufficient level of detail to enable readers to gain a good understanding by reading the book cover to cover in a reasonably short period of time.

This book will encompass many different subjects in the overall field of nuclear safety. There are many areas where much detail has been omitted and pointers to more detailed texts are given for the interested reader. One exception to this omission is with respect to radioactivity and basic nuclear physics. It is the basis of the entire discipline, and a nuclear safety assessor should have a good understanding of these aspects.

Safety case assessment and writing is occasionally seen as a 'black art' and 'difficult'. The truth is that nuclear safety is often quite easy, as it just requires logical thinking and thinking things through. In my experience, it is the engineers who do the clever stuff and have to provide the worked-out detail. The engineers generally do the hard sums to deliver what the safety assessors have asked for from their safety analysis.

This book assumes only a relatively basic level of physics, engineering and mathematics, though there are a small number of equations with differentiation ($\frac{dx}{dt}$) and integration ($\int$). It is rare that safety assessors require detailed mathematics to produce safety case documents, and the differentiation and integration are shown to give a proper mathematical framework for the physics. There are plenty of text books on the market (or even online sources) to explain differentiation and integration. A working knowledge of spreadsheets and the manipulation of data are useful skills for safety assessors to have.

Most of the material in this book is taken from experience gained in the industry. There are a number of essential go-to references that every safety assessor should be familiar with. One of the principal documents in the UK is the Office for Nuclear Regulation (ONR)'s Safety Assessment Principles (SAPs) [1]. Indeed, safety assessors should each have a battered copy of this document on their desk for easy reference. There are also Technical Assessment Guides (TAGs) and documents associated with risk such as the Tolerability of Risk (TOR) [2] and Reducing Risks, Protecting People (R2P2) [3], and these should be consulted.

This book focuses on the *principles* and *applications* of nuclear safety. In providing a sub-title of 'principles and applications', the intent is that this book will guide the reader through the 'why' and the 'how' of constructing a nuclear safety case. It is intended that this is not just a theoretical text that is removed from the real world. Where practicable, examples are provided on how safety cases may tackle a particular problem. The examples are as real world as possible within the constraints imposed by the fact that much of the material within actual UK safety cases is restricted on security and commercial grounds.

This book describes why we do nuclear safety, including the legal, financial and moral reasons. The concept of reducing risks to as *low as reasonably practicable* (ALARP) is fundamental in the nuclear industry and this is discussed. The safety case life-cycle is described, i.e. from design to commissioning to operations and decommissioning. Typical safety case methodologies are also discussed, including *design basis analysis* (DBA) and *probabilistic safety analysis* (PSA). In considering the applications of nuclear safety, I provide outline examples of how to do an assessment.

It must be remembered that the work undertaken in producing a safety case is not solely a theoretical exercise. The safety case must be implemented and adopted for use within the plant. Therefore, this book will describe how safety case documents can be utilised within the plant, e.g. via the inclusion within working instructions and clearance certificates. Fundamentally, in this book we seek to answer the following three questions:

1. Why write a safety case?

2. How do you write a safety case?

3. What do we do with a safety case?

The first part of this book provides an overview of safety cases, the different types of safety cases and an introduction to the regulator environment within the UK. The second part of the book provides an introduction to radiation physics and the processes used within safety cases to calculate radiation dose. More detailed understanding of nuclear physics can be gained from reading undergraduate texts such as Lilley [4] and Krane [5]. The third part delves into the detailed mechanics of safety case production.

The examples used in this book are based upon the fuel cycle associated with nuclear fission. Nuclear fusion for power generation is always 50 years away from delivery. However, we note that contrary to popular opinion, the application of nuclear fusion does generate some nuclear waste. Another application of nuclear fission is the ability to generate nuclear medicines. The principles of nuclear safety are the same for any nuclear application, and this book is also applicable.

I am indebted to colleagues who have proofread this book and who have offered helpful comments. Any errors or omissions are solely mine.

This book would not have been written without loving support from Rebecca, Thomas and Xavier, Mum and Dad, and Mark. I am grateful to them all.

Dr PF Coley
Hale, England
December 16, 2023

Part I

SAFETY CASE OVERVIEW

Chapter 1

Introduction

The nuclear industry is now a mature industry that has developed over the last 120 years or so. When X-rays and radioactivity were discovered at the end of the 19th century, a whole new branch of science was initiated that straddled the border between chemistry and physics. At the time, the scientists had no idea of what their early discoveries would eventually lead to. However, the power of the newly discovered X-rays soon proved their worth in the world of medicine as it was possible to image bone within the body.

The first phase of the nuclear industry involved the initial development of the science. Amongst other aspects, the different types of radioactivity were discovered, the laws of radioactive decay were formulated and the nucleus was split, i.e. artificial nuclear fission. These physical terms and many more are all relevant to nuclear safety and are described in this book. Nuclear fission is the realisation of the ancient alchemists' dream of transmuting one element into another. Rutherford's 1919 transmutation experiments at Manchester University were a long way from turning lead into gold. The experiments 'only' involved the transmutation of interacting nitrogen and helium nuclei (alpha particles) into oxygen and protons (hydrogen nuclei).

The fission of uranium was discovered by Hahn and Strassmann in 1938 with a theoretical framework developed by Meitner and Frisch in 1939. Scientists came to realise that the nuclear fission process could unleash useful stored energy in the nucleus. In particular, uranium and plutonium could support self-sustaining chain reactions, leading to a rapid release of energy. If uncontrolled this release could be used within a bomb, but if controlled this release could become a steady source of power generation.

The Second World War gave rise to the secret, urgent and complex race to develop the atomic bomb utilising nuclear fission: the Manhattan Project in the United States (US). This resulted in the use of the nuclear fission bomb over the cities of Hiroshima and Nagasaki, which rapidly brought an end to the war. With the existence of the nuclear bomb now in the open and with a leak of secrets by defectors in the Manhattan Project, the Russians soon developed their own atomic bomb after the war. The British developed theirs, as too did the French and others. With the proliferation of fission bombs, the US was then the first to develop the hydrogen or fusion bomb. A fusion bomb involves the use of a nuclear fission bomb to generate sufficient energy for nuclear fusion in isotopes of hydrogen to occur. In the sense that a fission bomb was a step change in destructive power from a conventional bomb, so too was a fusion bomb a step change from a fission bomb. Explosive yields were now being measured in tens of megatons[1] for fusion bombs against tens of kilotons for fission bombs, a factor of 1000 increase in destructive power. Again, the Russians and other countries quickly followed with their own fusion bombs.

Due to the urgency of the Second World War and then the Cold War, a significant step was the generation of plutonium for the nuclear fission bombs. Although isotopes of both uranium and plutonium undergo fission, plutonium is preferable for atomic bombs due to its smaller critical mass. Uranium can be mined as it is a naturally occurring material, though the isotope of principal interest for nuclear fission is ^{235}U, and this only comprises 0.7% of the uranium naturally found. For a nuclear bomb the uranium must be enriched with enhanced levels of ^{235}U to levels of 90% or so, which compares to ^{235}U enrichment for power reactors of up to 5%. By contrast, plutonium does not occur in nature and it must be bred in a nuclear fission reactor. Thus, early reactors were principally plutonium generators; uranium was put in and plutonium was produced and could be extracted chemically from the 'burnt'[2] fuel. In the UK, Windscale Piles 1 and 2 were used to generate plutonium; the notorious fire took place here in 1957.

At the time of the bomb development, many of the best scientists and engineers that could be found were deployed in the nuclear industry. At the time there was an increased awareness of the hazards posed by nuclear material. However, due care for the future disposal of waste was not always thought through. Waste material was simply dumped in shafts or silos or even the sea—a problem to be resolved at another time 'out of sight out of mind'. Consequently, much of the legacy nuclear material to be found in places such as Sellafield in the UK resulted from this development of the nuclear bomb, with the legacy waste from civil power generation just a fraction of all the waste. The early mind-set was that the plutonium had to be generated, almost irrespective of the future cost—the bomb was the drive. Fortunately, the subsequent decades saw an increasing awareness of and focus on the environment and health and safety.

From the late 1950s and 1960s, the commercial aspects of nuclear power were put in the fore with the ability to generate 'clean' and almost limitless energy without the need for fossil fuels. It was very much seen as the fuel of the future. Calder Hall opened at Sellafield in 1956 and was the first commercial power station, supplying energy to the national grid network until 2003. Many aspects of the nuclear industry were pioneered in the UK and nuclear power spread around the world. Of course, throughout this time, nuclear weapons were still stockpiled by the superpowers and others requiring the continued production of plutonium.

---

[1] Nuclear bomb explosive yield is measured in terms of equivalent tonnes of trinitrotoluene (TNT).

[2] In the nuclear industry we refer to the 'burn' of fuel, i.e. the amount of fission of ^{235}U. In no way do we mean the oxidisation of fuel such as occurs with petrol in an engine or wood on a fire.

Over its history the nuclear industry has had its ups and downs. Ups must be the relatively clean generation of power without the input of carbon dioxide into the atmosphere. The downs will include the nuclear accidents of which Chernobyl is the most significant. There have been other nuclear accidents for which much learning has been gained. These include the aforementioned Windscale fire, Three Mile Island and, Fukushima Daiichi and others.

1.1 Purpose of this book

The principles and applications of nuclear safety have developed over the nuclear industry's lifetime. At the very start of the industry, the hazards associated with nuclear material were unknown. Well-known pioneers of nuclear science, such as Madame Curie, succumbed to the effects of nuclear material. Over time, the hazards posed by the nuclear material were understood. The industrialisation of nuclear bomb and power generation led to the evolution of nuclear safety and its incorporation into the mainstream of the industry.

There are national regulators and international bodies solely concerned with the development of nuclear safety standards and ensuring that best practice is used around the world. Between them, these bodies provide much detailed guidance to nuclear safety assessors. There is deliberately no intent to reproduce all of this guidance verbatim in this book, as this can be read at leisure as required.

This book is intended to provide a simple introduction to the principles and applications of nuclear safety. The book also provides a number of worked examples to show how the concepts and principles may be applied in real-life nuclear situations, and the worked examples are provided in highlighted boxes. It is hoped that having read the book, the reader will be sufficiently informed to understand the full life-cycle of nuclear safety cases and how they may be constructed. In addition to the worked examples, a small number of *learning from experience* (LFE) anecdotes are given in highlighted boxes. These are intended to reinforce key messages.

The principles and applications of nuclear safety apply equally in any part of the world. The regulations and standards applied may, however, be specific to individual countries. The focus of this book is within the UK environment. In the UK, the requirement to produce a *nuclear safety case* rather than to just consider nuclear safety stems from UK legislation. A significant part of a UK nuclear safety case relates to hazard analysis, which involves the quantification of consequences and risks, and this book explains this quantification.

Overall, this book will introduce the reader to a range of topics including:

- The UK regulatory regime;

- Safety case composition and life-cycle;

- Radioactivity, detection, effects of it on the body and the calculation of radiological dose and risk;

- The assessment of radiological hazards including fault identification and the development of fault sequences;

- The designation of safety measures, the provision of defence-in-depth and engineering substantiation;

- Human factors;

- The implementation of safety cases;

- The reduction of risks to ALARP via the incorporation of safety-related improvements.

1.2   Common terms in a nuclear context

Nuclear safety is full of industry terms and three-letter acronyms (TRAs), and many of these will be introduced and described in this book. Within this book where important terms in common nuclear safety use are introduced, they will be *emphasised*.

The term *nuclear safety* is interchangeable with the term *radiological safety*. Confusingly, sometimes the term *nuclear safety* is considered to comprise *radiological* and *criticality* safety. The former is concerned with the releases of radioactivity or exposure to external radiation, whilst the latter refers to an uncontrolled nuclear fission *chain reaction* (which will also give rise to external radiation exposure).

If nuclear safety cases are anything, they are an assessment of the nuclear hazards and the likelihood of them manifesting themselves with their doses[3]—the risk. Within a nuclear safety case, there are references to a small number of fundamental terms that are common to any hazardous activity including those in a non-nuclear arena. Therefore, we will briefly describe these terms and place them into the context of a nuclear environment before discussing anything else. The relevant terms are:

1. Hazard;

2. Fault and accident;

3. Frequency;

4. Risk.

1.2.1   Hazards

We can define a *hazard* as the intrinsic property of something that has the potential to do *harm*, where harm is something bad that happens. The 'something' may be a piece of machinery; it may be a plant as a whole or a process within it. It may also be the physical or chemical property of something, be it a radioactive solid, liquid or gas. Some examples of hazards and harm are given in Table 1.1, which includes examples from everyday life.

---

[3]We will interchangeably refer to the terms *radiological consequence* or *dose* and mean these to be the same thing, but to be strict, we should say that the consequence of a nuclear accident is a radiological dose.

Table 1.1: Example hazards and harm with the type of hazard listed in *italics*.

Hazard	Harm
Cleaning windows at *height* on ladders	Falling leading to injury or fatality
Crossing the road with *moving traffic*	Collision leading to injury or fatality
Working in *confined spaces* such as underground tunnels or sewers	Asphyxiation or drowning leading to injury or fatality
Handling *radioactive materials*	Cancer leading to illness or fatality
Steam generator and distribution pipework	Burns leading to injury or fatality
Factory equipment with *rotating machinery*	Entanglement or crushing leading to injury or fatality
Maintaining *electrical* equipment	Electrocution leading to injury or fatality
Handling *chemicals* in a laboratory	Chronic exposure leading to illness or burns or poisoning leading to injury or fatality

We can see from Table 1.1 that we have defined harm as an injury, fatality or an illness for which we may expect injury and fatality to manifest themselves immediately or in a short period of time. Illness may not manifest itself for a long period of time, and this may eventually also give rise to fatality. The obvious example of an illness occurring is cancer that can be caused by radioactive exposure (or, e.g. from asbestos). It is well known that cancer tends to occur later in life and even with medical intervention it is often fatal. The cancer may arise many decades after the exposure to the radioactivity or radiation, i.e. the harming event.

It is important to note that there is no inference of the likelihood of the harm being realised in our examples. Only hazards that are *credible* or *realistic* from the activity should be considered in an assessment. We will examine what this means in the worked example below.

Finally, we can also think about how aspects of a plant might pose a hazard to other aspects of the plant. For instance, a crane will have a load at height, and by virtue of its height, it may pose a hazard to the primary containment of radioactive material below it. A fault in the crane may enable the load to be dropped and the harm realised.

> *Example: Credibility of Hazards*
> A domestic window cleaner has the obvious hazard of working at height. For most window-cleaning jobs, this may be the only hazard. A confined space hazard is not realistic or credible as no matter what happens the window cleaner will not be in an enclosed volume with the potential for a reduced oxygen environment.
>
> In contrast, a worker in a sewer may be in a confined space with the associated hazards, which will include the potential for a reduced oxygen content, drowning and exposure to toxic substances. In addition, there could be a working at height hazard whilst descending into the sewer or through unrevealed differences in level underground. These are all credible and realistic hazards.

For our purposes in producing nuclear safety cases, our definition of harm is generally that of a *premature fatality* normally due to cancer. For lower levels of exposure, this is found to be a *stochastic*[4] *hazard* in that there is a linear relationship between radiological dose and the chance of premature fatality occurring through cancer later in life. There are no immediate injuries from lower levels of exposure.

For larger exposures, direct injuries can occur, and this is known as a *deterministic hazard*. There will still be a risk of cancer later in life (if fatality does not occur in the short term), but there may be immediate burns to the body and damage to the body's organs, potentially leading to fatality in a time period of a few days or weeks. Hair loss, bleeding gums and sickness are well-known examples of short-term effects from exposure to high levels of radiation.

Nuclear safety cases are primarily concerned with the harm posed by radioactive materials. We note that nuclear safety cases also generally provide confidence that the other *conventional* or *industrial* safety hazards are adequately managed, but we do not go into detailed assessment of these unless they also pose a radiological hazard. Conventional or industrial hazards are interchangeable terms and relate to the hazards that may be found in any non-nuclear industrial plant.

A release of radioactive material might also do damage to the environment, but assessment of environmental damage is not a requirement of a nuclear safety case. There is alternative legislation covering environmental hazards. Within the UK there is a requirement that *best practicable means* (BPM) (in Scotland and Northern Ireland) and *best available techniques* (BAT) (in England and Wales) are used to minimise releases to the environment and waste disposals. The assessment of environmental hazards and BPM/BAT are beyond the scope of this book.

1.2.2   Fault and accident

A *fault* is an event that occurs that should not occur during *normal operations*. Normal operations of a plant refer to the operating conditions that are in line with how

---

[4]Stochastic means random, i.e. we cannot state with certainty when a cancer will occur or even that it will definitely occur, but we can predict the likelihood of it occurring as a function of exposure to radioactivity, and this is based upon statistical studies. There is assumed to be no lower threshold below which there is no chance of cancer occurring. If cancer does arise, its severity is not dependent upon the dose received.

Table 1.2: Recap of hazard, fault and accident.

Term	Definition	Example
Hazard	The intrinsic property of something that can do harm	Radioactivity
Fault	Something going wrong or a deviation from normal conditions that can give rise to the realisation of the hazard	Overfilling a tank due to control system failure leading to a release of hazardous material
Accident	The fault progressing to the point of release and dose	Ventilation system failure enabling aerosol from spilt tank liquor to migrate to the operating area

it was designed to operate. The normal operations should prevent or, at minimum, *mitigate* (minimise) routine exposure to the hazardous item or process within it. It is normally not practicable for a nuclear plant to entirely eliminate **all** exposure to radioactivity during normal operations, nor is it necessary—it is possible to reduce it to levels commensurate with natural sources.

The fault in a plant may be due to the breaking of a mechanical piece of equipment, or it may be due to an operator or computer error in a control system. The fault may progress with other failures occurring to give rise to a radiological consequence, i.e. the realising of a harming event. Strictly, this *fault progression* to a harming event where there has been exposure to radioactivity may be described as an *accident*.

Within the realm of safety cases, we will come across the terms *hazard*, *fault* and *accident*, and they may often be used interchangeably with little thought. In particular, it is not unknown for the terms *hazard* and *fault* to be used interchangeably, but there are differences and these may be subtle. Table 1.2 provides a recap of the strict definitions of our terms. Table 1.3 provides a small selection of faults leading to the realisation of harm.

1.2.3   Frequency

Frequency is the rate at which the event that causes harm occurs. Frequency is normally measured in units of per year (y^{-1}) (equipment failures are sometimes given in units of per hour (h^{-1}) or per second (s^{-1})). Through our hazard analysis we may conclude that a loss of cooling event gives rise to a release of radioactive material and a particular dose occurs at a frequency of 10^{-8} y^{-1}. In this example this is a very low frequency of receiving this dose.

Table 1.3: Example faults and realised harm.

Fault	Realised harm
Rung on a ladder breaking	Climber falling from height
Failure to isolate an electrical cabinet	Electrocution during maintenance
Over-raising a crane lift and 'double blocking'	Dropped load, container damage and release of radioactive material
Control valve on a discharge line erroneously opening	Discharge of radioactive material
Operator dropping a bottle	Bottle breaking and release of radioactive material
Operator selecting the wrong shield door for opening	Exposure to external radiation from containers inside

To give some context of what such a frequency means, we could *turn the frequency over*. Therefore, we could say that if a plant were to run for 10^8 years and with all things being the same, we might reasonably expect about one such event to occur. Of course, running the plant for this length of time is not really a realistic proposition (100 million years), but it can give a useful insight. On the other hand, a fault that has a frequency of 10^{-1}–10^{-2} y^{-1} has a reasonable chance of occurring in a plant lifetime (assuming it runs for a typical 30–40 years).

Faults or incidents, in reality, may occur at random times and will obey statistics. It is perfectly possible, but probably very unlikely, for a 10^{-8} y^{-1} fault to occur on consecutive years. Statistics allows for this. Truthfully, however, if two such events do occur, it probably means that we have got our analysis and frequency calculation wrong and there are factors that we have not adequately taken into consideration. In particular, the faults are unlikely to be truly random and there is likely to have been an underlying reason for their occurrence. Moreover, the lessons learnt as to why the first event occurred may not have been adequately processed with changes to prevent the event from occurring again.

We must also resist the temptation to actually believe such low numbers and *take them at their literal face value* even though there may be defined quantified targets to compare these frequencies against. Frequencies of such low magnitude are far beyond human experience. What such low numbers really should be taken to mean is that the particular event is very unlikely to occur.

There is a nuance to the term *frequency*, which is mentioned now but described in more detail in Section 8. The *initiating event frequency* (IEF) is the initial failure in a fault sequence and is often quite high ($10^{-1} - 10^{-2}$ y^{-1}). This should contrast to the *top event frequency* that takes into account all of the failures that must occur for a fault to progress to an accident. The top event frequency can be very low, as it takes into account coincident failures of the *safety measures*.

In some nuclear operations, the workers or the public may be continually exposed to the harmful item, though at low levels. This would be the exposure that occurs during normal plant operations and may be due to the background radiation levels or small day-to-day discharges of activity to the sea or atmosphere. Therefore, for normal operations, a frequency associated with the harm is taken to be annual.

1.2.4 Risk

Risk is simply the product of harm and frequency, i.e. the harm multiplied by the rate at which it occurs. For safety cases we have defined the harm as premature fatality, and there is a relationship between the chance of premature fatality and the size of the radiological dose. Mathematically, risk is written as

$$\text{Risk} = \text{premature fatality} \times \text{frequency}, \tag{1.1}$$

where frequency is the rate that the particular dose that can cause the premature fatality occurs. As an example, we might say in a safety case that the risk of a premature fatality to an individual from a loss of cooling accident and exposure to radioactivity is 10^{-9} y^{-1}.[5] Equation 1.1 may be used for accidents and even where the exposure is continuous due to normal operations. For normal operations there will be an annual dose that occurs with a frequency of 1 y^{-1}.

It is rare that there can be only one type of fault within a plant. Therefore, an individual may be at risk from a whole range of different faults that may have a total number of N. The individual's total risk is the sum of all the individual risks i that may affect them, i.e.

$$\text{Total risk} = \sum_{i=1}^{N} \text{risk}_i. \tag{1.2}$$

Equation 1.2 is used to demonstrate that the risk from nuclear activities compares favourably with the risks involved in everyday life. Nuclear plants would not be allowed to operate if there was near certainty that operations would lead to fatality.

We can never eliminate all risk, and we accept a level of risk in everyday life. Nuclear facilities will pose a risk to the workforce and the public due to their radiation hazards (and other aspects of an industrial site). We, as a society, tolerate this risk due to the benefit that nuclear power brings. Provided that this risk is perceived to be *tolerable*, we accept the level of risk. If the risk were to be higher, we might say that the risk is *unacceptable*. In contrast, we might feel more comfortable if we knew that

---

[5]Compare this value to the average annual risk of death from lightning in the UK, which is 1 in 18,700,000 or 5.3×10^{-8} y^{-1} [3].

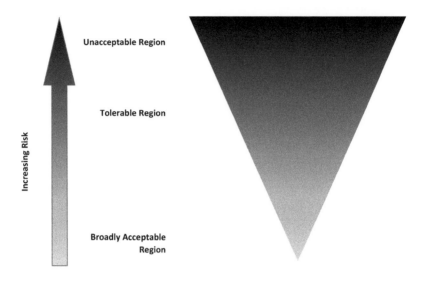

Figure 1.1: Schematic showing the tolerability of risk triangle. Adapted from [3].

the risk was much lower than just tolerable and it might be considered to be *broadly acceptable*. This is represented in Fig. 1.1, which is sometimes known as the *tolerability of risk triangle*. Nuclear plants should aim to pose a broadly acceptable risk, but sometimes their risk is only tolerable and improvements must be made to reduce the risk level. Occasionally, they pose an unacceptable risk and it may be necessary to suspend operations or make urgent improvements.

1.3 The what, why and how

So, what is a nuclear safety case and why do we write them? Why indeed does a safety case need a book such as this to set out the principles and applications of nuclear safety cases? How do we write a nuclear safety case,[6] and what do we do with it once it is written? This section will briefly answer these questions before the remainder of the book expands upon the topics.

---

[6] From this point, we will drop the term *nuclear* and solely refer to safety case.

1.3.1 What is a safety case?

In the first instance, a safety case is a set of analysis, logical argument and evidence that is presented to demonstrate how a plant, facility or process[7] operates as required and that the imposed hazards and faults from the operations give rise to a tolerable and ALARP level of risk to the public and the workers.

Generally, the safety case is comprised of one or more written documents that may be of a few pages in length to many thousands of pages. The length is determined by the number, type and severity of the hazards and the complexity of the plant or process. There will be a hierarchy of documents within the safety case, and this may include a top-tier safety report to summarise the safety *claims, arguments and evidence* (CAE) at a defined point in time. Underneath this report will be increasingly detailed technical documents and supporting analysis.

A safety case is not a static entity; rather it is a living document that has a life-cycle that will reflect the design and the operational stages of a plant. The safety case will be born when the design for a plant is first mooted, and it will grow as the design develops. The key broad stages of the safety case life-cycle include:

- Concept design stage;

- Preliminary design stage;

- Detailed design stage;

- Construction and commissioning;

- Operation;

- Decommissioning.

1.3.2 Why do you write a safety case?

With the life-cycle list presented above, it should be clear that safety cases will inevitably require a commitment of time and money that will be diverted from a company's profits. So why are safety cases written? We can simply state the following three reasons that will subsequently be expanded upon:

1. Legal;

2. Moral;

3. Financial/reputation.

---

[7]For the purposes of this book, we will define a *plant* as a building in which there is equipment and nuclear material. A plant is interchangeable with the term *facility*, but the latter may also refer to the whole nuclear site or refer to individual processing areas or storage areas not within a building, such as waste tips, storage rafts, and underground vaults. We will generically use the term *plant*.

Within all plants will be *process* operations associated with the nuclear material. The processes may involve many types of operations such as mechanical handling, laboratory work, storage and physical and chemical reactions.

Within the UK, it is a legal requirement for operators of nuclear sites to produce safety cases and this is the rationale for much of the form and content of the safety case. Over and above this legal reason, it is recognised by the operators of nuclear plants that there are moral reasons to write a safety case or at least to provide an adequate assessment of the hazards posed by the nuclear plant so that the potential for harm can be minimised.

We no longer live in the Dickensian (or pre-Dickensian) era where life was cheap for owners of factories with little concern over the hazards imposed on workers, the public or the environment. In the 2020s and beyond, the welfare of the workforce, the public and environment should take priority over all other aspects. There are self-proclaimed public commitments to *zero harm* and so on, and plant owners and managers want the workforce to go home at night in the same condition that they arrived. Managers of the plants take personal responsibility for the safety of their workforce, the public and the environment.

Finally, there are financial and reputational reasons for writing a safety case. An accident will cost money. This will be a direct cost because there may be compensation to be made to the victim(s). There will also be costs to clean-up and repair damaged equipment and remove contaminated material, leading to a non-operational plant that does not generate revenue. It is also highly likely that the owner will be prosecuted with the threat of significant fines and even personal criminal charges of corporate manslaughter. A poor reputation for safety can have a detrimental effect on investment, returns and the share price.

Despite best intentions and commitments, things do not always go to plan and accidents will still happen. Only human arrogance could state that an accident could never occur again in the future. However, by learning from the accidents that have occurred before, as well as learning from good practice where accidents have not happened, we can hope to reduce the nuclear risk going forwards as far as reasonably practicable. By ensuring that nuclear safety is given sufficient prominence in the design, operation, maintenance and then decommissioning of nuclear plants, the potential for an accident (or at minimum its severity) can be reduced.

1.3.3   How do you write a safety case?

We have discussed that safety cases are required to be produced to justify the operation of a nuclear plant. All safety cases, no matter what their size or complexity, follow the same broad major steps in their production, which are shown below. The steps are sequential and are largely start/finish.

This book will examine the steps in some detail to give an overview of the safety case process. For now, we will briefly describe what the steps involve to place the safety timeline into context. We also note that there are a range of different types of safety cases that can be produced, depending on what is required to be undertaken.

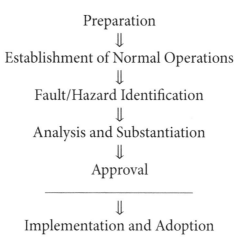

Preparation
⇓
Establishment of Normal Operations
⇓
Fault/Hazard Identification
⇓
Analysis and Substantiation
⇓
Approval

⇓
Implementation and Adoption

An interesting question, perhaps of semantics, is to ask whether we write a safety case or produce a safety case. Let's consider this: it is true that a safety case will consist of an overarching document and this will obviously be required to be written. There will also be supporting documents that will also be written—clearly a lot of documents and a lot of writing, which lends itself to the view that a safety case is written. However, this could be a somewhat simplistic view. To write a safety case may give the impression of a detached process with the author working away at a desk somewhere producing a piece of literature, probably at the back end of a project when all of the other work is done.

If we produce a safety case, we are making a product and we have to start at the beginning to make a product. The making of a product implies a more inclusive approach by working within a team, notably a team including engineers and operators. The safety assessors will have used their knowledge iteratively to influence how the plant and process operates. There will still be written documents in this product, but the best final output will be a plant and process that is safe, but also operable, maintainable and flexible as needs may require. In conclusion and in my view, whilst we may write documents, we do not write a safety case we produce a safety case.

Preparation

A site licensee may determine that a new safety case is necessary because a change to what currently happens at the site is required. Examples include:

- A brand new plant is to be built, e.g. a waste handling plant, a storage plant or even a new nuclear power station;

- An operational or physical modification to an existing plant is required, such as receiving a new stream of waste, changing from operations to care and maintenance and installing a new piece of process equipment;

- A plant is to be decommissioned, e.g. knocked down and the land returned to brown field status.

Moreover, the site may undertake a review of an existing safety case and determine that the extant safety case is determined to no longer be fit-for-purpose going forward. These reviews are undertaken every 10 years or so.

No matter what the reason for the new safety case, a period of preparation will always be required. This time may be spent to assemble a project team, obtain funding, gather relevant information, engage with stakeholders and so on.

Establishment of normal operations

The design of the plant and the manner of its correct operation will define the normal operations. It is essential that the normal operations are understood and clarified, as this will provide a baseline for the subsequent fault analysis. The hazards associated with the plant will be determined by the normal operations (such as the use of certain hazardous gases, use of heat sources or lifting equipment).

Fault/hazard identification

One of the first steps in the production of a safety case is the determination of the potential hazards and faults associated with the design and mode of operation. In Section 3 we will discuss the different types of safety cases that are produced.

Section 7.1 will describe some of the hazard and fault identification techniques used in the industry in more detail, but for the purposes here we state that a structured exercise will be undertaken to determine the nature of the hazards and faults that are applicable to the plant and process. One well established technique for doing this is the *hazard and operability* (HAZOP) study. The output of this and all fault/hazard processes will be a consolidated list of the hazards and faults relevant to the plant and process that will be assessed.

Analysis and substantiation

The hazards and faults will be required to be analysed to determine the risk proposed by the plant/process. This will be for normal operations and fault conditions. The manner of analysing the faults will be prescribed by the site licensee. Essentially, the analysis will determine the level of radiological dose that can be accrued, the risk that this poses and the safeguards or safety measures that must be in place to prevent those risks from being materialised. The risks will be required to be shown to be tolerable and ALARP.

Evidence will then be required to be obtained to demonstrate that the identified safety measures that are claimed in reducing the risks will do what is asked of them, i.e. that the *safety functional claims* in them are *substantiated*. It may be necessary to make changes to the plant to ensure that the risk is tolerable and ALARP. The substantiation will be of the engineering aspects and on the claims on human performance. The safety case will identify the appropriate limits and conditions to ensure safety, i.e. the *safe operating envelope* (SOE). It will be determined that the overall risk is ALARP and that there are no further reasonably practicable improvements to be made. A schematic of the overall process is shown in Fig. 1.2.

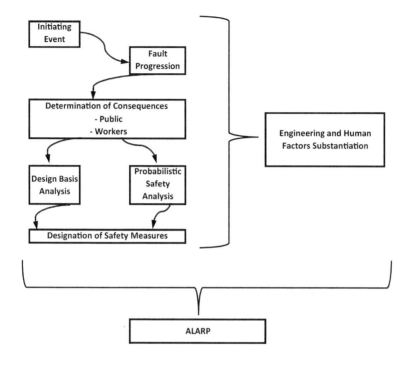

Figure 1.2: Schematic of the overall safety case assessment and substantiation process. Understanding how a fault initiates and progresses enables the calculation of consequences to be undertaken. The subsequent DBA and PSA will enable the appropriate number of safety measures to be determined together with their robustness (this will enable the calculation of risk). The claims on the engineering and operator action will be substantiated. All of these aspects will be brought together to determine the ALARP position, and to conclude that the risk is ALARP, there may need to be additional claims on safety measures.

Approval

A safety case justifies the operation of a nuclear plant for which the nuclear consequences of maloperation may be significant. An appropriate level of scrutiny must be applied to the safety case (including all of its supporting documents) to ensure the adequacy of the safety arguments. The hazard category will determine the approval steps that are required to be undertaken.

The steps required in safety case production will always involve a checking process (known as *quality assurance* (QA)), potentially followed by an *independent peer review* (IPR) prior to presentation to and approval of one or more *safety committees*. The most significant safety cases will require explicit approval by the ONR. The checking and approval process is known as *due process*. Appendix A.2 provides more information on the checking and approval processes.

Implementation and adoption

The process described so far has produced a new safety case that defines the limits and conditions of the operations to ensure safety. The safety case may identify procedures that operators must follow and may identify necessary pieces of engineering to ensure safety. There may even be recommendations to change how things are done or to provide additional or repair safety-related equipment to ensure risks are reduced to ALARP. At some point in time, the plant must begin to operate in accordance with the new safety case, i.e. it must now be *implemented* to enable its *adoption*.

This process of adoption will involve the cascade of the safety case's requirements into the actual operational working procedures within the plant. *Clearance certificates* may be one of the principal documents that tell the operators what they are 'cleared' to do. The clearance certificate will detail all the important safety-related equipment, operational requirements, limits and conditions as specified in the safety case. It becomes the handbook of what is permitted and the compliance steps that have to be documented.

Recommendations for safety improvement that have been accepted will be turned into modifications and the changes introduced. The modifications themselves may also need safety case justification and the modification process is discussed in Section 3.8. At a defined time, the plant will operate in accordance with the requirements of the newly adopted safety case.

It cannot be over-stressed as to the importance in adequately implementing a safety case. If it is not successfully undertaken, the safety case production process will have been wasted. The plant may not be safely run as the safety-related aspects identified in the safety case may not be adhered to or may even be removed with time. Subsequent chapters in this book will outline many of the aspects that are important during safety case implementation.[8]

1.3.4 What do you do with a safety case?

A safety case is produced and then implemented so that it can be adopted. Once a safety case has been adopted, the justified operations will continue in accordance with the new safety case until it is determined that a new safety case is required and the process described above repeats. Over time, there will be modifications to the plant or the processes conducted within it. These modifications could range from a new process line to a simple increase in operating temperature, and before they can come to fruition, a modification to the safety case will be required. The modification will be required to justify the change and ensure that the overall safety case encompasses the change. More detail on modifications is given in Section 3.8.

There must be continuous vigilance to ensure that the requirements of the safety case, including from any modifications, are adhered to. There will be *periodic reviews* of the safety case to ensure that cumulative changes from modifications do not have undue impact and that the safety case remains *fit-for-purpose* going forward. The periodic review of safety cases is described in more detail in Section 3.4.

---

[8][6] is a scholarly article on safety case implementation that provides useful insight into the challenges.

Chapter 2

The UK Regulatory Regime

The nuclear industry in the UK, as it is across the world, operates in a highly regulated environment. Regulation is not unique to the nuclear industry as regulation occurs across a wide spectrum of high-hazard industries where there is the potential to give rise to significant harm to the workers, the public or the environment. The aviation, rail and pharmaceutical industries are just three examples.

Within the UK, it is not possible for any person or organisation to simply operate a nuclear plant without first seeking legal approval from the UK regulator, the ONR. There are legal requirements on both the regulator and those operating or seeking to operate nuclear plants. This is to ensure the competence of those operating the plants in order to assure the safety of the persons working there and also the public who may all be affected by an accident and its associated release of nuclear material. Regrettably, despite regulation, accidents have been known to happen in the UK and across the wider world. This has often been facilitated by a mixture of poor safety culture at the plants together with happenstance leading to the initiating event and the progression of events to the accident. The quality of the regulation may also have been a contributory factor.

The purpose of this chapter is to outline how the UK nuclear industry is governed and why safety cases are produced from a legal perspective. Thus, the concept of the *nuclear site licence* (NSL) is introduced, which indicates a (hopefully high) degree of competence has been achieved by those seeking to operate or those currently operating nuclear plants. Those who hold a nuclear licence are known as *nuclear site licence holders* or *licensees*. The UK nuclear regulatory framework includes the *Nuclear Installations Act* (NIA) (1965) that establishes the requirement for an NSL and the provision of *licence conditions* (LCs) attached to it.

There are a number of numerical dose and risk criteria to which UK operators of nuclear plants must adhere to or at least strive to adhere to. Some of these are *legal limits* (LLs) that stem from regulations (i.e. The Ionising Radiations Regulations 2017 (IRR17)). Other numerical criteria are *targets* and should be met as far as is reasonably practicable. Many of these targets are described in the SAPs and these are touched upon in this chapter.

Finally, a key feature of all UK safety cases is the achieving of risk reduction to ALARP. ALARP is deeply and firmly embedded in all sectors of the UK industry and beyond. It is the legal stick stemming from the Health and Safety at Work Act (originally 1974) by which prosecutions of those organisations that have done harm to workers or the public are brought. This chapter will discuss ALARP and its utilisation in safety cases.

2.1   UK nuclear site licensing

The NIA (1965) is the principal law that governs the operation of almost all of the nuclear sites within the UK. UK legislation can be read for free on the government website. It is worth quoting verbatim from the current (revised) version.

Restriction of certain nuclear installations to licensed sites

1. No person may use a site for the purpose of installing or operating—

    (a) any nuclear reactor (other than a nuclear reactor comprised in a means of transport, whether by land, water or air), or

    (b) any other installation of a prescribed kind,

    unless a licence to do so has been granted in respect of the site by the appropriate national authority and is in force.

2. Such a licence is referred to in this Act as a "nuclear site licence".

3. The only kinds of installation that may be prescribed under subsection (1)(b) are installations (other than nuclear reactors) designed or adapted for—

    (a) producing or using atomic energy,

    (b) any process which—

        i. is preparatory or ancillary to producing or using atomic energy, and

        ii. involves, or is capable of causing, the emission of ionising radiations, or

    (c) storing, processing or disposing of—

        i. nuclear fuel, or

        ii. bulk quantities of other radioactive matter which has been produced or irradiated in the course of the production or use of nuclear fuel.

Note: Text from the NIA (1965) as amended.

Within the NIA, the appropriate national authority in relation to England, Scotland and Wales is the ONR. The ONR is responsible for ensuring both the nuclear safety and the conventional health and safety aspects of the sites. Conventional safety is associated with hazardous activities that may be found in any non-nuclear industrial facility, such as working at height, confined spaces, and moving machinery. The ONR also regulates the security of the sites, the transport of nuclear material around the UK and the safeguarding of the material.

There are a small number of UK defence sites that are owned by the Ministry of Defence (MOD) and are exempt from the NIA (as the NIA does not apply to reactors within means of transport, i.e. submarines). The MOD's own internal regulator the Defence Nuclear Safety Regulator (DNSR) takes the lead in regulating these sites.

The NIA is not the only health and safety law that applies to nuclear sites. All sites, including those operated by the MOD, must also comply with the Health and Safety at Work Act, from which the concept of ALARP stems. There is also a wide suite of regulations that must be adhered to that cover nuclear and non-nuclear aspects that include:

- IRR17;

- Radiation (Emergency Preparedness and Public Information) Regulations (REPPIR);

- Dangerous Substances and Explosive Atmospheres Regulations (DSEAR);

- Control of Major Accident Hazards Regulations (COMAH);

- Lifting Operations and Lifting Equipment Regulations (LOLER).

The ONR takes the lead in regulating these requirements across all nuclear sites. The MOD sites are sometimes known as having *dual regulation*.

As required by the NIA, a role undertaken by the ONR is the granting of NSLs to enable the undertaking of nuclear operations. The NSLs will normally have conditions attached (see below), which provide specific requirements and duties on the recipient of the NSL. The ONR provides a level of control on the operation of nuclear sites by only providing an NSL when they are satisfied that sufficient justification has been made. This justification is normally a safety case, but the ONR must also be satisfied that the arrangements for the management of safety and security and so on are adequate. The ONR provides judgement on the acceptability of submissions.

The ONR also provides guidance to the operators of nuclear plants and the designers of nuclear plants. This may occur in regulator meetings or through the provision of formal guidance documents, such as the SAPs and TAGs as discussed below.

The nuclear sites in the UK that are subject to regulation are involved in a wide range of operations of which only a minority are currently directly involved in civil nuclear power generation. The types of operations covered at the UK nuclear sites and covered by such regulations include:

- Power generation (civil and military for submarines) including design assessment of a proposed new build;

- Reprocessing (to be complete in the early 2020s);

- Care and maintenance, decommissioning and waste management;

- Long and short-term waste disposal and storage;

- Nuclear weapon production and research;

- Submarine reactor manufacture, fuel handling;

- Redundant submarine care and maintenance and decommissioning;

- Uranium enrichment and fuel production;

- Research and development;

- Nuclear medicine isotope production.

The ONR and the DNSR are not the only regulators of nuclear sites in the UK. The Environment Agency (EA), the Scottish Environment Protection Agency (SEPA) and Natural Resources Wales (NRW) are other regulators that the ONR will consult and take into account their requirements (as well as the DNSR for the MOD sites). The other regulators are focused on ensuring the minimisation of harm to the environment. For instance, this is through ensuring that discharges (radiological and non-radiological) are minimised as far as reasonably practicable and that BPM/BAT are used to ensure this.

The environmental aspects of a plant's design and operation are important considerations and may drive the installation of equipment and an operating regime that is more demanding than that may be required simply from a radiological dose point of view. Detailed discussion and explanation of environmental aspects, their regulation and application of BPM/BAT are beyond the scope of this book.

The ONR also works in conjunction with other national regulators and the International Atomic Energy Agency (IAEA) for which the UK is a member. Thus, the ONR collaborates and contributes to the development of international standards and guidance and seeks to ensure that these are embedded in the UK equivalent.

The regulation of industries in the UK (nuclear and non-nuclear) is described as *goal-setting*. Regulators in other countries can be *prescriptive*. A goal setting regulator will set broad principles that are expected to be met but will not provide specifics or standards that if met assure regulatory approval. Many of the LCs are themselves goal-setting. The UK regulators are effectively required to be convinced that adequate safety has been achieved through evidence-based assessment and deference to industry good practice. In contrast, a prescriptive approach can be seen as more of a 'box ticking' exercise with little demand to go the extra mile to provide additional safety.

The different style of regulatory approach can be challenging for engineers and operators from different countries and cultures coming to the UK to understand. In many respects, there is no definitive right answer in the UK regulatory model. This goal-setting approach is advantageous for the regulator because the regulator can defer to the industry and the industry experts to define the standards and procedures. The industry provides the expertise and operating history and with the right guidance and input from the regulator, can define *relevant good practice* (RGP) that will evolve with time.

Inevitably, from time to time, it is found that standards at nuclear plants fall below the expectation of the regulator. This is often a degradation of the safety margin and is not an immediate threat to public or workforce safety. It could also be because the arrangements for the management of safety are not up to the necessary standard. The ONR may serve an *improvement notice* on the plant requiring necessary improvements. A *prohibition notice* can also be served if the shortfall is considered to be so serious that there is a perceived immediate threat to safety. In the spirit of public accountability and openness, the ONR makes public the improvement and prohibition notices.

Ultimately, for significant shortfalls, a prosecution can be undertaken. In England and Wales, the ONR has the power to prosecute. Scotland has a different legal system and the ONR can only recommend to the Scottish Procurator Fiscal to initiate prosecution. Prosecution occurs, from time-to-time, when there has been a shortfall in delivering a statutory duty. Regrettably, this may follow an accident when a fatality or a release of radioactive material occurs leading to a dose to a worker (or the public). Fortunately, these events are rare and the rates compare favourably to equivalent accident rates in other industries. It is important to stress that prosecution can occur even without harm coming to an individual. Significant failure of a statutory duty is taken to be a serious failure due to the potential harm that could arise. The realisation of the harm may only have been prevented through good luck rather than sound judgement or planning.

2.2 Nuclear site licence and licence conditions

For the UK nuclear sites that are subject to the scope of the NIA, they must be granted an NSL for which we have said its granting is via the ONR (in England, Scotland and Wales). To recap, the organisation that receives an NSL is known as a *licensee* and the process untaken to receive a licence is known as *licensing*.[1] We also refer to sites that have a licence to operate as being *nuclear-licensed sites*.

Attached to each NSL are usually 36 standard LCs, which range from how to set out the site boundary to how to implement organisational changes (for the MOD sites, *Authorisation Conditions* (ACs) are equivalent to the LCs and are largely identical). The full list of the LCs issued by the ONR is available from the ONR website. Whilst all LCs are relevant to nuclear safety to varying degrees, the following are of particular interest and form the basis of much of the contents of this book.

LC 14 Safety documentation: Sets out the need to make and implement adequate arrangements for the production and assessment of safety cases consisting of documentation to justify safety during the design, construction, manufacture, commissioning, operation and decommissioning phases of the installation. This LC sets out the principle of the evolving life-cycle of safety cases that reflects how knowledge of the plant will change through design, operation, decommissioning and so on.

LC 15 Periodic review: Sets out the requirement for periodic and systematic review of the safety case. Within the industry this is generally interpreted as a short-term review (annually) followed by an in-depth review that is often every 10 years. This LC will ensure that the safety case takes stock of the cumulative impact of modifications made to the plant that were implemented in accordance with LC 22. It also offers an opportunity to seek improvements to ensure that RGP in equipment and modes of operation are utilised as far as reasonably practicable.

---

[1] Note the UK spelling of licence, licensed, licensee and licensing.

LC 19 Construction or installation of new plant: Sets out the need for the licensee to make and implement adequate arrangements to control the construction or installation of any new plant. Whilst LC 14 establishes that there must be arrangements to ensure the production of safety case documentation, LC 19 requires that a plant can be installed or constructed safely, i.e. taking into account the potential to damage other nuclear plants or safety-related infrastructure on the nuclear site.

LC 22 Modification or experiment on existing plant: Sets out the need for the licensee to make and implement adequate arrangements to control any modification or experiment carried out on any part of the existing plant or processes which may affect safety. This LC ensures that a safety case is kept up to date and that there is sufficient documentation to justify the safety of modifications.

LC 23 Operating rules: Sets out the need for any operation that may affect safety to have an adequate safety case to demonstrate the safety of the operation and to identify the conditions and limits necessary in the interests of safety. These conditions and limits are known as *operating rules* (ORs). Within this LC is the term *adequate*, which can mean different things to different people (see Appendix A.1). Essentially, the LC sets out that the boundary or envelope of the safety case needs to be understood.

LC 24 Operating instructions: Sets out the need for all operations that may affect safety to be carried out in accordance with written instructions known as *operating instructions* (OIs).

LC 27 Safety mechanisms, devices and circuits: Sets out the requirement that a plant is not operated, inspected, maintained or tested unless suitable and sufficient *safety mechanisms, devices and circuits* are properly connected and in good working order. Essentially this LC ensures that sufficient safety measures are available at all times, recognising that there may be as many hazards during periods of shut down and maintenance as there are during actual operation.

It should be clear that the law of the land in the UK sets out the requirements for a safety case to be produced. To some degree the law of the land also dictates what aspects need to be considered to assure safety and what a safety case must do, e.g. it must identify limits and conditions (LC 23) and it must ensure sufficient account is made of changes to the plant (LC 22). How this is then undertaken on a particular licensed site is determined by the individual licensee who will establish their own *written arrangements* for the production, approval, adoption/implementation and management of their safety cases together with how they will comply with their own safety case process requirements.

The individual licensee will also determine the methodology that they will utilise to produce their safety cases. The methodology will include consideration of:

- How worker and public dose is calculated, e.g. what dispersion models are used to determine how radioactivity travels from the point of release to the point where an individual is exposed to it;

- The approach to the designation and classification of safety measures;

- How claims on safety measures are assured or substantiated.

Aspects of all of the above are discussed in this book.

There are different sectors associated with the UK nuclear industry, e.g. the civil nuclear reactor sector, nuclear waste management and reprocessing sectors, uranium enrichment sector, military reactor and warhead production sectors together with the *research and development* (R+D) sector. Therefore, these different sectors have evolved similar, but sometimes different, processes for the production, adoption and management of safety cases. Similarly, the methodologies employed are broadly equivalent, but there are differences. There are increasing efforts to share good practice across the industry for the betterment of all. A nuclear accident or near miss would have implications across the board so it is in the interest of everyone to help to mitigate this risk by sharing what works well and just as importantly, sharing what does not work well. The movements of personnel between the sectors and the regulator, together with industry seminars, and so on, are vehicles by which improvements across the industry can be brought to bear.

The LCs are written at a high-level (goal setting) and are not intended to be working instructions for individual personnel to utilise. Therefore, as noted above, nuclear licensees produce their own written arrangements that demonstrate how the LCs cascade into the working procedures and practices on the site. Flowing from this is a hierarchy of site documentation that is produced by the licensee. This documentation may start at a policy level, then cascade to procedures and guidance notes and so on. Safety cases will be produced, adopted and managed in accordance with these policies, procedures and guidance notes. At a working level, it is likely that most personnel may not have direct sight of the underpinning LC, but they should have sufficient knowledge to understand that the LCs exist and form the basis of why they do what they do.

For example, LC 22 sets out the requirement for there to be control of any modification on the plant. At the working level, the site will have established a process by which changes to plant are undertaken. Different terms are given to this across the industry, but we may take the generic term *modification proposal* for the document that is written and approved before the change is made.

The modification proposal will set out what is proposed to be changed, which could range from an increase in operating temperature to the installation or removal of a piece of equipment. The proposed change will then be assessed for its impact on safety, justification given and which lower-tier documents may need to be changed, such as the OIs. Only following the modification proposal's review and approval by peers and management on the plant, site or even the regulator can the change be implemented. Thus, there is control of the modification through the modification proposal and LC 22 is satisfied.

A nuclear-licensed site will, by definition, have an NSL. Within the site, individual plants may be in operation or in phases of care and maintenance or decommissioning (much of the UK nuclear industry is associated with the latter two phases). The nuclear regulator may also be required to grant a licence for new plants that may wish to be built on the existing site or for significant changes to an existing plant that may have the potential to give rise to public or worker doses if incorrectly implemented. The regulator would grant approval for the new build or installation by the issuing of a *licence instrument* on satisfactory review of the safety case submission.

2.3   Safety assessment principles

The SAPs were written by the ONR to provide a framework for their inspectors to make consistent regulatory judgements. They can also be used by designers and operators of nuclear plants, bearing in mind the true intended audience for them. More detailed guidance on various topics covered by the SAPs has been written by the ONR in the form of TAGs and they cover a wide range of issues such as criticality warning systems, human reliability analysis and essential services.

By definition, the SAPs provide principles and also guidance. They were written with a view to alignment with international standards, such as those written by the IAEA having relatively recently been benchmarked and revised (2020). Not all of the SAPs apply to all nuclear plants. For instance, there is a section on graphite, which is not relevant to many non-reactor sites.

As noted, the SAPs and TAGs were strictly written for the ONR's inspectors and are not written for site licensees or safety assessors in the supply chain. However, by understanding what these documents say, the wider community can gain an understanding of what the ONR's expectations are; we can at least know the criteria by which the 'homework' will be judged. Meeting the ONR's expectations is always good advice if the aim is to gain or retain an NSL. Moreover, meeting their expectations is part of ensuring RGP is adhered to. As we show in Section 2.5, demonstrating alignment with RGP is an important mechanism by which we can achieve ALARP.

The SAPs themselves are detailed and offer a wide depth of guidance and information across the full range of disciplines that may contribute to safety of nuclear plants. However, the SAPs as presented are not simply a shopping list of things that should be considered or achieved. They do contain inbuilt background of why the SAPs are what they are and justification for many of the aspects covered. Much of the information covered is common sense and would be applied in any high-hazard industry not just the nuclear industry. For example, how safety systems should work, be independent of control systems and fail to safety are principles that should be applied in rail, aviation and so on. Conversely, there are many aspects covered by the SAPs that are only relevant to the nuclear industry such as the sections on radiological dose and risk.

Much useful and relevant information can be taken from a reading of the SAPs and by having them to hand as a reference. They are not, however, an easy read overall. They are not a textbook per se, but there is a narrative. In my view every safety assessor and safety engineer should have a copy of the ONR's SAPs to hand especially if an assessor or engineer needs an understanding of disciplines other than their own. Even if a site's processes and methodology are well developed, the relevant parts of the SAPs should be handled and understood. The ONR will work to their SAPs and generally not a site's specifics, so understanding how licensee arrangements meet ONR requirements is always a sensible idea.

The SAPs provide detailed advice on the aspects covered by the LCs, but in more detail and in many cases with objective and quantified criteria. A large part of the SAPs involves the development of numerical criteria which set out the range of hazards to be assessed and the risk levels that must be achieved.

2.4 Numerical targets

In producing a safety case, a logical and robust argument, supported with evidence, forms a large part of the safety justification and this will go a long way in securing the necessary adequacy of the case presented. In addition to this, within the UK, there are objective *numerical criteria* or *targets* which a safety case will be required to achieve. These generally require a degree of explicit numerical calculation. Some of these criteria are legal maximum values, known as LLs and defined in legislation for which it is not possible to exceed these even with justification. For other criteria, the expectation is that they are met, but there is some latitude if they are not—with suitable justification and with a view to doing all that is reasonably practicable to meet the targets, i.e. to make improvements in a defined period of time. The targets are defined by the ONR and the targets are given in terms of the *basic safety levels* (BSLs) and the *basic safety objectives* (BSOs) for which some BSLs are also LLs.

The ONR's expectation is that for a new plant, the BSLs should be met. For an older plant built to earlier standards or subject to degradation, the BSLs may not be met. If so, steps should be undertaken to reduce the risk unless it is grossly disproportionate (see Section 2.5). Even for a new plant that meets the BSLs, the licensee has a duty to reduce the risks as far as reasonably practicable and meeting the BSL itself is not a justification that the risk is ALARP.

The BSOs are benchmarks that reflect modern safety standards and expectations. That is, a new plant should aim to meet the BSOs. Should a plant meet the BSO, the ONR may not seek further reduction of risk, though there is still a legal requirement to reduce risk as far as reasonably practicable. Simply put, should a plant reach the BSO, the ONR may seek to spend their finite effort on higher risk plants. This is simply common sense and reflects a proportionate approach to regulation.

There are BSLs and BSOs that apply to normal conditions and also separate BSLs and BSOs that apply in fault conditions. We will discuss some of the BSLs and BSOs in this book, as this gives context to the framework in which UK safety cases are constructed. The reader should defer to the SAPs to gain insight into all of the targets and the rationale for their numerical values.

Fundamentally, the rationale for the defining of the targets is to favourably place the risk from nuclear operations or accidents with that posed by other hazardous industries.

2.4.1 Targets: normal operations

There is a limit to the effective radiological dose an individual can be exposed to in a calendar year through the normal operation of the plant, i.e. through routine (non-

Table 2.1: Numerical effective dose targets in any calendar year for normal operations. Those with an * are also the LLs. Information taken from the ONR SAPS [1].

Group	BSL mSv	BSO mSv
Employees working with radiation	20*	1
Other employees on the site	2	0.1
Average employee	10	0.5
Public off-site	1*	0.02

accident) releases of radioactivity and from the background radiation levels. Therefore, the dose may be accrued through inhalation or ingestion of radioactive material or through direct exposure to radiation. The LLs are embedded in the UK legislation (IRR17) and are also specified in the SAPs. One target has the desirable effect of preventing excessive dose sharing between lots of workers by introducing a BSO for average dose. The target dose values in terms of the BSLs and BSOs are given in Table 2.1. The safety case must demonstrate that the LLs are achieved under normal operations. If an LL is not achieved, the licensee must take steps to ensure compliance. We should be clear that these LLs apply to normal operational doses. It is quite acceptable for safety cases to predict doses far in excess of these LLs under fault conditions, but there must then be sufficient protection to ensure that the likelihood of these doses being realised is sufficiently low and that the overall risk is tolerable (and ALARP).

We may wonder why, for instance, has 20 mSv been chosen as the LL? From a detailed study of the stochastic risk from radiation exposure, it is found that the chance of premature fatality is $0.04 \, \text{Sv}^{-1}$ (see Section 5.2.5). Therefore, with an exposure of 20 mSv, the chance of premature fatality is $8 \times 10^{-4} \, \text{y}^{-1}$. This is just below the risk value of $10^{-3} \, \text{y}^{-1}$ defined in R2P2 [3] as the limit of tolerability. For the public and an LL of 1 mSv, the corresponding risk is $4 \times 10^{-5} \, \text{y}^{-1}$, which is below the R2P2 limit of tolerability of $10^{-4} \, \text{y}^{-1}$ for the public. It is left as an exercise for the reader to determine how the risk associated with the BSOs equates to R2P2.

2.4.2 Targets: fault conditions

It is inevitable that even for the simplest plant or process, there will be the potential for deviations from normal operations that can lead to elevated dose from fault conditions. If the fault were to occur, this would be in addition to the dose accrued from normal operations. The analysis of the faults and their potential doses forms the basis of a significant component of the analysis presented within a safety case. This gives rise to the assessment of *accident risk* and its management. As we have discussed above, we define risk as the chance of a premature fatality (Section 1.2.4). This premature fatality may be due to stochastic or random effects (from lower levels of exposure) or due to deterministic effects (from higher levels of exposure). More detail on these issues is given in Section 5.2.5.

Table 2.2: Numerical target risk values for accidents at the site. The values for the public and workers are the same, but it is worth noting that the workers will more than likely receive a much larger dose during normal operations than the public. Their overall risk will be the sum of the risk from normal operations and from faults, which together should be $< 10^{-3} \, y^{-1}$. Information taken from the ONR SAPS [1].

Group	BSL y^{-1}	BSO y^{-1}
Any person on site	10^{-4}	10^{-6}
Public off-site	10^{-4}	10^{-6}

Table 2.3: Frequency dose targets for total accidents in an individual plant for any person off the site. The targets mean that the total frequencies for all accidents in any dose band should be combined for a plant, i.e. a running total. This is subtly different from that of the workers. Information taken from the ONR SAPS [1].

Effective dose mSv	BSL y^{-1}	BSO y^{-1}
0.1–1	1	10^{-2}
1–10	10^{-1}	10^{-3}
10–100	10^{-2}	10^{-4}
100–1000	10^{-3}	10^{-5}
>1000	10^{-4}	10^{-6}

Similar to the dose targets for normal operations, there are risk targets for accidents with their corresponding BSLs and BSOs. These targets are shown in Table 2.2. However, there are no LLs as defined in the UK legislation for the risk targets, but there are strong expectations of where the risk should lie.

The ONR also defines frequency targets for *dose bands* within which the accident doses may lie during fault conditions. These targets are known as the *frequency staircase* due to the shape made if plotted on a graph (another exercise for the reader). The frequency targets for the public and workers are shown in Tables 2.3 and 2.4.

Should there be large public doses (>1 Sv) from an accident that can give rise to over 100 public deaths (immediately or eventually), there is another target (Table 2.5).

Individual sites normally set their own more restrictive limits than those given in the BSLs and BSOs. A nuclear site may comprise of many different individual plants and each plant poses a nuclear risk to the public. The public is solely concerned with the risk from the nuclear site *as a whole* and not from individual plants within it. Therefore, it is common practice to allocate a *risk allocation* or *risk budget* to individual plants, with each allocation being a fraction of the overall site declared risk target (e.g. $\frac{1}{10}$th or even $\frac{1}{100}$th for large sites). Provided each plant is within its own target, the total site risk will meet the overall site target.

Table 2.4: Frequency dose targets for any single accident for any person on the site. Unlike the public, this does not correspond to a running total of frequency within each dose band. Information taken from the ONR SAPs [1].

Effective dose mSv	BSL y^{-1}	BSO y^{-1}
2–20	10^{-1}	10^{-3}
20–200	10^{-2}	10^{-4}
200–2000	10^{-3}	10^{-5}
>2000	10^{-4}	10^{-6}

Table 2.5: Numerical target frequencies for the site where there may be over 100 public fatalities. Information taken from the ONR SAPs [1].

Targets	
BSL	$10^{-5} \, y^{-1}$
BSO	$10^{-7} \, y^{-1}$

From time-to-time, it is necessary for one plant to 'eat into' a part of another plant's allocation. This is fine provided there is enough margin overall. There is always an exercise for each nuclear site to keep track of the total site risk from all of the plants, which can become a significant undertaking for a large and complex site. There is further complexity if there are transient and relatively short-term activities. We should note that for very short-duration transient tasks that are a small fraction of a year (such as days or weeks), it is not really appropriate to consider 'annualising' the risk over a year. The focus should be more on the deterministic arguments with the demonstration that there is defence-in-depth.

2.5   As low as reasonably practicable

The concept of ALARP is deeply embedded in the safety case process, and ALARP is about reducing the risk to as low as reasonably practicable. We have mentioned ALARP in the preceding sections and further explanation is now provided.

First of all, it is important to state that the term *reasonably practicable* is a subjective term and there is no hard and fast right answer to any particular solution. Within the safety case process, there are clear objective criteria such as the risk targets, but if the BSOs are met, for example, it does not necessarily imply that the risk is ALARP. Meeting numerical targets helps to make an ALARP argument and it can help in formulating what is reasonable to do.

ALARP requires an understanding of both the risks and the options to reduce the risks together with the benefits and disadvantages (detriments) of the options. In simple terms, an option may be considered to be 'reasonable' if there is clear benefit in doing it in comparison to the disadvantage of doing it. An option may be considered to be 'practicable' if it can be undertaken. ALARP brings the two together.

Unlike other high-hazard industries, working in a nuclear and radiation environment always brings risks simply from turning up to work or living close by as there will always be some level of exposure to radiation. This radiation exposure can cause fatal cancer. Therefore, ALARP must apply to these normal operational doses. In addition, accidents may lead to greater exposure, but a key aspect of ALARP is the determination that the likelihood of the accidents occurring and/or their severity is reduced as far as reasonably practicable.

A point of clarity is that the nuclear industry generally uses the term ALARP on a day-to-day basis. The key legislation from where ALARP stems (the Health and Safety at Work Act) refers to *so far as is reasonably practicable* (SFAIRP). The two terms can be considered to be equivalent.

To help in the understanding of what reasonably practicable means the term *great disproportion* is used. The term stems from an important legal case: Edwards vs the National Coal Board when the court had to determine whether the UK Coal Board should have spent more money to shore up a road in a coal mine. The court determined that an improvement is not *reasonably practicable* if there is a 'great disproportion' between the risk on one side and the sacrifice involved (time, cost or trouble) in making the improvement. We discuss more about great or *gross* disproportion and what this might mean in objective terms in Section 13.1. One can sometimes make an argument that the risk reduction of making a change makes too little difference to justify the disruption caused. It follows directly that a key test in making an ALARP case is to provide evidence of *optioneering*. This does not have to be a fully detailed optioneering study and multi-page report, but can sometimes include a short-reasoned argument weighing up options for improvement against the detriment of implementing them.

Evidence that a solution is ALARP can also be provided by demonstration that the solution aligns with RGP. RGP is the way of doing things or designing things in a manner that is recognised by regulators and industry experts as the benchmark by which things should aim to be done by. RGP is defined in sources such as:

- Approved code of practice (ACOP);

- Defined codes and standards;

- Industry guidance;

- Custom and practice.

It is important to note that what constitutes RGP will change with time. This should be obvious from owning a car—the level of safety equipment on a modern car is significantly greater than that on a car from 10 or 20 years ago. We simply would not tolerate buying a car without seat belts and so on.

Finally, in formulating an ALARP argument, the position in the hierarchy of risk reduction can be important to consider, which we will now discuss.

2.5.1   Hierarchy of risk reduction

An essential aspect in the demonstration of ALARP is the position in the *hierarchy of risk reduction* and the justification that there are no reasonably practicable improvements in the position. Related to this is the provision of defence-in-depth. The term *safety hierarchy* is also used inter-changeably with the hierarchy of risk reduction.

The preference for a plant is an inherently safe plant, i.e. a plant that avoids hazards rather than manages or controls them. Another term often used is the *elimination* of hazards.

Inevitably it will not be possible to eliminate all hazards. By its nature, a radioactive material will always possess radiation or contamination hazards to some degree. However, the processes adopted in the plant can eliminate hazards that may disrupt normal process operations. For example, the elimination of lifts or the elimination of compressed gases will provide an inherently safe plant in terms of the relevant hazards associated with lifts and gases.

A deviation from the normal operation of a plant may progress to an unsafe state, if not corrected. This is the essence of a fault and the preference is that the deviation is towards a safe condition, but if this is not possible the change in plant state to a dangerous situation should be long so that safety measures can act. Safety measures will either stop the fault progression or minimise the doses.

The hierarchy of risk reduction places passive safety measures ahead of active safety measures. Passive safety measures require no moving parts, requirement for services or operator action and will effectively have zero probability of failure on demand (or very low). Such safety measures would always be present. Examples of such passive measures include:

- Shield or containment walls;

- Steel cladding in-cell bunds/sumps;

- Container flasks;

- Pipework or vessels.

Active safety measures may be automatic acting or require operator intervention, with the preference normally for the former. Examples of active safety measures include:

- Interlocks and trips;

- Alarms and subsequent operator action;

- Operator surveillance checks and action.

Last in the hierarchy of risk reduction is mitigation. By definition, mitigation means that the public or workers receive a dose, which is not an ideal situation in a fault. Examples of mitigation include:

- Ventilation extract systems including filters;

- Evacuation;

- Respirators.

Let us be clear that the hierarchy of risk reduction represents a preference in an ideal nuclear plant. ALARP is about making reasoned argument and justification that the chosen plant design solution is what is reasonably practicable for the plant in question. This will depend on the nature of the plant, its age, the operations being conducted and so on. Numerous safety cases, with a tolerable level of risk, are made on the basis of the safety measures being mitigation. An ALARP justification is made that it is not reasonably practicable to move higher up in the hierarchy of risk reduction.

It is also worth recognising where a safety measure may feature in the fault development. It is preferable to terminate the fault close to the initiation of the fault and this may make preferable claims on automatic systems compared to passive features.

Example: Hierarchy of Risk Reduction

Liquor is transferred to a vessel. Overfilling of the vessel may lead to a loss of containment to the cell bund and release of aerosol. The bund is stainless steel clad and is within a sealed cell ensuring minimal transfer of activity to the operating area. The cladding and the cell structure are passive features and could be considered to be high in the hierarchy of risk reduction. It is not possible to eliminate the need to transfer the liquor.

The bund and cell structure are clearly important, but terminating the flow before overflow seems like a sensible approach. Overflow and aerosol release may still result in some dose even if air release from the cell by any ventilation system is filtered. Moreover, there will be contamination and future decommissioning complications.

Finally, in our example, we should note that if the liquor is fissile, the bund should be passively safe to prevent an unsafe geometry forming should there be a liquor spill. This would increase the importance of the passive nature of the bund and would be preferable to an unsafe geometry that requires safety measures to prevent overflow—safety measures of this nature cannot protect against any failure in the vessels or pipework.

The hierarchy of risk reduction is sometimes phrased in terms of *eliminate, reduce, isolate, control, personal, discipline* (ERICPD), though the terms really stem from conventional safety convention. The principles are essentially the same as described above, i.e. eliminate the hazard and rely on operator action/mitigation last.

Principles of defence-in-depth

At the core of hazard analysis and demonstration of ALARP is the principle of *defence-in-depth*. Defence-in-depth provides for multiple layers of protection or barriers to ensure that faults cannot progress to a significant radiological dose. No single barrier,

Table 2.6: Example defence-in-depth layers of protection.

Layer	Example
Prevent deviations from normal operations	Well-designed control system to minimise failure and error correct. Conservative design and tolerance of the duty system
Provide safety margins to enable deviations to be detected and terminated	Operating within a well-defined envelope. Provision of alarms to enable the deviations to be detected and operators to respond in a timely manner
Protect against unsafe conditions arising before there is a release	Safety measures such as interlocks and trips to terminate the fault progression (ideally without relying on operator action)
Provide barriers to prevent significant releases	Containment buildings, isolation of ventilation systems to prevent forced discharge
Mitigate the effects of a release	Emergency arrangements, evacuation, respirators, iodine tablets

no matter how robust, will be 100% infallible and defence-in-depth helps to mitigate against this fallibility.

Sometimes, the principle of defence-in-depth is illustrated by a *Swiss cheese model*. A Swiss cheese is full of holes, and if these holes line up there is a path through from one side of the cheese to the other. The model is a symbolic means of explaining that no combination of protection can be perfect, and if there are enough failures (holes), a fault may progress to an accident and a dose to the public or workers. So how does this model of defence-in-depth translate into a nuclear context?

Defence-in-depth involves the use of multiple and independent barriers that encompass aspects of operational design and physical *structure, system or components* (sscs). Therefore, the barriers relate to different stages in the fault progression. Multiple and independent barriers ensure that there is redundancy and diversity in the protection to maximise the likelihood that at least one barrier is successful (redundancy and diversity are explained in Section 8.3). The principle of defence-in-depth also includes emergency arrangements to mitigate the doses of an accident should it occur, which is clearly the last line of defence.

Defence-in-depth must always be applied in a proportionate manner with the most significant hazards requiring the greatest number of barriers that are of the highest levels of quality and robustness. Table 2.6 shows example barriers that provide defence-in-depth.

Chapter 3

Development of the Safety Case and Its Life-Cycle

Every nuclear plant has a life-cycle that spans from the earliest stages of its design to its construction, operation and eventual decommissioning. For each stage of this life-cycle, an appropriate and proportionate safety case is produced. This chapter will provide an introduction to the plant life-cycle and the corresponding safety cases.

Within this chapter we will introduce and describe common safety cases associated with the design process that leads to the production of a *preliminary safety report* (PSR) and a *pre-construction safety report* (PCSR). The delivery of these documents is important in the design process and the PCSR is often required for authorisation of construction or for the installation of significant mechanical equipment to begin.

Following the construction of a plant or the installation of significant equipment, there will be a requirement to *commission* the plant/equipment. This is to ensure that the plant/equipment functions as intended in the design and as required by the safety case. Commissioning is initially performed using inactive (not radioactive) material or simulants, known as *inactive commissioning*. This commissioning is followed by *active commissioning* with radioactive material that will culminate in the utilisation of the actual process material utilised by the plant. This chapter describes the common safety cases associated with the commissioning processes that typically culminate in the production of a *pre-inactive commissioning safety report* (PICSR) and a *pre-active commissioning safety report* (PACSR).

There are many common elements within safety cases irrespective of the stage in the plant life-cycle and these will be explored in this chapter. These include the requirement to clearly define the scope of operations and the principal hazards and how they are managed. A typical breakdown of the sections within a safety case is provided. Conversely, there are some key differences between the different safety cases. An obvious difference is in terms of the tense used: a design safety case shows how a plant *will* operate, as opposed to how it *does* operate when an operational safety case is written.

This chapter will also describe how safety cases are reviewed to ensure that they remain fit-for-purpose. This is an important aspect of the life-cycle particularly given that a plant can be operational for 50 years or more, and in this time there are many factors that could undermine the original safety arguments, age and degradation being obvious examples. Safety cases will, from time-to-time, require modification to reflect changes that occur within the plant, either due to the introduction or removal of equipment or changes to processes undertaken. The process for modifying safety cases is described.

Finally, it is recognised that safety cases need to be proportionate to the *harm potential* that the plant poses. The proportionality is not only in terms of assessment, but the rigour applied to the checking, approval and permissioning. Therefore, the concept of *categorisation* of the safety case is introduced.

3.1   Scope, boundaries and interfaces

Common to all safety cases, irrespective of their position in the life-cycle, is an understanding of the *scope* of the safety case. A safety case must be clear in the description of the scope of coverage and what the purpose of the safety case is. As we will show in the subsequent sections, there are key differences between safety cases for each stage of the safety case life-cycle.

The scope of the safety case will need to be written down within the actual safety case documentation. Additionally, it can be convenient to write a separate *scope of works* document and/or a *safety case strategy* document, particularly for more complex safety cases. These documents can identify principal issues that may relate to:

- The purpose of the safety case and which licence conditions apply (e.g. an LC 15 review or an LC 22 modification);

- Nature of any permissioning sought and proposed period of validity of the new safety case;

- Other safety cases impacted;

- Single-stage safety case delivery or multi-stage, such as a civils PCSR followed by a mechanical, electrical and instrumentation (ME+I) PCSR;

- Processes and (safety case) methodologies to be followed;

- Provisional category;

- Key stakeholders and success criteria;

- Delivery strategy in terms of organisations, intelligent customer roles and so on.

By ensuring that the correct stakeholders 'buy-in' to the scope or strategy before committing time and money into producing the safety case, the potential for a late challenge can be minimised.

In writing the scope of the safety case, the boundaries and interfaces of the safety case should be clear. Sometimes this is written in a separate *boundaries and interfaces* document. On a complex plant with many interactions with other plants this can be very detailed. The understanding of the interfaces may change as the safety case is produced and the document may need to be revised as the safety case matures. Aspects to be considered with respect to boundaries and interfaces may include:

- The physical scope of the safety case, including the geographical coverage of the case and the physical extent of the plant (this aspect may be by reference to marked up drawings);

- Interface points where one safety case begins and the other ends, even down to which 'shared' valve is covered in which safety case;

- The inventory and *conditions for acceptance* (CFA) of material, or effluents (liquid or gases) passed between one plant and another;

- Where and how interfacing hazards are addressed.

The last point above can be important and potentially difficult to resolve. Let us consider *Plant 1* that sends radioactive packages to *Plant 2*. If *Plant 1* erroneously sends the wrong package or an incorrectly configured package to *Plant 2*, where is the hazard assessed if the dose is only realised in *Plant 2*? The potential realisation of the dose in *Plant 2* suggests that *Plant 2* should address the hazard and this may require safety measures to then be designated in *Plant 1*. In this instance, there are clear interface issues that need to be understood, documented and complied with across two different plants, two different safety cases and two different teams of operators. The key point is that interfacing hazards need to be captured, addressed and agreed between the *safety case owners* of the plants.

3.2 The design process

A requirement for a new nuclear plant is identified. This could be a new business venture such as a new nuclear power station or a fuel manufacturing plant, or it could be a new plant to handle, process or store nuclear waste. From the initial idea in a company board room to the operation of the plant there may be a time period of 10 or more years. During this time a design must be developed, a construction contractor appointed and building work undertaken. Eventually, the plant will be ready to be commissioned and to commence operations. This section will focus on the design phase of this process.

The design of a new nuclear plant is a multi-stage process that sees increasing levels of design and understanding as each stage develops. The safety case is one component of the overall project to deliver the new plant. In industry there are *broadly* three fundamental stages of design and these will be labelled here as:

1. Concept design stage;

2. Preliminary design stage;

3. Detailed design stage.

Following design, the project must move into construction and then commissioning (inactive and active) prior to operations commencing. The design, construction and commissioning stages within the project to deliver the plant will generally follow funding stages whereby the project can only move onto the next stage following approval of the previous stage. This is a project risk mitigation strategy as it helps to avoid all of the money being spent on a project in the early stages when it may prove to be non-viable. It is also easier to raise and then release funding in smaller amounts from those that hold the purse strings rather than releasing a huge block, potentially for billions of pounds.

Within the project funding stages are also key deliverables in terms of the safety case. Approval of the safety case is generally required at certain key stages, notably to authorise construction, active commissioning and active operations. For high-hazard plant, the regulator may be required to give explicit consent at these stages.

It is possible for a design to progress from one stage to the next even if the safety case is behind schedule. This is generally ill-advised as there may be abortive work if the safety case requires changes to be made to the design when it catches up. Conversely, if the design moves too far ahead compromises to the safety case may have to be made leading to a less robust means of managing hazards. This is far from ideal, but is what actually can happen in the real world and it makes it more difficult to demonstrate that the risks have been reduced to ALARP. The commercial reality comes into play and can temper the idealism of the safety case even though the design is still on paper at this time. Project managers will rarely wait for the safety case to catch up in a major design project.

We will now describe each stage in turn. It is important to stress that different organisations may utilise different terms to those given here and they may also have more design stages. We simply seek to give an overview of the principal stages and the approach adopted in the industry.

3.2.1 Concept design stage

The initial design stage is associated with the very earliest phases of the design process and will commence once the need for a new plant or process has been identified. It is unlikely that any significant expenditure on the project will have commenced at the start of this stage and any project team may be very small, perhaps a handful of key leads. There may be a few project documents, perhaps a *basis of design* (BOD) for the required plant. The BOD would outline, at a high level, what the plant is required to do such as:

- When the plant is required and for how long, i.e. its lifetime;

- What it will do and any inputs and outputs;

- Fundamental technology (if known);

- Throughput and nature of the inventory.

At this design stage, there may initially be very little knowledge of what the plant will look like, how it will operate and so on. There may be many unknowns in terms of technology or chemical processes that necessitate a programme of R+D. This R+D may take many years to complete and there may be many risks within the project should it not come to fruition as hoped. It may be necessary to secure funding to enable this R+D to commence.

One early means of capturing the hazards associated with the proposed plant is through the conducting of a HAZOP 0 study, which is described in more detail in Section 7.1. This HAZOP will focus on hazards rather than faults or operability issues, as the design will be too immature to understand these two issues.

From the identified hazards, it will be possible to develop an initial *hazard management strategy* (HMS). The aim of the HMS is to seek solutions to eliminate hazards by design or, if this cannot be achieved, identify the high-level means of managing the hazards that are as high in the safety hierarchy as reasonably practicable. The HMS will develop a series of Level 1 *safety function requirements* (SFRs) for the forthcoming design process to incorporate. The development of Level 1 SFRs and examples of them is given in Section 9.

The HMS may not be a safety case deliverable in terms of a regulator submission, but it is a very useful vehicle for demonstrating that safety has been embedded in the design process from the earliest stages. It therefore helps in the demonstration of ALARP. Getting the HMS right is key to a successful design project and can save considerable sums of time and money.

3.2.2 Preliminary design stage

The preliminary design stage will see the design process rapidly escalate with the assembled project team potentially increasing dramatically in size with the range of disciplines involved also expanding. The largest of projects may begin to include many hundreds of engineers from a multitude of contracting organisations. These will include engineers associated with civils, heating, ventilation and air-conditioning (HVAC), control and instrumentation (C+I), construction together with safety, both nuclear and non-nuclear. The future operators of the plant will also be included in the design team to ensure that the design will meet their expectations and requirements, i.e. it will be operable as well as safe. At this still early design stage, there may be uncertainty in how things will be done in the new plant, which may lead to a number of different options being available. The options could be in terms of:

- Location of the plant;

- Fundamental processing and/or handling technology;

- The end state of the product and so on.

Optioneering studies provide a means of down selecting the available options and these may be undertaken (more information on the optioneering process is provided in Section 13.1.1). There may still be decisions to be made in later design stages, but there should be enough information to start representing the design on drawings, notably the *process flow diagrams* (PFDS), *ventilation flow diagrams* (VFDS), *mechanical flow diagrams* (MFDS) and *general arrangements* (GAS).

At this stage of the design, the fundamentals of the hazards associated with the process will begin to be understood though there may be significant unknowns. The knowledge of the hazards should feed into the optioneering studies as discussed above. It may be possible at this stage to select options or technologies that can intrinsically eliminate hazards and make the plant safe by design. These could be in terms of plant location, plant size, processes and technology used, the end state of the plant's process and so on. There may be uncertainty in how the plant will be constructed, which can be a significant issue on an existing site where they may be hazards to other plants. Consequently, during this stage, optioneering may be undertaken with a view to down selecting a final chosen option or to a reduced field of options for the next design stage to consider further.

Example: Submarine Refit Plant
A requirement has been identified to refit nuclear submarines, and the submarines are required to be taken out of the water to do the work. There are many locations in the country (or abroad) where refit work could potentially be undertaken. An optioneering study would examine each potential site to determine the optimum solution. This could involve decisions based upon: location of a skilled workforce, security, safety of the site, available infrastructure and so on.

Once a site has been chosen, the process for extracting the submarine from the water needs to be determined. There are alternative technologies such as different types of lift or dry-docking plants. Again, optioneering would help to inform the decision-making process. The output of the optioneering may determine that a dry-docking plant in location *Happy Sands* is the optimum.

The design team may be unsure of how some processes will work due to a lack of industrial knowledge. This uncertainty may be related to uncertainty in the physics or chemistry of the process and how it should be controlled or the mechanical behaviour of items during normal operations or even fault conditions. Therefore, this may necessitate a programme of R+D that may not conclude until the next design stage.

Eventually, the design should begin to mature and a number of key deliverables will be produced by the design team. Safety should be embedded in this process. From a designer's perspective, the engineering may be expected to produce a number of key outputs including those provided in Table 3.1.

There is no harm in re-emphasising that the contents of Table 3.1 should all be produced collaboratively with input from safety assessors, i.e. safety led (or at worst influenced). As the design begins to mature, the safety assessors can begin to understand the relevant hazards and potential faults that may arise from maloperation or

Table 3.1: Example concept design deliverables.

Deliverable	Description
BOD documents	Outlines how key systems are expected to be developed, what they are expected to handle or process, principal codes and standards to use and success criteria for the design
GA drawings	Schematics showing the physical layout of the plant both externally and internally
PFDS	Schematics showing principal vessels, pipework and methods of control and how gas and liquor streams will move through the plant
MFDS	Schematics showing how solid material will move through the plant and key steps associated with its physical form or containment
Outline construction strategy	A description of potential construction methods that may require optioneering in this stage or in the next detailed design stage

failures of equipment. This should be from a natural development of the HMS and the Level 1 SFRs produced during the concept design stage.

Formally, many of the contents of Table 3.1 will feed into fault identification exercises. A HAZOP 1 study would utilise the PFDs, VFDs and MFDs, and the HAZOP process is described in more detail in Section 7.1. Following the HAZOP 1 it should be possible to commence (and complete) concept level safety assessment. This will lead to the defining of the Level 2 SFRs.

The ultimate deliverable at this design stage will be the PSR that will:

- Explain what the plant is intended to do and how;

- Summarise the output of any optioneering and give an indication of where further optioneering is required, i.e. justify the chosen options where possible;

- Summarise any outstanding R+D and what impact this may have on the validity of any arguments presented in the PSR;

- Summarise the relevant hazard and fault analysis and demonstrate that the future risks will be tolerable from both normal operations and fault conditions;

- Provide confidence that the chosen HMS through the implementation of the Level 1 and 2 SFRs can be delivered by demands placed upon engineering or operators;

- Demonstrate that, as things stand, the risk is considered to be ALARP and that as the design develops, the final design will ensure that the risk from operation will be ALARP.

In addition, a PSR is expected to outline the expected waste arisings and the disposal routes for these. There would also be consideration of any airborne or liquid discharges to the atmosphere or sea and the means by which these are expected to be abated. These aspects also stray into environmental consideration and environmental aspects are beyond the scope of the book.

Should there be any particular early indications of issues with construction or commissioning, then these would be discussed and there may be some initial construction or commissioning assessments. For example, construction of a plant on a crowded nuclear site can impose hazards onto other plants. At this design stage the construction contractor may not have been engaged, but consideration as to the viability of construction should be considered. The optioneering of site selection is crucial in ensuring that the chosen option with the associated construction risks will be ALARP.

Example: High-Hazard Plant Location

A high-hazard plant was required to be built on a crowded nuclear site adjacent to an older high-hazard plant. When joining the project, the safety case team repeatedly asked the client for the optioneering justification of the site selection given the potentially significant construction hazards that would be imposed. The request was repeatedly knocked back: 'It's there because it needs to be'. Eventually, the client relented and commissioned a detailed optioneering study.[a] The optioneering did conclude that the chosen site was the optimum even when taking on board the construction risks (which themselves were able to be significantly mitigated against by the further optioneering of construction strategy including crane selection and siting).

When the safety case eventually made it to the highest nuclear safety committee on the site, the first question asked was 'Why are you building it here?' The reply was that the location had been fully optioneered and the reasons were x, y and z as given in a fully referenceable optioneering document. Thanks were then expressed by the client representative for the perseverance in requesting this study and providing a 'get out of gaol card'.

---

[a]Given that the plant had not yet been built and solely existed on paper, it is fair to say that the optioneering study was commissioned rather than (as often occurs) backfitted, but it still occurred later than was ideal.

The PSR would be unlikely to be formally categorised in terms of its safety significance as no regulator permissioning is sought. However, there may be a notional categorisation and it would go through the relevant due process of checking, review and approval. Ultimately, the PSR may be submitted to the regulator for information and confidence building.

3.2.3 Detailed design stage

The detailed design stage is the real 'hard core' phase of the design process and it is where the majority of the design and safety development will occur. It is at this detailed design stage that the outstanding design issues from the PSR, any R+D and the results of the previous optioneering should come together to produce more or less a final design. We say 'more or less' as even at the detailed design stage, there is likely to still be further design work to be done, for instance, the incorporation of selected vendor design information and any design modifications to cater for their specifics so that they can integrate within the plant. There will also be the final 'nuts-and-bolts' design where manufacturing and construction drawings will need to be produced.

At this detailed design stage, the design should be sufficiently developed that it is possible to conduct a detailed safety analysis on a design that is mature. For instance, the design would have developed such that the PFDs will become more detailed and will have transitioned into *piping and instrument diagrams* (P+IDs). Likewise, MFDs will be supplemented by *mechanical handling diagrams* (MHDs). Thus, all of the processes, vessels, pipes, mechanical handling systems and process and safety systems should become known. Some of the principal design documents produced at the detailed design stage are outlined in Table 3.2.

It is worth noting that organisations attach project milestones and funding stages to the completion of detailed design. However, organisations can take different views on the term *detailed design* and the level of design maturity that this truly means—caution is recommended to ensure that all parties in a project understand what is expected at this stage. It is not unknown for there to be contractual wrangles over the completeness of projects having completed (or not) 'detailed design'.

Table 3.2: Example detailed design deliverables.

Deliverable	Description
Plant inventory and/or flow-sheet	Details of radiological material in terms of chemical form, quantity and mass balance through the process
Plant and process description	An overview description of what the plant will do, what it looks like and how it operates
Detailed layout drawings	Physical layouts of the plant both externally and internally including major process systems and mechanical equipment
P+IDS	Schematic diagrams showing the pipes and their falls, valves, vessels and piping tie-in points, instrumentation and control and safety systems such as alarms and interlocks

Table 3.2: Continued

VFDS	Schematic diagrams showing the ventilation systems including the air-conditioning units, air-handling units, fans, filters together with the stack or discharge points and the cascade air flows through containment boundaries
MHDS	Schematic diagrams showing cranes and other mechanical handling equipment used to transport solid material, such as the import of new clean containers into a system their filling of material and export from the plant
Classification of areas and normal radiological dose assessment	An assessment of radiation and contamination levels in different rooms, cells and process areas. Determination of radiological dose during normal operations
C+I configuration diagrams	Schematic diagrams showing C+I systems and how safety-related systems are arranged from detection to logic to termination
C+I cause and effect documents	How the process control and safety interlocks and alarms function, what trips the interlocks and alarms together with the cascading consequences of their trip
Construction methods, drawings and optioneering	How the plant will be constructed and demonstration that an ALARP process has been selected

The safety case at the detailed design stage will be summarised in the PCSR. The safety analysis will normally be based upon HAZOP 2 of the P+IDs, VFDs and so on as shown in Table 3.2 (more details of the HAZOP process are given in Section 7.1). Some specific aspects unique to the PCSR stage are described below.

Accounting for construction

The PCSR is the safety case that seeks permission for construction to start. For high-category plant, it is normal for construction to only be authorised by the regulator following review and acceptance of the PCSR. This is by the granting of a licence instrument.

It is essential that the hazards posed by construction to other nuclear plants on the site are understood and demonstrated to be tolerable and ALARP in the PCSR. There may be direct impact hazards to other plants or disruption to safety-related services routed to these plants. Ideally, the new build should be far enough away from the existing nuclear plants that there is no hazard. However, this is not always practicable in an existing and crowded site. Moreover, the new build plant may be required to directly interface with the existing plants, such as a new retrieval plant to remove waste from an historic waste vault and this will involve interconnecting civil structures and mechanical systems.

Evidence of optioneering in construction strategy can be an important aspect of justification and this can be especially true in the selection and siting of cranes. Cranes can pose significant hazards to adjacent plants due to their reach and mass at height.

Accounting for normal dose

An assessment of radiological dose during normal conditions will be required to demonstrate that this will be both tolerable and ALARP. The dose criteria given in Table 2.1 form the basis of this demonstration with an expectation that the BSOs should be met for a new build, as far as reasonably practicable.

During the detailed design stage, the *radiological classification of the areas* will have been undertaken and there will be an understanding of the predicted radiation and contamination levels in each room, cell or process area. There will also be knowledge of the operator's working patterns in terms of activities, their durations and locations in areas of elevated radiation or contamination. Therefore, it will be possible to calculate the radiological dose for the operational tasks for comparison with the doses in Table 2.1.

Similarly, an estimate of normal operational discharges via ventilation routes to the atmosphere or liquid discharges to the marine environment should be demonstrated to lead to tolerable and ALARP levels of dose to the public. This last aspect will also stray into the environmental side of the permissioning through the need to demonstrate BAT/BPM, i.e. that potential harm to the environment has been reduced to ALARP.

Accounting for decommissioning

Given that a PCSR is seeking permission to build a plant and once built, it is likely to be too late to make significant corrections, it is important that the PCSR broadly sets out how the plant will be decommissioned. The decommissioning may not occur for many decades to come, but the lessons of previous failures to consider decommissioning in plant design should have been learnt and incorporated.

It is not expected that a fully detailed decommissioning process is known at the outset, as this will be dependent upon the future life history. However, the broad principles and strategy for how decommissioning will be undertaken should be developed. To help in showing the strategy, the safety case should include a range of information including aspects of:

- Knowledge of what will constitute 'end of life';

- What design processes and internal features will be incorporated to aid decommissioning;

- How future decontamination may be undertaken;

- Expected decommissioning waste routes and the quantities of waste;

- Reliance on other plants to aid decommissioning.

As an example, cells containing radioactive liquor vessels may be expected to have stainless steel clad bunds and wash rings. This is to ensure that if there is a leak, activity migration into concrete is minimal and that the steel liner can be washed down prior to decommissioning. This may enable much of the concrete to be consigned as *free release* and not require disposal as *low-level waste* (LLW).

Accounting for change

A final, but important, note to make is that during the detailed design stage, the design is likely to be *frozen*. The freezing of the design is normally required prior to the HAZOP to ensure that the safety analysis is based upon a design that does not change under its feet without knowledge. Until this point, it is likely that drawings will be produced and updated as required to ensure a workable design. After the freeze point, a formal change process will be required to be instigated to control modifications to the design even though these are 'on paper'. This is often via the issuing of a *design change notification* (DCN) for review that should include the safety assessors as well as the relevant engineering disciplines and operators.

Significant changes introduced via a DCN after the PCSR will generally still occur and they may require their own supplemental safety case justification at the time. The next safety case submission will normally be associated with commissioning and this should incorporate all of these changes and ensure that any cumulative effects are accounted for and justified as acceptable. If the DCN has been done well, there should be no unpleasant surprises when the PICSR is written and the impact of the changes assessed. The PICSR is discussed in the next section.

3.3   Commissioning

The construction of a plant or the installation of mechanical equipment into a new plant will generally be undertaken in an inactive environment. At some stage the plant will be required to operate and go *active* in order to receive, process, generate, export radioactive material and so on. Going active in this manner is an important milestone and is often subject to a regulator hold point for significant plants or installations. Once a plant goes active, the process parts of it will become radioactive and it will no longer be straightforward to correct any deficiencies. Moreover, 'pressing go' will lead to a step change in the decommissioning cost of the plant and it is important to be confident that the plant will work. Can we imagine the scenario of a multi-million-pound new build project commencing nuclear operations only for a fundamental and life-limiting defect to be detected at the core of the nuclear process? Unbelievably, plants have been built costing millions of pounds only for a fundamental flaw in the process to be identified.

The commissioning of the plant is therefore an important step in transitioning a plant from non-active to active. It is a controlled process and quite often is a two-step process involving the production of two separate safety cases with two separate top-tier safety reports: to reflect *non-active* and *active* commissioning. The top-tier reports are generally known as the PICSR and PACSR, respectively, and they provide the justification that the hazards associated with commissioning can be undertaken safely. We will briefly discuss each in turn.

3.3.1 Pre-inactive commissioning safety case

The pre-inactive commissioning safety case is written following the construction of the plant or the installation of major equipment into an existing plant and the safety case is summarised in the top-tier report: the PICSR. The intent is that the PICSR builds upon the safety case presented in the PCSR and should include an evolution of the safety arguments previously presented. In simple terms, the PCSR reflects how the plant is *expected* to be built whilst the PICSR reflects *how* the plant was built. The two states are not necessarily the same!

The design drawings, such as the P+IDs and GAs, should achieve *as-built* status showing the actual configuration installed within the plant. However, there may be changes introduced during construction and aspects of the safety case between the PCSR and the PICSR may diverge. Changes during construction may be due to construction errors or changes in equipment because the original specified equipment could not be delivered. It may also be found that there have been late changes in the project scope and the plant is required to operate slightly differently to that originally justified in the PCSR. This would require interim safety case justification. Therefore, the PICSR will reflect any late design changes and changes introduced during construction.

A key aspect of the PICSR is to demonstrate that the plant will be commissioned safely. By definition, the plant or system will remain inactive during this commissioning stage and there should be no radiological doses during inactive commissioning other than those associated with working in the plant's location on the nuclear site. The PICSR will describe the managerial arrangements that will be in place to underpin the commissioning with reference to the relevant risk assessments.

So what exactly is commissioned on the plant? Essentially, many of the aspects of the plant are checked and tested to confirm that they work as the design intended, which is referred to as the *design intent.* This checking and testing may involve the use of simulants or dummy non-active material, such as containers, etc., to confirm the functionality of the process and mechanical handling equipment.

The use of simulants may require temporary abatement systems to treat off-gases to prevent the discharge of noxious chemicals into the atmosphere. This may be because active tie-ins to existing nuclear process ventilation systems may not yet have been made. Strictly, the potential discharge to the atmosphere is an environmental issue as the simulants will not be radioactive. However, the safety case is likely to be required to provide some confidence that there are adequate arrangements to manage any hazards associated with the chemicals and also to provide evidence to demonstrate that the simulation sufficiently resembles the nuclear process it is trying to represent.

The preceding PCSR will have developed a schedule of safety-related SSCs, which will include the safety systems such as alarms and interlocks with their associated safety functions. These SSCs will be included on a *commissioning schedule* and their commissioning will ensure that the safety functions are adequately delivered in line with the safety case requirements and the design intent. The commissioning schedule will also justify how the systems are commissioned, noting the restriction that testing must use inactive methods and this may pose certain limitations in the accuracy of the results obtained. This is not a problem—it is about confidence building. The commissioning schedule will detail the pass/fail criteria for the testing. Justification will also be provided in the commissioning schedule (or a supporting reference) for not undertaking commissioning of specific sscs if this is not reasonably practicable.

During commissioning, should defects be found, these will normally be corrected to bring the item in line with the original safety case specification. However, there may need to be accompanying changes to the safety case to justify the installation of new replacement systems or to take into account changes in performance. The latter situation is not ideal, as it will require an ALARP justification to justify the acceptance of something that is not as good as it should be. We will illustrate the situation by the use of two examples.

Example: Shield Wall Thickness—Insufficient During Commissioning
This example is one from real life on an active plant that contains a number of shielded cells that handle high gamma radiation sources. The cells incorporate shield walls made from reinforced concrete. It was determined during commissioning testing that there were a number of small voids in the wall giving rise to areas of reduced shielding thickness compared to the design intent. These should have been detected and rectified during construction, but for whatever reason they were not. To correct the defect would take a considerable cost in terms of time and effort that would have a detrimental effect on the operations and so on.

It was found that the actual shielding present was still sufficient to ensure very low-dose levels to the operators. It was, therefore, relatively simple to construct an ALARP justification to accept the reduced shielding thickness. The marginal dose rate experienced by operators was still tolerable and sufficiently low that any increased risk was deemed to be negligible.

On the other hand, what if the deficiency was so significant such that the dose rates were no longer tolerable or were very high? In this case, the ALARP justification would be difficult to make. Whilst pulling down the wall and starting again may not be reasonably practicable, additional measures could be justified to be employed to reduce the dose rate back towards the original design intent. This could necessitate the placing of additional shield blocks around the area or impose access restrictions to the area, and both of these solutions could give rise to significant operability issues. In this case, the actual solution to be determined would depend on the specifics of the deficiency, its magnitude and impact on the operational plant.

Example: Safety Case Interlock—Fails During Commissioning
During inactive commissioning of a process waste plant, it may be found that a safety interlock system does not work as intended. This failure could be because it was a novel interlock that was based upon process parameters that had never been used before and there was no LFE on which to refer to. During the design process, when

the interlock was solely on paper, it may or may not have been recognised by the engineers that there was uncertainty in the viability of the system.

Irrespective of what the designers originally thought, there is nothing as good as real data. During commissioning it may be found that the system gives spurious trip signals or it may simply not function at all when the trip parameters are met. There may also be found to be unintended consequences that were not predicted.

These commissioning results may give rise to a considered joint opinion between safety, engineers and operators to do away with the interlock system given the trouble it will cause during actual operations. On review of the safety case, it may be found that there are alternative systems that could be used or an ALARP justification made that the plant can be actively commissioned and operated with the interlock removed from service. It may be found that there are no reasonably practicable alternatives and that the risk, whilst numerically higher, is still tolerable.

3.3.2   Pre-active commissioning safety case

Following successful inactive commissioning, permission will be sought to commence active commissioning. This is often achieved through the delivery of the pre-active commissioning safety case, which is summarised in the PACSR. As its name suggests, *active* commissioning will involve the introduction of radioactive material into the plant, and once this is undertaken it will be very difficult to 'roll the clock back' and make changes in areas that have been exposed to such material. Therefore, the PACSR will build upon the PICSR and incorporate the results of the (hopefully) successful inactive commissioning. An active commissioning schedule will detail the commissioning tests to be undertaken with their pass/fail criteria.

In the spirit of the 'R' in the ERICPD, the radioactive inventory initially used during active commissioning may be *reduced* from that associated with the eventual operations. Thus, should things go wrong, the consequences will not be as severe as they could be. As an example, liquors of low radiological content may initially be used or a waste drum towards the lower end of the inventory range. There may not be any alternative but to use material representative of the typical inventory to be processed in the plant. A reactor starting up for the first time will produce significant numbers of fission products, but it would not go to full power until confidence that the systems work as intended.

As the example with the reactor suggests, there will be a series of hold points to ensure that all of the systems are working as predicted and there will be an increased level of checking and supervision during these tests. Once the conditions of each hold point are satisfied, authorisation will be granted to progress to the next stage. This could be the movement of a waste drum through the process, the transfer of liquor from a holding tank to a process vessel or the increase in power output of a reactor. It may be found that the regulator has only granted initial approval for a certain number of commissioning tests to be undertaken with further safety case submissions required for the next stage.

It is sometimes found that one active plant interfaces directly with another active plant. This may be because they are physically next door to each other and material is transferred from one to the other, such as waste drums via mechanical handling systems that straddle the two plants. Plants may also be physically separated and connected by ventilation pipework, or liquor transfer pipework or rail transfer systems to move material from one building to the next. The implication of this is that our newly designed, built and inactively commissioned plant must make *active connections* or tie-ins into an existing radiological plant. Process ventilation systems and liquor pipework in particular may have the highest potential for contamination release when active connections are made.

A key aspect of the PACSR is the demonstration that the active tie-ins can be undertaken safely. This in itself may be an involved process and require a detailed safety assessment. If the tie-in were to go wrong, there may be not only a release of activity but also an impact on the adjacent interfacing plant. The safety assessment may be required to assess the hazards on multiple plants. The management of this process and the delivery, approval and authorisation to undertaken the work can become very complicated if there are multiple stakeholders, noting that it is possible for some stakeholders not to be too keen on the operation going ahead. A ventilation system can interface with a dozen individual plants that all have their own safety cases and all can be affected by the modification.

3.4   Operational safety case

Following active commissioning of a plant, the plant will transition to operations. One would not expect the plant to continue to operate in accordance with the PACSR as the plant will be beyond the commissioning stage. After a relatively short time, the safety case should be revised to become an *operational safety case*. This should be a very minor change in the written documentation; there may be some minor amendments to reflect the results of active commissioning. This safety case should then become the baseline safety case for the foreseeable future operation of the plant. In many respects, this is the safety case that the design life-cycle safety documentation has been building up to.

It is recognised that the operational safety case for a plant will be written and implemented at a specific time. The plant may operate in one form or another for 50 years or more. The safety case should be kept up to date as the plant is modified either through the incorporation of new processes or changes to plant equipment. The plant may have transitioned in scope of operations in that time and may have actually have been under an extensive period of care and maintenance. We will discuss the management of changes in Section 3.8, but there should be a plethora of safety case justifications associated with modifications that have been raised in the operational history. Over time, this may make the safety case unwieldy and hard to follow.

One question we can reasonably ask for an existing plant with its safety case is 'would a safety case written many years ago for a plant be the same as if it were to be written today?' The answer is probably 'no'. This is because understandings of processes and hazards change and views on the acceptability of risk levels may also change. The way safety cases are written may fundamentally change in this time period, and this may or may not be more demanding in terms of the requirements for safety-related equipment and procedures.

Finally, we must recognise that over time, life-limiting factors may come into play. This can lead to a reduction in safety margins. For some items they can be replaced, but if they are fundamental and embedded in the nuclear process and within areas of high-radiation and contamination, their replacement may be impossible. Graphite cores of reactors or vessels containing highly radioactive liquors are obvious examples that will define the life-limiting factors of the plants.

Example: Plant End-of-Life Criteria

A safety case for a new plant was written 30 years ago and it was commissioned and successfully operated. Towards the end of its operational life, the safety case for the plant was being reviewed and it was discovered that the original safety case was based upon an expected operational life of only 15 years. No evidence that an engineering assessment had been undertaken to justify a life extension could be found. Of concern was that important pipework that was providing primary containment of radioactive material had no effective secondary containment.

The radioactive material also possessed significant chemical hazards. The pipework was subject to thermal cycling and internal corrosion, and there was a concern expressed that if fractures were to develop there could be a release and the consequences severe.

Whilst there were clearly failures in the management of the safety case, once identified corrective action was immediately instigated. This included the commissioning of pipe stress analysis modelling and a programme of non-destructive testing to confirm the integrity of the pipework. The results of the modelling and testing were satisfactory, enabling justification for the plant to continue operating over a longer time period. It is noted that the plant operations were not suspended when the issue was raised. An ALARP justification to continue operating was made. Whether this was or was not the right approach will not be judged here, but it can be a big call to take a money-generating plant offline if there is no actual evidence of an imminent chance of failure. Should the results of the modelling and inspection have been less positive, a different decision would have been made.

3.4.1 Short-term safety case reviews

A long-term periodic review of a safety case (which we will subsequently discuss) can be a significant undertaking in terms of disruption to key staff, time and money. If the safety case is not well managed in the interim periods, there can be a significant number of surprises. It is also unclear how adequate control of the safety case can be demonstrated if there is no interim assessment of the safety case.

Good practice in the industry utilises a process of conducting a *short-term periodic review* of the safety case. These are often undertaken annually, but there is no defined frequency of conducting them in legislation and so on. A plant subject to a significant number of modifications may require an annual short-term review, but others that are more or less static may be able to justify a more relaxed timescale. We will, therefore, resist referring to these as annual reviews of the safety case and use the more generic *short-term reviews* of the safety case.

The purpose of the short-term review of the safety case should be focused on ensuring that:

1. The chronic effect of changes introduced by modifications is understood.

2. There are no unexpected trends in deterioration of plant performance in terms of: reliability of safety-related sscs, accidents, near misses and events, radioactive discharges to the atmosphere and normal operational dose.

3. The overall safety case comprising of the base operational safety case supplemented by the totality of safety case justifications for the modifications continues to be adequate. Additionally, that the envelope of operations and the safety measures to ensure this envelope is not breached are adequately defined.

In achieving items (1) and (3) above, it may be necessary to tabulate and provide a commentary for all the modifications. Particular emphasis in the commentary is placed on those of higher safety category. The short-term reviews of the safety case therefore become a useful 'go-to' place when it is necessary to understand the status of the plant and modifications that have been made to it.

As a word of caution, it is not unheard for these short-term safety case reviews to become cluttered with all sorts of information that is perceived to be of interest. This is all very nice, but can distract from the core message and there should be more appropriate vehicles for the collation and distribution of this information. The safety case review should be proportionate and focused. The skillset and knowledge of the person writing the reviews needs to be one with an understanding of the safety case for that plant and the day-to-day operations and how these may have changed over the review period.

Once written, the short-term reviews are normally submitted to review by a safety committee that is responsible for nuclear safety in the plant and will include senior members from the plant's management. The committee will, therefore, have the capability to instigate investigations and/or corrective action if undue concerns are raised. The short-term reviews can be an important source for information for longer-term reviews, which we will now discuss.

3.4.2   Long-term safety case reviews

Over a longer time period to that of a short-term review there is a more detailed and in-depth review of the safety case. Timescales for review of 10 years are not uncommon in the industry. The review process can be time consuming and costly for personnel and involve a wide range of disciplines from safety, human factors and engineering as well as operational and maintenance personnel on the plant. A long-term review will need to be treated as a project and managed accordingly.

Technically, the long-term periodic review leads to a revalidation of the current operational safety case. In reality, it may lead to the production of a new safety case that must subsequently be implemented and this should occur before the validity of the current operational safety case expires. The production of a new safety case does not mean a wholesale rewrite of the current case—the mantra should always be to 're-use' and not to 're-write'. Indeed, the rewrite of the safety case should only be on the basis that the review identifies that the operational safety case is not-fit-for-purpose. This does not mean that the safety case is necessarily wrong, but it may not be suitable for future operations or that the future condition of the plant may need to be more accurately reflected in the safety case. Therefore, the long-term review should be *forward looking* as well as reviewing the plant's operational history. The principal aims of such a long-term review include:

- To review the current operational safety case and to confirm that it is still adequate, e.g. that it reflects current and future operations (to a reasonable extent);

- To provide a comparison with current standards and expectations, and evaluate any shortfalls making recommendations to improve safety;

- To demonstrate that life-limiting factors of plant and equipment are understood and are accounted for;

- To revalidate the safety case for a defined period of time.

The long-term review will be reported in a top-tier safety report, which may be known as a *long-term periodic review* (LTPR) *report* or *continued operations safety report* (COSR). The top-tier safety report will describe the process undertaken, summarise the safety case going forward and provide the evidence that the risks are tolerable and ALARP. To undertake the underpinning review, there will be a number of key steps that will include:

1. Confirmation of the scope of the review in terms of time, physical extent, radioactive inventory and processes;

2. Establishment of a baseline of operations by reviewing modifications since the last review and consider their cumulative effect;

3. Confirmation that the current suite of hazard analysis adequately reflects the cumulative changes, e.g. that there are no gaps or areas where the analysis is wrong and make recommendations as necessary (against observations or shortfalls);

4. Review of the engineering substantiation to ensure that there are no gaps and provide a comparison with current standards making recommendations as necessary;

5. Review of other aspects such as human factors, incidents, operational doses, discharges making recommendations as necessary;

6. Produce new hazard analysis, engineering substantiation and so on as required;

7. Undertaking ALARP reviews;

8. Summarising the process in the long-term report, gaining approval and implementing the revised case or revalidating the current case.

Example: Self-Defeating Safety Case

A plant manager responsible for a safety case admits that the inherited safety case was difficult to follow. This was because it was too long and complicated for what was a relatively simple plant. The safety case comprised over 40 individual safety analysis documents and a voluminous engineering schedule.

As an example, for the drop of a package there was a whole suite of analysis in one document considering the release of aerosol from the package due to a loss of containment. There was another document, with overwhelmingly the same paragraphs, assessing external radiation from a breach in shielding of the same package in the same drop event. There were over 20 pages of words and argument for each assessment and the doses were actually found to be trivial and of no real concern. The structure and analysis were disproportionate, overly complex and ultimately not-fit-for-purpose. It was not surprising that it was difficult to follow. Note that this was an issue of documentation and not an issue of the safety of the plant.

As part of an LTPR, the safety case was reduced significantly and eventually comprised only a few documents of safety analysis. Therefore, it became proportionate, readable and, ultimately, fit-for-purpose.

3.5 Post-operational clean-out

At the end of the life of a plant, there may be a period of *post-operative clean-out* (POCO). This is a process by which residual inventory within the plant is systematically removed with a view to facilitating its eventual decommissioning. The POCO stage is likely to utilise the existing plant infrastructure and may well follow normal operational practices. It is clearly preferable to undertake POCO before waste removal and processing equipment have been decommissioned and removed from the plant. Examples of POCO operations include:

- The removal of residual liquors from storage or processing vessels followed by a system wash-out with the wash-out liquor utilising the existing discharge routes;

- The removal of bulk material from gloveboxes followed by the decontamination of the inner surfaces with the material bagged out and sentenced via the solid disposal route;

- The handling of reactor fuel if this is within the scope already justified in the safety case.

The above examples show that POCO does not necessarily require a modification to the existing safety case and POCO can simply be considered to be the final suite of operations. The reduction in the plant inventory can have a beneficial effect of reducing the safety classification of the plant. This is because the reduction of bulk inventory will likely lead to a step change in potential doses to the public and workers from a fault. Therefore, a modification proposal can be raised to reduce the category. A plant may be in a state of POCO for some time whilst decommissioning strategies are developed, but it will clearly be of benefit to decommissioning to have removed the inventory as far as practicable before it commences.

3.6   Decommissioning safety case

At the end of the plant's operational life, it is likely it will undergo POCO as we have discussed above. Eventually there will be a requirement to restore the plant's location to a green or brown field site, leaving as little evidence of the nuclear history as practicable. The plant will, therefore, be decommissioned. Decommissioning is unlike normal operations and may be a more hazardous working environment. As with any dismantling operation, there will be hazards associated with removing and size reducing heavy industrial equipment and dismantling civil structures, but with the added complication of residual nuclear material. For older plants record keeping may not have been as good as it should have been and it is possible to discover unknown sources of radioactivity (e.g. seepage from a historic leak). Additionally, physical sections of the plant may not match the configuration expected.

Constructing a safety case for decommissioning can, therefore, be challenging. This is because:

- There may be uncertainty in the inventory especially as historic hard to reach or forgotten places are eventually accessed;

- Decommissioning by its nature is transient and there is likely to be a short-term increase in risk for greater long-term risk reduction;

- The use of industrial equipment brings its own industrial hazards and may lead to new nuclear hazards;

- There will be the generation of sharps and the use of cutting equipment will increase the contaminated wound hazard;

- Key personnel with a knowledge of the plant may have long since retired or left by the time decommissioning occurs;

- Many tasks will be one-off tasks and operators will be unfamiliar with the new environment and be able to bring limited LFE;

- It may be necessary to remove or over-ride safety systems;

- There may be uncertainty at the start of decommissioning as to how all of the plant will be decommissioned.

The safety case associated with decommissioning will need to be different from that produced for an operational plant. It is not usual to continue with an operational safety case and to introduce modifications to justify decommissioning. A decommissioning safety case may be structured with an over-arching framework outlining the main steps, results of optioneering, hazards and controls together with ALARP justification. This may then need to be supported by individual safety case submissions within the framework to reflect the next phase of decommissioning and the removal of uncertainty. A decommissioning mind-set is required with complex ALARP arguments to be made balancing short-term increases in risk against the longer-term risk reduction. Outlining the approach to be adopted for the safety case in a strategy paper is essential to minimise project risk.

3.7   Contents of a safety report

We have established that a safety case should be proportionate to the harm potential and to an extent the complexity of the plant or process within it. The actual contents will also differ to some degree depending on these factors and whether the safety case is for design, commissioning, operation, decommissioning and so on. The sections above have indicated the typical contents to be included at each stage. Generally, this will all be provided in supporting references that comprise the overall safety case. The top-tier safety report document is the summary document that tells the story in a digestible form that ideally should be able to be read within a few hours. In contrast, the underpinning safety case may comprise of many tens or hundreds of documents.

The safety report is intended to be read by key plant personnel, safety committees, regulators and interested parties to gain an overview of the safety case and to be able to make an informed decision as to the adequacy of the overall case. Primarily, the safety report (and the overall safety case) is for those directly responsible for safety.

There are common elements to all safety cases and by extension, safety reports. We will briefly highlight the contents that may be found in a typical safety report. We should note that individual licensees will tailor their safety case and safety report structure to suit their needs and preferences. The contents of what might be found in a typical safety report are shown in Table 3.4. Some licensees may structure their safety reports in a more explicit CAE structure. A CAE structure is a hierarchical structure that begins with a fundamental *claim* that may be supported by lower tier *sub-claims*. Each claim should be supported by an *argument* and then *evidence*:

Claim: The claim that the plant presents a tolerable and ALARP level of risk;

Argument: The written rationale of why the plant presents a tolerable and ALARP level of risk;

Evidence: The detailed assessments, hazard analysis, calculations, design codes, substantiation and so on.

The CAE structure can extend into the hazard analysis and engineering substantiation with appropriately worded claims and so on. For instance, a claim can be made that the risk from a particular tank is *tolerable and alarp* with arguments and evidence to demonstrate that:

- There is a robust control system;

- Faults have been identified and assessed;

- SSCs have been identified and substantiated;

- Recommendations for improvement have been sentenced and incorporated accordingly.

When shown on a page, a graphical map of the CAE can be a powerful tool to visually show the safety arguments. A skeleton CAE is shown in Fig. 3.1.

3.8 Safety case modifications

A safety case for an operational plant should reflect the physical status of the plant and the processes undertaken within it. As we have noted, within the body of the safety case documentation, there should be sufficient information to know what is being undertaken on the plant. This may be encompassed within written documents or engineering drawings such as the P+IDs, VFDs and GAs. Over time, there will be changes to the plant, which may involve physical modifications or modifications to operational processes. These could be due to:

- Installation of new equipment to undertake a new process;

- Installation of new safety measures to satisfy the requirements of an LC 15 review;

- Replacement of a physical component for another one of a different type;

- A change in a maintenance regime;

- A new way of working such as a change to an operating temperature or a liquor level;

- A change to an alarm level;

- An experiment being undertaken;

- Adoption of a new safety case.

These modifications cannot be just undertaken as LC 22 requires there to be adequate control of the modifications. The control is exercised by the use of a modification procedure, sometimes known as a *modification proposal* depending on the

Table 3.3: Example safety case categorisation scheme. No numerical criteria are defined in our example and a licensee would be expected to develop their own numerical criteria to define what is meant by 'low' and 'significant'.

Category	Description
A	Potential for significant on- and off-site doses
B	Potential significant on-site doses, but limited off-site doses
C	Low on- and off-site doses
D	Trivial or no on- and off-site doses

licensee. The modification proposal is normally a pro-former type document (that may use an electronic database system) to describe the modification and provide justification of the modification. The proposal is a vehicle to introduce a new aspect of a safety case, i.e. a modification to an existing safety case. It can also be used to move from one safety case to another, i.e. to adopt a new safety case. An example of adoption would be to move from an operational safety case to a decommissioning safety case.

Changes to a plant that do not involve the nuclear plant (or services that support them) do not normally require a formal modification procedure produced in line with LC 22. Such exclusions would include modifications to kitchens, or office buildings away from the nuclear plant. Similarly, like-for-like replacements of equipment during maintenance do not normally require a modification proposal. A change in equipment type, even if it is doing the same operation or providing the same safety function, may require a modification proposal. This is due to the potential to introduce an error or introduce a new aspect of operation or failure from the new type of item.

The modification proposal will be categorised on the basis of the nuclear hazard that the modification introduces. This hazard may also be because the change is incorrectly planned or implemented. The categorisation should take no account of controls or safety measures that will be put in place to prevent these hazards from occurring. Like all safety cases, the quantity of assessment and information presented within the proposal will generally be proportional to the safety significance of the modification, i.e. its category. Again, this reflects the concept of proportionality. In addition, the due process route for the proposal will also be determined by the safety category. Categorisation schemes for modifications will be similar to those presented in Table 3.3.

For simple modifications, potentially of low safety significance, the modification proposal document itself may be sufficient to include all of the necessary information. However, more complex modifications may require a number of safety and engineering documents to justify the modification. For modifications of Category A or B (see Table 3.3), safety case documents such as a PCSR may need to be written. A PCSR may require peer review and approval by safety committees and they may ultimately require approval from the regulator.

Table 3.4: Example sections and their contents within a safety report. There will be differences in the sections depending on the nature of the safety case. For example, a PCSR may expect to include details of construction schemes within Section B as these are the normal operations of the process and there would then be a summary of the assessment of construction hazards in Section D, should construction pose a hazard to other nuclear plants.

Section	Title	Contents
A	Introduction	Introduction to the safety case, project stage, relevant design deliverables, methodologies used, success criteria, safety case structure, what the safety case is for
		Scope and boundary of the safety case in terms of processes, time, plant state, feeds (inventory) and outputs, exclusions
		Main hazards and summary of key hazard management strategies
B	Plant and Process Description	Plant location
		Summary of the plant physical structure and internal layout
		Summary of key processes
		Feeds and outputs
		Solid, liquid and gaseous waste arisings and discharges
		Management arrangements including how the NSL is complied with, roles and responsibilities (not personal names), plant instructions and compliance arrangements
C	Operational History	Plant history and effect of cumulative changes if relevant
		Incidents and near misses
		Waste arisings, discharges, trends and future predictions
		Normal dose to public and workers, history, trends and future predictions
		Trends from maintenance and future maintenance requirements
D	Hazard Analysis Summary	Summary of hazard identification process
		Summary of radiological and criticality hazard analysis including demonstration that risks are tolerable and relevant criteria are satisfied (or discussed if there are shortfalls)
		Summary of any other significant hazards
		Discussion of the safe operating envelope of the plant, defined by operating rules, safety instructions and key safety equipment

Table 3.4: Continued

Section	Title	Contents
E	Substantiation Summary	Discussion of shortfalls and recommendations Collation of safety claims on engineering (engineering schedule) Engineering substantiation of key safety equipment, including a description of processes undertaken, limitations, key findings including shortfalls and recommendations Human factors substantiation of claims made on operator behaviour and reliability Analysis of the role of humans in the plant, including whether the processes and environments are optimised to minimise errors and maximise the potential for a safe operating environment, *human machine interface* (HMI) issues
F	ALARP Summary	Demonstration that the normal operations of the plant are ALARP (discharges, dose to the public and workers), safety hierarchy in dose minimisation Demonstration that the process is ALARP from a fault perspective, engineering substantiation and human factors perspectives Discussion of key recommendations and ALARP processes undertaken including evidence of optioneering and forward action plans to incorporate changes to reduce risk
G	Conclusions	Summary of safety case, processes undertaken Summary of key hazards, hazard management strategies and substantiation of claims on engineering and operator action Conclusions that the risks are tolerable and ALARP and that there are forward actions in place to further reduce risk (if appropriate) Anything else pertinent
-	Miscellaneous	References Figures, tables and appendices

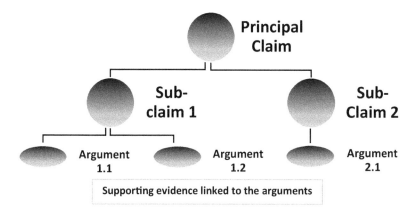

Figure 3.1: Skeleton CAE structure. The principal claim may refer to the fact that the facility provides an acceptable level of safety such that the risks are tolerable and ALARP. As many supporting claims and sub-claims as necessary will feed into the structure. For instance, a sub-claim may be that all faults have been identified; argument being a description of the HAZID processes; evidence being the minutes of the HAZID meetings, fault listing and so on.

In practice, a modification proposal can be considered to be an *enabling document*. It is then a signposting document to demonstrate that all of the relevant work to make the change has been done. In addition to the safety case assessment, this may include:

- Engineering substantiation;

- Drawing updates;

- Commissioning schedules;

- Cascading of safety case requirements into procedures on the plant;

- Production of (conventional) risk assessments;

- Training of personnel.

Approval of the proposal through the due process will eventually give rise to the final signature giving *authorisation to implement* the change. The work can then be undertaken to implement the change.

Once the change has been completed the modification proposal should be *closed-out*. Again, this will require signatures to demonstrate that the work has been satisfactorily completed in line with the proposal. This is an important process and it is not untrue to say that after the 'excitement' of making the change, the close-out process can take a while to complete. It is important to reflect that without closing out of the proposal, it may not be clear to future interested parties whether the modification was completed or not. This will make safety case reviews difficult to ascertain what has been changed on the plant. As an example, it is an important exercise to ensure that the drawing registry contains the latest drawings reflecting the as-built modification.

Example: Poor Drawing Control
A large plant was undergoing an LTPR. The review determined that a HAZOP was required, as the original records were scarce and patchy and considered to be not-fit-for-purpose to underpin a modern safety case. However, the drawing registry had not been kept live following numerous modifications. It was unclear what the actual plant configuration was. The HAZOPs were delayed as a team of personnel was employed to survey every pipe and system on the plant (as far as practicable) to ascertain the as-built status and produce up to date drawings. This cost a lot of money.

3.9   Categorisation

As we have been describing, safety cases are required to justify the operations of nuclear plants. However, not all plants are equally hazardous. For example, consider a nuclear reactor that may pose a societal risk due to the potential for faults to lead to significant releases of activity (examples being Chernobyl or the Windscale fire) and a low-level waste plant which contains encapsulated solid waste. Even within a nuclear site itself, there will likely be a range of hazardous plants. To ensure a proportionate approach to production, review and scrutiny, a safety case *categorisation* scheme is used. The highest category safety case may require approval from the regulator before it can be adopted and used.

Therefore, it is important to define such a categorisation scheme. These are typically based upon the nature and magnitude of the doses without regard for likelihood of occurrence. That is, the categorisation should take no account of controls or safety measures that will exist to prevent the faults from occurring or to mitigate their doses.

The highest category will be reserved for the plants that can give rise to significant off-site doses with the tier below restricted to the plants that may give rise to significant on-site doses but limited off-site. Table 3.3 gives an example categorisation scheme for modifications that can be applied for safety cases. It is worth noting that numerical values have not been assigned to the terms in Table 3.3, as these will be specified and justified by the individual licensee. As a guide, significant doses may be determined to be equivalent to the LLs (Table 2.1), i.e. 20 mSv (worker) and 1 mSv (public).

Part II

RADIATION PHYSICS AND DOSE

Chapter 4

Radioactivity and Nuclear Processes

By definition, nuclear safety involves the safe use, handling, processing and storage of nuclear material. We define nuclear material as material that is either radioactive, fissile or both. It is important to have an understanding of what radioactivity is and why it is of concern if one is involved in the preparation or use of safety cases. It is, after all, the hazard we are trying to manage. Understanding radioactivity and the dose implications of exposure to it can help to dispel the myths associated with the subject. We are constantly exposed to radioactivity in the natural world and the nuclear industry should only increase an individual's exposure by a small amount in comparison to that associated with nature.

Radioactivity involves an unstable parent nuclide decaying into a more stable, lower energy, *daughter* nuclide. This involves the emission of a particle and/or the emission of a photon of light (gamma or X-ray). *Radioactivity* is therefore the process of radioactive decay (the change), and the emissions from the nuclide are known as the *radiation*. When radioactivity occurs, the resulting smaller daughter nuclide may itself be unstable and decay and so on until a stable nuclide is eventually reached. This is known as a radioactive *decay chain*.

The nuclear *fission* and *fusion* processes associated with power generation and weapons involve making changes to the nuclear structure leading to the production of different nuclides. Fission involves the splitting of uranium or plutonium nuclides, which can be induced by an interacting free neutron. The nuclides are *fissionable* and some are also known as *fissile* nuclides due to their ability to undergo fission when the neutron has low energy.

Nuclear fusion involves the joining together of light elements, notably hydrogen or helium nuclei. The nuclear energy sector only utilises the nuclear fission process, but there are research centres around the world that are trying to develop nuclear fusion. The nuclear fission and fusion processes may lead to instabilities in the newly produced nuclei that lead to their radioactive decay. This is a particular problem in nuclear fission where very complex decay chains can arise.

This chapter provides a background to the subject of radioactivity and radiation. After a brief history, it begins with the basics in terms of the different types of radioactivity and decay modes, i.e. *alpha*, *beta* and *gamma* decay and other lesser-known decay modes. The laws of radioactive decay are introduced and the units of measurement typically used are described with a focus on the modern-day unit of the becquerel[1] (Bq). Inevitably, there is physics involved in discussing radioactivity, but the material presented is no more advanced than that associated with a sixth-form school or first year at university. We introduce the concept of a plant *inventory* and *fingerprint*, which quantify the radioactivity and the nuclide breakdown of the radioactive or fissile material within a plant. Having knowledge of the inventory and fingerprint is fundamental in developing a safety case. The process of determining the fingerprint is sometimes known as *characterisation*.

Nuclear fission is the basis of the overwhelming majority of the nuclear industry, and a basic understanding of the process is required for all safety assessors. Criticality safety assessors will specialise in the nuclear fission process and they will need an in-depth understanding of fission for which there are industry standard packages for their detailed training. In this book we only provide an introduction to the basic terms including *moderator* and *neutron multiplication factor*. Additionally, the operation of fission reactors is considered to be beyond the scope of this book and reference should be made to more detailed and specialist texts (e.g. [4]) to gain an understanding of their operation if needed.

For completeness, we will also briefly mention nuclear fusion. Nuclear fusion is not a process that is used for power generation, but there are organisations researching and developing fusion systems. The fusion process does generate relatively small quantities of radioactive waste and there are radiation hazards when operational. Facilities include the Joint European Torus (JET) in the UK and will include the forthcoming International Thermonuclear Experimental Reactor (ITER) in France scheduled for operations in the late 2020s/2030s.

4.1   Discovery of radioactivity

It was the study of uranium minerals by Becquerel in Paris at the end of the 19th century that led to his serendipitous discovery of radioactivity. He was originally researching the luminescence properties of the minerals and discovered that the emission of rays (later defined to be gamma rays) was an intrinsic property of the mineral and did not involve the initial absorption of light.

The term *radioactivity* was coined by two of the most famous pioneers of the fledging field of nuclear science: the Curies, in 1898. With the work of Rutherford and others, the nature of this radioactivity began to be understood. The laws of radioactivity

---

[1] It is a little known convention that even when units are named after an individual, they are written in full in lowercase, but the first letter of the symbol will use uppercase. Hence, the unit named after Henri Becquerel is written as the becquerel with symbol Bq. The unit is also a mathematical entity rather than an abbreviation and can be manipulated in an equation accordingly. Bureau International des Poids et Mesures [7] provides an excellent guide to the official use of International System of Units (SI).

were formulated and it was ascertained that there were different types of radioactivity, i.e. alpha, beta and gamma decay. These terms are still used today. In the early experiments, it was also determined that alpha and beta decay involve the loss of matter from the nucleus and the transmutation of matter from one element to another.

The early pioneers initially had no knowledge that radioactivity was harmful to health. Even when evidence began to arise that it was harmful, it was ignored in the pursuit of the science. Precautions were sometimes taken when the radioactivity was found to interfere with their experiments! Rutherford kept and prepared samples of radium in a shed outside the laboratory building in Manchester [8]. Eventually, the radioactivity took its toll on the health of many of the scientists with Marie Curie herself succumbing to radiation-induced disease. Even over 100 years later, laboratories and equipment used by the scientists were still found to be contaminated.

4.2 Definition of radioactivity, laws and types

So, what exactly is radioactivity for which nuclear safety is the theme of this book? For a start, we can state that it is an entirely natural phenomenon and it is an intrinsic property of particular unstable nuclei. Experiments have shown radioactivity cannot be altered by chemistry, heat, pressure or any other external influence. Indeed, this is the basis of the difficulty of dealing with nuclear waste and why it will be around for many thousands of years. Only time is the known way to reduce the amount of radioactive material. We should note that whilst radioactivity is a natural process, nuclear safety involves consideration of the radioactivity of plutonium which is not a naturally occurring isotope. In order to understand radioactivity, we need to understand what an atom is, i.e. the atomic nucleus and electrons, and this is what we will proceed to do.

4.2.1 Atomic structure

An atom consists of a positively charged nucleus that contains protons and neutrons (nucleons), which is surrounded by a cloud of negatively charged electrons. This basic atomic structure was determined in 1911 by Rutherford's scattering experiments in Manchester. It is from the nucleus that the radioactive emissions originate, though some modes of decay indirectly lead to the emission of an X-ray from an electron orbital.[2] In a neutral atom, the number of protons exactly matches the number of electrons so that there is no overall electrical charge. This is shown schematically in Fig. 4.1.

Atomic diameters are of the order of an Angstrom which equates to 10^{-10} m, whilst a hydrogen nucleus has a diameter of the order of a femtometre, which equates to 10^{-15} m, but this will increase by a factor of 10 for larger nuclei. Thus, an atomic nucleus is 100,000 times smaller than its overall atomic diameter, which is solely defined

---

[2]An X-ray photon can have the same energy as a gamma photon; convention is that the photon is generally known as a gamma ray if it originates from the nucleus and an X-ray if it is from an electron changing atomic orbital.

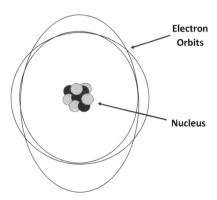

Figure 4.1: Schematic of an atom showing the nucleus consisting of positively charged protons and neutrons (no charge) with negatively charged electrons orbiting the nucleus. The schematic is not to scale, as the diameter of a small element nucleus is of the order of 10^{-15} m, whilst the diameter of the atom (that is defined by the orbit of the electrons) is of the order of 10^{-10} m. In reality, there is no clearly defined round shape of neutrons and protons, and electrons do not orbit in the traditional sense like satellites around the Earth. A true picture of atomic structure requires quantum mechanics.

by the orbit of the electrons. It is the interaction of electrons between neighbouring atoms that give rise to chemistry. Nuclear fission and fusion solely involve the atomic nuclei.

Just like two north poles of two magnets, like charges repel each other. Being all positively charged, the protons in the nucleus do not want to be constrained in their small nuclear volume and experience a repulsive electromagnetic or Coulomb force. Fortunately, there is an overpowering 'strong' nuclear force that acts over a range of femtometres to enable the protons (and neutrons) to be bound into the nucleus; i.e. it takes energy to separate the protons and neutrons. The nuclear binding energies are orders of magnitude greater than the energies involved in binding electrons into atoms. This is why nuclear processes involving nuclear binding energies are so attractive for power and bomb use. Chemistry solely involving electromagnetic energies simply cannot compete.

A chemical element is defined by the number of protons, for which we have stated that neutrally charged atoms have an equal number of electrons in orbit; the atomic number Z is the number of protons. The atomic mass number A is the number of protons and neutrons. As a convention here, we may write $^{A}_{Z}X$, where X is the chemical element and this can be shortened to ^{A}X because stating the atomic number as well as the chemical element abbreviation is superfluous. It is found that there are many different combinations of protons and neutrons that can come together to form individual *nuclides*. *Isotopes* have the same atomic number, but different atomic mass numbers and are chemically identical; i.e. isotopes of the same element have different numbers of neutrons. As examples, common uranium and plutonium isotopes encountered in the nuclear industry are:

- ^{233}U, ^{235}U, ^{238}U;

- ^{240}Pu, ^{241}Pu, ^{242}Pu.

All atoms of uranium have 92 protons and hence 92 electrons, but there are a number of different isotopes as illustrated above. Because chemistry involves atomic electrons, different isotopes behave the same way chemically speaking and it is not possible to separate out different isotopes through chemical processes. Separation can only be achieved by exploiting the slight mass differences through physical mechanisms.[3]

As the atomic number increases (a measure of the number of protons), the number of neutrons in stable (non-radioactive nuclei) initially broadly matches the number of protons. That is, the atomic mass is approximately double the atomic number. However, larger nuclides begin to have proportionately more neutrons than protons and they become more neutron rich. Neutrons carry no repulsive electric charge, but they do provide binding energy. As the nucleus gets larger with more protons, proportionately more binding energy from the neutrons is needed to bind the nucleus together to overcome the longer range electromagnetic repulsive force between protons. Both fission and fusion are energetically favourable because the average binding energy of the nucleons increases.

It is the neutron-rich nature of uranium and plutonium that explains why nuclear fission leads to so many radioactive species being produced. The large neutron-rich uranium or plutonium nuclei split into two smaller nuclei each with approximately 50% of the original protons and neutrons plus a small number of free uncontained neutrons (which can then go on to split other nuclei in a chain reaction). The two new lighter nuclei have proportionately too many neutrons to the number of protons to be stable. Thus, they are radioactive and need to shed the excess neutrons, e.g. by a neutron decaying to a proton and a beta particle (electron) and an anti-neutrino. Beta decay efficiently and simultaneously removes an excess neutron and increases the number of protons, which moves the new nuclide closer to the point of stability.

4.2.2   Rate of radioactive decay

Radioactivity is a random process and we do not know when a particular nuclide will decay. We know of no physical mechanism that can influence the rate of radioactive decay. From experimental knowledge, all we can assign is a probability of decay in a particular time period. Fortunately, because atoms are so small and numerous in the material world, statistics comes into play and we can confidently understand how a large sample will behave and change with time. We can readily measure the *half-life* of a sample and know with certainty how that sample will change through radioactive decay with time. The half-life is defined as the time taken for half of the nuclei in a pure sample to decay.

---

[3] Typically, centrifuges or diffusion processes that exploit the physical mass difference are used to enrich the ^{235}U content of uranium for power generation or bomb production. The fractional mass difference between ^{235}U and ^{238}U is small and it is an energy-intensive and physically extensive process to produce bulk quantities of enriched uranium through centrifuge or diffusion technology.

Table 4.1: Activity conversions.

1 PBq	=	10^{15} Bq	=	10^3 TBq		
1 TBq	=	10^{12} Bq	=	10^3 GBq	=	10^{-3} PBq
1 GBq	=	10^9 Bq	=	10^3 MBq	=	10^{-3} TBq
1 MBq	=	10^6 Bq	=	10^{-3} GBq		

Mathematically, the probability that an individual nuclide will decay in unit time is given by the *decay constant* λ. For N radioactive nuclides in a sample, the rate of decay is

$$\frac{dN}{dt} = -\lambda N. \tag{4.1}$$

The minus sign is because the radioactivity decreases the number of parent nuclides present. Integrating the above gives, at time t,

$$N_t = N_0 e^{-\lambda t}, \tag{4.2}$$

where N_t is the number of nuclides left at t and N_0 is the number at $t = 0$. In simple terms, if we know what the nuclide number of a sample is at a particular time, Eq. 4.2 lets us calculate its value at any time in the future. The decay rate is exponential. The SI unit of radioactivity is the *becquerel* (Bq), which corresponds to one disintegration per second; i.e. $dN/dt = \lambda N = 1$. It is therefore a very small unit. The term λN is known as the *activity* and as this is proportional to N, it reduces exponentially.

The half-life, $t_{1/2}$, is the time taken for half of the nuclides to decay and it is related to the decay constant by

$$t_{1/2} = \frac{\ln 2}{\lambda}. \tag{4.3}$$

Therefore, with a knowledge of the half-life, we can determine the decay constant. We can plot Eq. 4.2 as a function of time to graphically see how the activity of a sample (rate of decay) decreases with time. This is shown in Fig. 4.2 for an illustrative initial sample of 10^{12} Bq of ^{137}Cs.

It is often found that the inventory of nuclides of interest will be in the region of mega-becquerels (MBq), giga-becquerels (GBq), tera-becquerels (TBq) or even peta-becquerels (PBq) for the most radioactive of systems. The relationships between the different units and their orders of magnitude is given in Table 4.1. Safety assessors should be familiar with the units and moving between them.

The unit of curie (Ci) is mentioned in (generally older) safety case documents. It has a value of 3.7×10^{10} Bq equating to the activity within 1 g of ^{226}Ra. However, in the modern world of metric, the Ci is not a very user-friendly unit and is in decreasing general use.

We must be very careful to remember that Eq. 4.2 applies to the activity of a specific nuclide, e.g. ^{240}Pu or ^{137}Cs as shown in our example above. The equation does not apply to the collection of different radioactive nuclides *as a whole* within a bulk of inventory. A real bulk inventory will have many different radioactive nuclides that will have different half-lives potentially ranging from fractions of a second to billions of years. In addition, the daughter nuclides of radioactive nuclei may also be radioactive, which will then decay after being created in accordance with their decay curves and the rate of their production (the rate of decay of the parent nuclide). These facts can lead to a complex relationship of overlapping decay chains that is beyond the scope of this book. Suggested reading includes Lilley [4] and specialist advice may be needed for any safety assessor tasked with determining the inventory in a complex real-world situation.

4.3 Types of radioactivity

So far, we have discussed the laws of radioactivity and the rate of decay, but have not discussed what exactly happens and what the radiation emissions are. Radioactivity occurs because the parent nuclide is in an unstable state or is known as being *excited*. The emission of the radioactive particle enables a loss of energy to occur and the transition to a more stable state. This is analogous to an object falling under gravity. If a ball is held aloft it has potential energy and if let go, it will minimise its potential energy by falling to the ground and gaining kinetic energy. Whilst held aloft with potential energy, the ball is in an excited state and is capable of doing work. Parent nuclides can be considered to have potential energy and seek to lose this by radioactive decay (the ball being let go and falling).

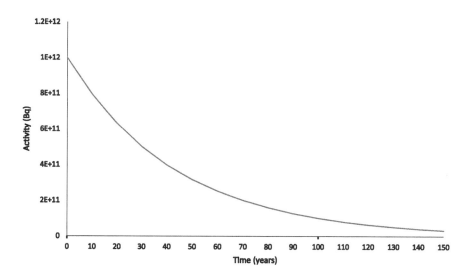

Figure 4.2: Radioactive decay curve for an initial sample of 10^{12} Bq of ^{137}Cs, which has a half-life of 30.2 years. After 30.2 years the activity is half the initial value (5×10^{11} Bq) and after 60.4 years it is a quarter (2.5×10^{11} Bq) and so on.

The principal modes of decay are *alpha*, *beta* and *gamma* decay and these are described below. For completeness, *electron capture* and *internal conversion* are also mentioned as these modes are not well known. *Spontaneous fission* is also a mode of radioactive decay and occurs naturally and should not be confused with artificially induced fission that is described in Section 4.6.

4.3.1 Alpha decay

Larger nuclides, including the transuranic nuclides,[4] will often decay by the emission of an alpha particle (α). This particle comprises two tightly bound protons and two neutrons, i.e. a helium nucleus ^4_2He. Thus, a nuclide decaying in this manner loses both mass and charge and results in the transmutation of the nuclide from one element to another. The daughter product may or may not be stable and if it is stable, it will undergo no further decay. The decay process can be represented by

$$^A_Z X \longrightarrow {}^{A-4}_{Z-2}X' + {}^4_2\text{He}, \tag{4.4}$$

where X and X' are the chemical symbols of the parent and daughter nuclide, respectively, A is the atomic mass number and Z is the atomic number.

Alpha particles are emitted with specific energies and an alpha particle is highly ionising due to its large charge. The particles quickly lose energy when travelling through a medium, such as air, skin or clothing. Sheets of paper are sufficient to block the passage of alpha particles. Consequently, alpha-emitting nuclides are only of concern if they enter the human body through inhalation, ingestion or injection into the blood and they are extremely dangerous inside the body. For plants processing alpha-emitting nuclides, containment of the nuclides is of principal concern rather than shielding. Examples of alpha-emitting nuclides are ^{233}U and ^{240}Pu.

4.3.2 Beta decay

Neutron or proton-rich nuclides may decay via negative or positive beta decay, respectively. Negative beta decay (β^-) involves the conversion of a neutron (n) in the nucleus to a proton (p) with the emission of an electron (the beta particle (e^-)). An anti-neutrino ($\bar{\nu}$) is also emitted.

Likewise, the conversion of a proton to a neutron will lead to the emission of a positron (the anti-matter equivalent of an electron (e^+)) and a neutrino (ν) and is known as positive beta decay (β^+). The reactions are shown as

$$\text{n} \longrightarrow \text{p} + e^- + \bar{\nu} \quad \text{and} \quad \text{p} \longrightarrow \text{n} + e^+ + \nu. \tag{4.5}$$

Neutrinos (and the anti-matter equivalent the anti-neutrino) are massless[5] and chargeless particles that do not readily interact with matter. Their interaction with

---

[4]Transuranic elements are those with atomic numbers greater than uranium (such as plutonium) that do not occur naturally in nature. They are produced by artificial means, e.g. within a nuclear reactor.

[5]They are believed to have zero rest mass (m) or at least a rest mass very close to zero. The rest mass is the inherent mass possessed by particles, which is given by the well-known equation for energy E from Special Relativity; i.e. $m = E/c^2$, where c is the speed of light.

matter is so small that they are capable of passing directly through the entire planet Earth and will not be troubled by the human body. The decay of the neutron or proton leads to the transmutation of the nuclei of mass A and atomic number Z from one element X to another X'. The decay process can be represented by

$$\ _Z^A X \longrightarrow \ _{Z\pm1}^A X'. \tag{4.6}$$

For negative beta decay, the atomic number Z is increased by one, but for positron emission it is decreased by one. The atomic mass number being the sum of the protons and neutrons is unchanged.

The beta particles are emitted with a continuous distribution of energies rather than at discrete values. The particles are less massive and not as ionising as alpha particles, but do lose energy relatively quickly in a medium. They will only travel a few metres in air, and can give rise to skin burns if external to the body. They also pose a hazard if taken into the body. Examples of beta emitting nuclides of relevance to the nuclear industry are ^{90}Sr and ^{241}Pu.

4.3.3 Gamma decay

Gamma decay (γ) involves the emission of a gamma ray of a specific energy from the nucleus, which is effectively very energetic light (a high-energy photon). The emission itself involves no change in the nuclide's mass number or charge, but will result in a decrease in the energy of the nuclide. However, alpha and beta decay is sometimes accompanied by the emission of a gamma ray, which may actually be emitted by the daughter nuclide, as the emission of the alpha or beta particle still leads to a nucleus in an excited state.

Gamma radiation is very penetrating in matter and can pose an external radiation hazard that can give rise to dose remote from the nuclides. Therefore, the principles of shielding, distance and time are required to minimise dose (see Section 5.3).

4.3.4 Electron capture and internal conversion

Electron capture involves the absorption of an orbital electron (e$^-$) by a proton (p) in the nucleus leading to the production of an additional neutron (n) and the emission of a neutrino (v). This is shown as

$$p + e^- \longrightarrow n + v. \tag{4.7}$$

As previously stated, the neutrino poses no hazard to human health because it has a negligible cross section with matter. However, an X-ray is likely to be emitted as an electron in a higher orbital drops down to fill the vacancy of the absorbed electron. The X-ray is hazardous due to its ability to cause ionisation and in many respects is similar to a gamma ray.

Internal conversion involves the de-excitement of the nucleus by the ejection of an orbital electron. This electron should not be confused with the electron emitted in beta decay that is produced from the decay of a neutron in the nucleus. The emitted orbital electron is also hazardous due to its potential to cause ionisation. Due to an electron vacancy in the atomic orbital, an X-ray can subsequently be emitted as a higher orbital electron fills the vacancy, which is hazardous.

4.3.5   Spontaneous fission

Fission is generally considered to be an artificial process due to it being used in reactors and bombs (see Section 4.6). However, there are nuclei that can spontaneously undergo fission without the need for initial capture of an external neutron. *Spontaneous fission* can therefore be considered to be a form of radioactive decay, as it is entirely random and is not affected by environmental conditions.

From one initial nuclide X, the process leads to the production of two lighter nuclei (X' and X''). The lighter, daughter nuclei are not rigidly defined like the daughter nuclei in alpha and beta decay and there is a statistical distribution of the daughter nuclides produced. The daughter nuclides are themselves neutron rich and will, therefore, be radioactive. The process also leads to the instantaneous emission of one or more unbound neutrons (n), which can then initiate fission in other nuclei. The spontaneous fission process is given as

$$X \longrightarrow X' + X'' + \text{a few n}. \qquad (4.8)$$

The production of the free neutrons can go on to form a *chain reaction* or *criticality*. Hence, the requirement for criticality of safety cases is to ensure that *critical masses* of uranium or plutonium cannot accumulate even if there are no artificial sources of neutrons. Spontaneous fission is also a concern in the design of nuclear bombs as it is essential that fission occurs at the right time to ensure optimal yield and is not triggered early by a random neutron from a spontaneous fission event.

4.4   Radioactivity in the natural environment

Whilst this book focuses on the nuclear safety of nuclear plant, it is worth briefly mentioning radioactivity in the natural environment. The material that makes up most of the universe (primarily hydrogen) was created in the big bang with many of the larger nuclides (to iron) produced by nuclear fusion in the cores of the first generation of stars. The largest of these stars underwent supernovae spreading much of the stars' material into the galaxy. The violence of the supernovae and other galactic events also led to the production of many more massive nuclides including thorium and uranium.

Much of the material produced in the supernovae was radioactive, but over the subsequent billions of years the nuclides have decayed away. Consequently, only the longest-lived nuclides from these events are present today. It is the accumulated heat from natural radioactivity deep in the Earth that results in the molten core. In turn, this ensures a magnetic field enabling compasses to work and the deflection of charged particles from the sun.

Example: Isotopes in the Earth
Let us consider the age of the Earth and different isotopes that would be present during its formation from the material previously released by supernovae. The Earth's age is ~4.5×10^9 years, which is the same as the 4.5×10^9 year half-life of ^{238}U. There are even longer-lived nuclides, such as ^{232}Th that has a half-life of 1.4×10^{10} years. Since the Earth was created with the uranium present in the supernovae clouds locked

into the body of the planet, only half of the ^{238}U initially present has decayed away. Compare this to the half-life of ^{14}C of 5730 years, which equates to nearly 8×10^5 half-lives of decay since the Earth was formed. This gives a remaining fraction since ^{14}C was locked in of $0.5^{(8 \times 10^5)}$, which is too small for most calculators to process. However, ^{14}C is naturally produced in the atmosphere due to cosmic rays interacting with the atmosphere and the supply is replenished.

The long-lived thorium and uranium are physically and chemically locked up in the Earth's rocks and so too are the majority of their decay chain nuclides. If undisturbed, the radioactivity poses no hazard. However, radon is a decay product of uranium and thorium and is a noble gas. It is, therefore, not chemically bound and can be released to the atmosphere from fissures in the rocks. This is a well-known natural hazard in uranium mines as well as in granite areas such as Aberdeen and Cornwall in the UK. Building basements are areas where the gas can accumulate and forced ventilation systems and monitoring systems are necessary to ensure sufficient air changes and removal of the gas.

There are also residual radioactive nuclides in the atmosphere from the use and testing of nuclear weapons, nuclear accidents (e.g. Chernobyl and Windscale) and the normal (low-level) discharges from nuclear plants. Cosmic rays also contribute to a background of natural radiations.

4.5 Plant radioactive inventory

Nuclear plants will, by definition, contain nuclear material that is radioactive. How much radioactivity and what form it takes are important and will define the hazard posed by the plant and how severe this hazard may be. In simple terms, the *inventory* is defined as the amount of radioactive material that is present. It is clearly very difficult to write a comprehensive and robust safety case if the radioactive inventory is not known.

The inventory is normally given in terms of absolute activity (Bq) or it may be given in terms of per unit mass (kg^{-1} or g^{-1}), per unit volume (l^{-1} or ml^{-1}) or occasionally per mole (mol^{-1}). The inventory can also be known as the *source term*. It is the inventory that is hazardous to human health.

The chemical and physical properties of the inventory need to be understood as the hazards will differ depending upon these characteristics. The hazards associated with liquid waste will differ from those of solid waste even if the radioactive inventory of the plant is the same. We can generally consider that plants processing liquid radioactive material pose a greater harm potential than plants handling solid material for the same inventory. Liquors are more mobile than solids and may be more susceptible to mixing and chemical reactions.

It is not enough to simply know how much radioactive material is present, but also which nuclides are present and the activity of each: the *fingerprint*. Knowledge of the fingerprint and the inventory determines whether the principal hazards arise from external radiation (e.g. gamma emitting nuclides) or from internal radiation (e.g. alpha-emitting nuclides) or a mixture of the two.

Some plants may have a limited number of different nuclides present, but others will contain many tens if not hundreds of different nuclides. In particular, material that has been processed through a reactor will contain fission products as well as uranium and plutonium and all of their decay chains. This can lead to very complex source terms for which specialist software can be used to determine the inventory and how the inventory in terms of the isotopes and their quantity changes with time. The inventory and fingerprint can be generated on both conservative and best-estimate base.

Example: Uranic Fingerprint
A theoretical conservative example fingerprint of uranic material processed in a plant is shown below. The fingerprint is for uranium enrichments of up to 60% ^{235}U (natural uranium is only 0.7% ^{235}U). The remaining fraction of uranium, as determined by assay, is primarily a mixture of ^{234}U and ^{238}U. For conservatism, also included is a notional trace contamination level of plutonium which is at the parts per million (ppm) level, as some of the material may have been exposed to plutonium.

In our theoretical example, on a best-estimate basis, it may be possible to justify not accounting for the plutonium being present. This is on the theoretical basis that it is only a trace contaminant in a very few items, if any, processed in the plant. Given the knowledge of the mass of uranium in any part of the plant and the fraction that may be released in a fault, it is possible to calculate the dose.

Isotope	Fraction
^{235}U	60%
^{234}U	20%
^{238}U	20%
^{240}Pu	1 ppm
^{241}Pu	0.01 ppm
^{242}Pu	0.01 ppm

It is possible and occasionally necessary to decay correct the inventory of a plant by utilising Eq. 4.2. This can be especially useful to plants that may process legacy fission product material that will contain a wide range of nuclides that have a range of relatively short-term decay half-lives. Many of these nuclides are of radiological concern, e.g. ^{106}Ru, which has a half-life of just over one year. By accounting for radioactive decay, it may be possible to reduce the source term from a historic benchmark and hence reduce the magnitude of the doses from a release by an appreciable factor.

An inventory for a plant may state that the inventory is *decay corrected* to a particular date and this must be recognised by the safety assessor. This approach is useful for a new build safety case where legacy waste that must be processed in the future has a particular known fingerprint during the early design phase. By the time the plant is built and operational, which in the nuclear industry typically takes 10 years, it is clearly prudent to take into account radioactive decay, as this may impact on the integrity of the shielding or containment that is required.

It must also be recognised that decay products can also be radioactive and hazardous. For example, ^{241}Am is a daughter of ^{241}Pu and is a gamma emitter. The quantity of ^{241}Am in a plutonium store will increase with time, leading to an increase in the background external radiation dose rate.

Radioactive decay involves the liberation of nuclear energies which partly manifest themselves in the kinetic energy of the emitted particles. Section 5.2 will discuss the potential damage mechanisms that the particles can do to living tissue. Over and above this, it must be recognised that items that are highly radioactive can generate significant levels of heat.

For example, plutonium stores may need to be cooled to prevent the cans containing the plutonium from bursting; fission product liquors produced during reprocessing can generate heat at levels of the order of 10 W l^{-1} and require cooling to prevent the liquors from self-heating to boiling. Reactors also need their decay heat to be removed should the reactor be tripped and the nuclear fission reactions curtailed. The management of this radioactive heat is very important and can pose technical challenges to ensure sufficiently reliable systems and back-up systems are in place.

For more complex process plants, a *flowsheet* is produced. The flowsheet will determine how much radioactivity is present at each stage of the process, and it will account for the physical and chemical processes that may occur in the processing of the material. The flowsheet must ensure that the total inventory of the nuclides is preserved between the different process stages; i.e. there should be no unaccounted losses.

It would not be usual for safety assessors to produce the flowsheet or the fingerprint of an inventory. These require specialist information. Process engineers would typically produce the flowsheets.

Example: Evaporator Flowsheet

As an example, consider an evaporator held under a depression that, through the application of heat and reduced pressure, boils waste liquor to remove volatiles and hence concentrate up the liquor. The volatiles are cooled and the condensate is collected in a distillate collection vessel. There are also off-gas flows to the ventilation system.

To construct a safety case, a flowsheet is required to specify the inventory of the feed material and the inventory of the concentrate at the end of the batch. In addition, the process will give rise to carryover of radioactive nuclides into the distillate stream and into the ventilation off-gas system. The flowsheet will be required to determine the inventory transferred to the distillate stream and the off-gas system. This may be important in determining the clean-up systems required.

4.6 Nuclear fission

We have previously described spontaneous fission as a form of radioactive decay and it only occurs in the largest nuclides. The fission process can also be induced through the absorption of neutrons. This is the basis of a nuclear reactor and nuclear bomb operation whereby a fission event occurs leading to a self-sustaining chain reaction. The chain reaction involves one fission event leading to a release of neutrons that go on to induce more fission events and so on. In simple terms, a nuclear reactor will ensure that this process is controlled whilst a bomb is designed to ensure that the chain reaction runs away with a very rapid increase in fission events.

Let us consider a fission event involving ^{235}U that is induced by an incident neutron. This is absorbed by the target nucleus and technically gives rise to an excited state of ^{236}U*; i.e. the nucleus has absorbed a neutron and remains that of a uranium nucleus but is an isotope of uranium due to the different neutron numbers. This excited nucleus may decay by γ emission to a lower energy state of ^{236}U. However, it is more likely to undergo fission and split into two components, plus a release of free neutrons. Equation 4.8 is a representation of spontaneous fission and we can adapt it with a real fission example:

$$n + {}^{235}U \longrightarrow {}^{236}U^* \longrightarrow {}^{87}Br + {}^{147}La + 2n + 200 \text{ MeV.}^6 \qquad (4.9)$$

The nuclides on the right of the second arrow are *fission products* and together with the free neutrons will carry kinetic energy. This is a *prompt* release of energy and these neutrons are known as *prompt neutrons*, as they are released immediately on the fission event. The fission products are neutron rich and are, therefore, radioactive with decay via the emission of γ and β radiation. Additionally, some fission product nuclides decay by neutron emission, which may occur over timescales of seconds or minutes. These are known as *delayed neutrons* and it is these neutrons that enable nuclear reactors to be controlled, as the delay enables neutron-absorbing control rods to be manipulated. Some of the fission products actually have large cross sections for neutron capture and these fission products can act as *poisons* and will reduce the number of fissions taking place. This is an important aspect to take account in the operation of reactors.

The local physical medium will be heated by the released kinetic energy of the fission products, neutrons and radioactive emissions. In a commercial reactor, it is this released energy from all of the fission events that will eventually be transformed into electrical energy that will be distributed to homes and factories and so on. The radioactive decay of fission products will continue long after a reactor is shut down and is the reason why cooling of spent nuclear fuel is required to be maintained even if all fission reactions have been stopped.

---

[6]MeV is a million electron volts, which is a unit of energy traditionally used for subatomic particles, nuclides and atomic reactions. One electron volt is the energy gained by an electron accelerating through a potential difference of 1 V, which is equivalent to 1.602×10^{-19} J. Therefore, 200 MeV = 3.2×10^{-11} J.

4.6.1 Moderation

The overwhelming majority of naturally occurring uranium is the isotope ^{238}U (> 99%), and this isotope has a large scattering cross section for the energetic or *fast* neutrons released in fission events. Neutrons scattered in this manner can be 'lost' from the fission process and only a fraction of the neutrons undergo fission in ^{238}U. Thus, it is not possible for a reactor containing solely natural uranium to operate as too many fast neutrons are lost to enable a chain reaction to occur. A fast reactor requires the uranium to be enriched in ^{235}U. However, ^{235}U has a much higher fission cross section at lower or *thermal* energies (where the neutron has energy commensurate with the thermal energy of the medium) with a broadly 1/velocity dependence; ^{238}U does not undergo fission at thermal energies. Therefore, ^{235}U is one of a number of *fissile* isotopes that undergo fission when bombarded by thermal neutrons.

To make a uranium-based thermal reactor, the ^{235}U component is enriched (typically to a few percent). Neutrons released in a fission event must be slowed down or *moderated* to achieve thermal energies and achieve the large fission cross section in the ^{235}U. Moderators are comprised of light nuclei that have a good scattering cross section for neutrons. Traditional moderators comprise of water or graphite (carbon).[7] A key feature in many safety cases is the control of moderation. For example, fissile material is handled in many nuclear plants such as laboratories, stores and process plants. The control of moderation is a key factor in ensuring safety.

4.6.2 Neutron multiplication factor

A single neutron can induce fission that will lead to a release of more than one neutron. Each of these can then go on to produce further fission events, i.e.

$$1n \longrightarrow 2n \longrightarrow 4n \longrightarrow 8n \longrightarrow 16n \longrightarrow \text{and so on.}$$

Thus, there is an exponential increase in the number of neutrons assuming *all* of the neutrons go on to produce fission events. This is an example of a *chain reaction*. In reality, some neutrons will be lost through capture or scattering out of the fissile material and take no further part in fission reactions. Therefore, we can define the *neutron multiplication factor* k as the number of neutrons in one generation compared to the preceding generation. If $k < 1$, then the system is *subcritical* and the chain reaction will die out, if $k = 1$ it is *critical* and the chain reaction is self-sustaining and will proceed in a steady state. If $k > 1$, the system is *supercritical* and the chain reaction increases.

It is of course desirable for $1 < k > 1$ within a nuclear reactor depending on its operational state. As previously noted, there is an important role for delayed neutrons in a nuclear reactor, which ensures that the rate of increase in neutrons is not instantaneous and can be controlled. However, a key aspect of nuclear safety is ensuring that accumulations of fissile material outside of a reactor do not give rise to k

---

[7]Occasionally, heavy water has been used that utilises deuterium which is an isotope of hydrogen that has one proton and one neutron in the nucleus. Both heavy water and graphite have low-neutron absorption cross sections and can be used as moderators in natural uranium reactors.

approaching 1 and instigation of a *criticality*. A criticality outside of a reactor can never be tolerated. Site licensees set their own sub-critical safety criterion for values of k, such as $k \pm 3\ \sigma \le 0.95$, where σ is the standard deviation of the mean calculated value. The safety assessments will be required to demonstrate that this value of k is never approached (or exceeded) during normal operations or foreseeable fault conditions.

The determination of k for a system can be undertaken by the use of computer codes for complex systems or via reference to standard look-up tables or graphs for simple systems. These will be based upon known quantities of the mass of fissile material or its concentration within liquids and so on. The computer codes utilise *Monte Carlo* calculation techniques to model the neutron transport through the fissile material taking due account for moderation and fission events, reflection, geometry and so on.[8] A nuclear safety assessment will need to take account of the normal conditions and fault conditions which may lead to changes in the degree of the parameters that affect criticality.

Consequences of a criticality

In the unlikely event that an unplanned criticality occurs, there will be a release of gamma radiation and neutrons that, if not shielded, lead to a significant radiation dose in the local area. A number of workers have died in the past when such events have occurred many directly initiated by the workers. Of interest, but of no concern in itself, is that witnesses have reported seeing a blue flash of light. This is believed to be caused by fluorescence of excited ions produced by the radiation or even Cerenkov radiation.[9]

A criticality event may also lead to a release of fission products, though these are of secondary concern, but may pose an issue off-site if they are released to the environment. Criticality accidents rarely lead to physical damage or explosions. However, in high power density reactor systems, containment integrity may be compromised with significant damage leading to a release of fission products from the core.

It is found that criticality events can self-terminate due the physically disruptive nature of the event with the majority of the fission events occurring in the initial *excursion*. However, there may be a steady continuum of events after this initial spike and there may even be oscillations of enhanced criticality over subsequent hours. This is a feature of liquid-based systems and is known as an *oscillating criticality*. It may be that intervention is required to terminate the criticality, such as through an injection of poison or disrupting the geometry. These would all need to be done remotely and may be difficult to achieve. The emphasis in a criticality safety case must be on preventing the event in the first place rather than actions on recovery or mitigation of dose.

---

[8]The parameters that influence whether a criticality can occur are: mass, absorption, geometry, interaction, concentration, moderation, enrichment, reflection and volume (MAGIC MERV).

[9]Cerenkov radiation occurs when charged particles travel through a dielectric medium with a velocity greater than the velocity of light within that medium, such as the eyes or the fluid if the event occurs in a liquid system. Cerenkov radiation itself is not hazardous.

Historic criticality accidents have been assessed to have had a range of total fission events (the initial excursion and any oscillations or continuum), which typically are in the region of 10^{15}–10^{19} fissions. In absolute terms, this is a small number of events compared to the total fissile mass present and available for fission. One mole of ^{235}U, for instance, would have a mass of 235 g and would contain Avogadro's number (N_A) of ^{235}U nuclei, i.e. 6.022×10^{23}; historic fissions involve a small fraction of a mole.

4.7   Nuclear fusion

Nuclear fusion is a process by which energy is liberated when light nuclei combine together to form a larger single nucleus. However, whilst nuclear fission can take place at low temperatures, nuclear fusion requires very high temperatures. This is because the positively charged nuclei need to have sufficient kinetic energy to overcome the repulsive electromagnetic or Coulomb barrier between the two nuclei. For fusion to occur, the nuclei have to approach sufficiently close that the attractive strong nuclear forces between the nuclei dominate the Coulomb repulsion. Within experimental inertial confinement plants, this requires temperatures of the order of 10^8 K and at these temperatures the matter breaks down into a *plasma*, which is a mixture of atoms stripped of their orbital electrons. The plasma requires strong magnetic fields to ensure that it is contained and prevent physical contact with the structure of the fusion reactor.

The principal fusion reaction performed in experimental plants involves deuterium (^{2}H) and tritium (^{3}H) for which tritium is another isotope of hydrogen that contains two neutrons. The fusion reaction is of the form

$$^2\text{H} + {}^3\text{H} \longrightarrow {}^4\text{He} + \text{n} + 18 \text{ MeV}.$$

Reaction-for-reaction, the energy released in fusion is a factor of 10 less than that of fission. The neutron is not constrained by magnetic fields and will transfer energy to the surrounding medium. Once captured by nuclei, the neutrons can lead to their activation and radioactive decay. The tritium used in the fusion reaction is radioactive with a half-life of only 12.3 years and so is only available in trace amounts in the Earth or the atmosphere. It can be manufactured by the bombardment of lithium targets with neutrons. Therefore, the clever use of lithium targets around the fusion reactor can generate the tritium fuel for the next cycle.

Finally, we note that nuclear fusion is not devoid of the generation of radioactivity and there are neutrons to shield against. The radioactivity will come from the activation of fusion reactor components and shielding. However, the radioactive waste problem is not of the same order as that generated by the nuclear fission cycle. For instance, it does not lead to the generation of long half-life actinides, such as the uranium isotopes or plutonium isotopes.

Chapter 5

The Physics of Radiation Interaction

As with all living matter, the human body is susceptible to damage from radiation. The human body is exposed to natural background radiation all of the time. Nuclear safety is concerned with ensuring that workers and the public are not exposed to significantly enhanced levels of radiation from the nuclear industry over and above that received during the normal course of life. Their exposure to radiation from the nuclear industry must be both tolerable and ALARP.

The mechanism for radiation damage to the body is complex. There may be initial direct damage to the cells as the radiation's energy is transferred to the body's tissues leading to their death. The radiation's interaction with the body's matter can also produce chemically active species such as free radicals that can give rise to further damage. With very large exposure the damage may be so severe that the body is irreparably damaged with physical effects occurring immediately (acute effects). After all, the radiation particles all carry energy and if absorbed in sufficient quantities will cause burns to the skin. At low levels of exposure, the risk may be chronic with the potential for cancers to form in later years.

There have been a large number of studies into the effects of radiation on the human body. The atom bombing of Hiroshima and Nagasaki in World War Two have provided a lot of information on the effects of radiation. This is both in terms of the acute effects and the stochastic risk of cancer forming from lower levels of radiation exposure.

There have also been a number of accidents in the history of the nuclear industry. These have provided additional information on the effects of radiation. Chernobyl is one such significant accident where there was a large range of radiation exposure. Many of the first responders received fatal radiation doses and died within a few days. Many millions of people across Europe were exposed to different levels of radiation. There have also been a number of criticality accidents across the world, which have led to very large acute doses to a small number of workers close to the incident.

There is good scientific consensus concerning the risk posed by large radiation doses, e.g. from a criticality. The effects are inevitably fatal. For smaller exposure levels, it is less clear on the risks associated with radiation exposure. A linear risk model is used such that the stochastic risk is proportionate to the amount of exposure. Whether this linear risk model actually holds true at small doses is unclear.

This chapter will provide an introduction to how radiation interacts with matter. This will introduce the terms of *radiological dose* and how the dose received is a function of the type of radiation, the exposure duration and which part of the body is irradiated. Thus, the terms of *equivalent dose* and *effective dose* are defined. It is worth noting that there is a confusing range of units associated with dose and different units can be preferred in different countries. Clarity to the modern units generally used in the UK is given. *Dose coefficients* and numeric risk values associated with radiation exposure are discussed. The basic *principles of radiation protection* are provided.

Inanimate matter can also be vulnerable to radiation damage. This chapter will also discuss some of the principal concerns of inanimate matter to radiation damage. Finally, a discussion on radiation detectors commonly used in the nuclear industry is given. Working knowledge of these systems is essential for all safety assessors.

The *attenuation* of radiation through matter and the *inverse square law* are introduced for which the latter is purely a geometric function.

5.1   Radiation interaction

Section 4.3 has described how there are different types of radioactivity and radioactive emissions. Each of these emissions will interact with the human body in a slightly different way due to their different penetrating powers in matter. Nuclear safety is concerned with shielding and containment of radioactive material and it is necessary to understand how radiation affects matter.

- Alpha particles (α) are helium nuclei and are charged particles. When travelling through matter they interact with the target's electrons due to the electric field between the alpha particle and the host body's atomic electrons leading to ionisation of the target's atoms. For a given energy of an alpha particle, there is a well-defined penetration distance in matter with matter ionisation occurring along its track. The majority of the ionisation and hence damage to the tissue is deposited at the end of the alpha particle's track.

  Alpha particles do not travel far in the air (the order of cm) and are stopped by skin. Consequently, they can only cause significant damage if taken into the body and irradiate sensitive organs. Alpha particles do not pose hazard outside of the body.

- Beta particles (β) are electrons or positrons and are also charged particles, but with only half the charge of an alpha particle. They also interact with the target matter's electrons through the electric field. In comparison to alpha particles, they have a negligible mass (5.5×10^{-4} of the mass of a proton). They are, therefore, more penetrating than alpha particles, but are more easily scattered. Consequently, beta particles will distribute their energy over a larger volume than that of alpha particles.

In addition, as the particles are scattered, they change direction and speed (known as acceleration) and accelerating particles emit *bremsstrahlung radiation*, which is simply a photon carrying away energy that can be deposited in a wider volume of tissue leading to additional damage. Should the beta particle be a positron it will eventually interact with an electron leading to their annihilation with the release of a gamma ray, which itself will be damaging over a large volume. By losing energy over a larger volume, beta particles are less likely to destroy individual cells than alpha particles, but may damage more cells.

- Gamma rays (γ) are photons of light and are uncharged. Compton scattering is the main mechanism for energy transfer from the gamma ray to the target tissue (human tissue is primarily made from light elements of hydrogen, carbon and oxygen for which Compton scattering is most efficient). The scattered electron will travel through the target tissue leaving an ionisation trail just like that of a beta particle. Pair production[1] and photo-electric absorption will also occur, of which the former will produce electron-positron pairs and the latter will liberate electrons. These will then traverse through the medium causing damage similar to that of beta particles.

- Neutrons (n) are uncharged particles and will therefore not directly affect the target's electrons. Neutron radiation is not directly ionising radiation. However, if of low energy, they can be absorbed in the nuclei of the target's atoms, which can then activate them making them neutron rich and radioactive. Higher energy neutrons on impacting nuclei can cause them to recoil and subsequently travel through the target's medium. This will then leave an ionisation trail causing damage along the track of the recoiling nuclei.

5.1.1   Attenuation of radiation

As radiation traverses through matter, the interaction between the radiation and the matter in the medium leads to the transfer of energy from the particle of radiation to the medium. Logically, therefore, when the particle's energy is all expended, there will be no further energy transfer to the medium. Eventually, alpha particles will capture stray electrons and will simply become helium gas and escape. Beta particles, simply being electrons, will likely attach themselves to a positive ion somewhere.

Free neutrons will eventually be captured in an atomic nucleus or themselves beta decay to a proton, an electron and an anti-neutrino because neutrons outside of the nucleus are unstable. Gamma rays may eventually impart all of their energy by liberating an electron from an atomic orbit via the photo-electric effect or, for the highest energy gamma rays, produce an electron and positron in pair production. The gamma ray itself will then no longer exist.

---

[1]This is the creation of mass (matter) from energy, which contrasts to the nuclear fission and fusion processes that involve the conversion of mass to energy.

Gamma rays and neutrons have significant penetrating power and can be scattered from surfaces. Neutrons can be scattered by target nuclei like billiard balls and will only be captured when their energy is sufficiently low for the nuclear forces to take hold. The Compton scattering of gamma rays will also lead to re-direction of the gamma ray (together with a recoiling electron to preserve the conservation of momentum). This means that if a beam of neutrons or gamma rays is incident on the matter, the beam will be scattered away from the direction of travel and attenuated in that direction. Moreover, the mechanisms for capturing the neutron or gamma ray (e.g. photo-electric effect) will also attenuate the beam by removing the neutron or gamma ray entirely. In simple terms, as we move through the matter medium away from the point of origin the flow of radiation is reduced.

A term used is the *flux* of radiation which represents the number of particles (gamma rays, beta particles, etc.) passing through unit area perpendicular to the direction of travel per unit time. Flux has units of cm^{-2} s^{-1} (or equivalent). Another term is the *fluence*, which is the flux of radiation over a period of time and has units of cm^{-2} (or equivalent). Let us consider a well *collimated* beam of radiation of intensity I_0 as it enters the medium. Collimated means that the radiation direction can be considered to be parallel to our defined axis. The intensity of the radiation at distance x in the medium is given by

$$I_x = I_0 e^{-\mu x}, \tag{5.1}$$

where μ is the linear attenuation coefficient and is based upon the probabilities of both the absorption of the radiation and the scattering[2] of the radiation out of the axial direction. Equation 5.1 shows that radiation traversing through matter is reduced exponentially. If plotted, a curve of the radiation through the medium would be of the form shown in Fig. 4.2 because both are based upon an exponential equation. An exponential reduction means that if 10 cm of shielding material is required to reduce the flow by half, 20 cm would reduce it by a quarter and 30 cm by an eighth and so on. Thus, it can take many half-thicknesses of material to reduce the radiation to a 'safe' level. It is impracticable to shield *all* of the emerging radiation (e.g. from a reactor) as it would require shielding of infinite thickness.

Equation 5.1 is a fundamental equation from which radiation shielding calculations are undertaken. It must be remembered that μ is a function of energy of the particle. Hence, for distribution of radiation energies, which is what happens in the real world, the reduction of intensity with distance is more complex than that represented by a simple single exponential curve.

There are other real-world complications that are not represented in Eq. 5.1; it solely assumes single scattering of the radiation particle out of the beam's axial direction. If a particle can be scattered more than once, it can be scattered back into the beam's direction, particularly if the scattering medium's extent is much larger than the mean scattering path length. Thus, Eq. 5.1 would over-estimate the attenuation.

---

[2]Safety assessors may come across the term *cross section*, which is the probability of a scattering or reaction event occurring. It is used with respect to criticality where there is a variation of the likelihood of fission occurring with the energy of the initiating neutron and the uranium isotope. The unit of cross section is the barn (b) and is equivalent to 10^{-28} m^2.

Equation 5.1 also assumes that the beam is thin and collimated; i.e. all of the radiation particles are travelling in a parallel direction and the beam is of no significant width. A real-world beam will not be truly collimated and will have a non-negligible width. For radiation particles that are not collimated, particles initially travelling in an off-axis direction, i.e. not parallel, can be scattered just once back into the axial beam direction.

Both multiple scattering and non-axial travel can lead to a *build-up B* of radiation in the beam's direction. This results in an attenuation rate of less than that calculated by Eq. 5.1 and is given by a modified equation of the form

$$I_x = BI_o e^{-\mu x}. \tag{5.2}$$

Modern computer codes used for the calculation of the flux of radiation take into account the real-world geometry and include the build-up factor.

5.1.2 Inverse square law

We have shown above how radiation is attenuated by matter. It is also true that increasing the distance from the source of radiation will decrease the flux of the radiation simply through geometric considerations. Remember that the flux of radiation is the number of particles or energy passing through each cm^2 per second. Let us consider a transparent ball surrounding an isotropic source of radiation. Isotropic means it emits the same flux of radiation in all directions. The ball has radius R_1 and has a surface area of A_1, which is given by $4\pi R_1^2$. Therefore, all of the radiation must pass through this area as it travels from the source to the wider environment. For any 1 cm^2 of the ball's surface area, the flux of radiation will be inversely proportional to the surface area, i.e.

$$\text{Flux} \propto \frac{1}{A_1} \propto \frac{1}{R_1^2}. \tag{5.3}$$

Equation 5.3 is known as the *inverse square law* and is well known in physics. Newton's law of gravitation is one example of an inverse square law where the gravitational force between two masses is inversely proportional to the square of their distance. The inverse square law means that doubling the distance from an isotropic source will quarter the radiation flux.

Within safety cases, the radiation flux is sometimes expressed as a dose rate in Gy s^{-1} or Sv s^{-1} if this has been calculated knowing the type of radiation. If we know the radiation dose rate D_1 at a distance R_1, we can calculate the radiation dose rate D_2 at a different distance R_2 by the ratio

$$D_2 = D_1 \frac{R_1^2}{R_2^2}. \tag{5.4}$$

Gamma radiation is not significantly attenuated in air and it is possible to use Eq. 5.4 to work backwards from a remote radiation measurement to determine the dose rate close to the source. Alpha radiation is attenuated in air within a few centimetres, beta radiation within a metre or so. Therefore, the use of Eq. 5.4 for alpha and beta radiation would underestimate the dose rate if working backwards as the 'remote' measurement is only of the radiation that has survived scattering and absorption in the intervening matter medium.

Even for gamma radiation, the inverse square law tends to break down at close distances when the distance to the source is not significantly greater than the geometrical size of the source. At this scale, the radiation will not necessarily be isotropic. Moreover, each part of the emitting source is at a different distance to the chosen dose point. At close distances, this can make an appreciable difference. For complex geometry and situations in the near field, more sophisticated models may be required. Specialist software is available.

5.2   Radiation dose

The *absorbed radiation dose* received by a target is a function of its intensity (or flux) and the exposure time together with the type of radiation and its energy. There are a number of different and confusing units for the measurement of absorbed radiation dose of which many are no longer routinely used. In this book we will only use modern units and we introduce the SI unit of absorbed dose: the gray (Gy). In this section we look at the biological effect of radiation dose on the human body and discuss the *effective dose* and the *equivalent dose*, for which the SI unit for both of these is the *sievert* (Sv).

Finally, we note that inanimate objects exposed to radiation will receive a radiation dose. The effect on the objects will differ to that on living things, as there is no potential to damage living matter (the cells within the body's tissues and organs). However, the radiation can still damage these inanimate objects, through ionisation of the object's constitute material or through physical displacement of atoms within the lattice structure of the material. This can become a life-limiting factor on material exposed to radiation.

5.2.1   Absorbed dose and dose rate

All material, inanimate or living, will absorb energy from radiation, some material more effectively than others. The absorption of the radiation is a function of the radiation type, its energy and the nature of the absorbing medium. The absorption of radiation (together with scattering) forms the basis of the attenuation equation (Eq. 5.1). We therefore define the absorbed dose D as the energy imparted into the material. The SI unit of absorbed dose, as we've noted above, is the gray (Gy), which is equivalent to the imparting of 1 J of energy into 1 kg of matter, i.e. $1 \, \text{J kg}^{-1}$.

A related quantity of great usefulness in nuclear safety is the *dose rate* and is simply the absorbed dose per unit time, i.e. Gy s^{-1}. For a given source, geometry and shielding, radiation computer codes can produce dose rates at given locations. Safety cases use dose rate information to calculate the absorbed dose by applying a suitable *exposure time*. This can be for both normal conditions and under fault conditions.

5.2.2 Equivalent dose

It has been found that not all radiation is equally damaging to living organisms and this includes humans. The type of radiation and also its energy can influence the damage to living tissue. More penetrating high-energy gamma rays, for instance, are able to penetrate further into the body and damage internal organs rather than solely the skin and sub-surface layers. However, gamma rays will deposit their energy over a longer path length than alpha and beta particles. In particular, alpha particles are quickly attenuated by the skin and do not penetrate into the body. Thus, the potential for individual cell damage (for the same absorbed energy overall) is greatest for those alpha particles if there is a route for them to penetrate into the body.

The *equivalent dose H* is defined to take into account the relative differences between radiation type/energy and its effect on the human body. A dimensionless radiation weighting factor w_R is introduced. Therefore, the equivalent dose in a tissue or organ is given by

$$H_T = w_R \, D_{T,R}, \tag{5.5}$$

where $D_{T,R}$ is the average absorbed dose in organ or tissue T from radiation type R. Tables of w_R are given by the International Commission on Radiological Protection (ICRP) and example values are reproduced in Table 5.1.

Table 5.1 shows that the equivalent dose from 1 Gy of alpha particles requires 20 Gy of gamma radiation to be received to accrue the same equivalent dose. This is an important aspect that safety assessors should be aware of; alpha particles are much more damaging to the body than gamma rays (on the proviso that they are within the body).

The total equivalent dose to a tissue or organ is then the sum of the different radiation types absorbed.

5.2.3 Effective dose

We have established that the radiation's effect on the human body is dependent upon the type of radiation and its energy. It is also found that the part of the body irradiated makes a difference in the effect of the radiation on the body. Logically, consider applying a large radiation dose solely to the finger compared to the brain. We do not need to be medically trained or well versed in radiation science to take a view on what would be of greatest concern.

Table 5.1: Example radiation weighting factors. Data from [9].

Radiation	Weighting factor
Electrons and gamma rays	1
Neutrons	5–20 (depending on energy)
Alpha particles	20
Fission products	20

This gives rise to the definition of the *effective dose* whereby account is taken of which organs are irradiated and whether the radiation affects the whole-body. The latter gives rise to the *whole-body dose*, which is a term most encountered in safety cases. A set of dimensionless tissue weighting factors (w_T) are used to modify the equivalent dose calculated for each tissue and organ. The tissue weighting factor accounts for how the equivalent dose in a tissue or organ is weighted to represent its contribution to that resulting from uniform irradiation of the whole body.

The whole-body dose is the sum of the individual equivalent doses to each tissue and organ. The whole-body effective dose E is the sum of the equivalent doses to all of the different tissues and organs and can be written as

$$E = \sum_T w_T \sum_R w_R D_{T,R}. \qquad (5.6)$$

The unit of effective dose is again the Sv. Generally, safety cases utilise the effective whole-body dose and this is more often than not simply referred to as the *dose*. It is advantageous for safety assessors to understand how this dose is built up from the dose absorbed (in Gy) and then modified by the weighting factors. It is rare that safety assessors need to calculate whole-body doses from first principles as tabulations of (whole-body effective) dose per Bq inhaled or ingested are provided in licensee methodology documents.

From time-to-time, doses to extremities, such as the fingers, need to be calculated. This could be for hands-on work within gloveboxes where there is handling of material that emits beta radiation. There are different radiation limits to extremities compared to the whole body.

One important point to note is that should there be a very large absorbed dose (1 Gy) in a short period of time, such as from a criticality, the dose is normally solely given in Gy and not Sv. The tissue-weighting factors are based upon the effects of long-term damage to tissues and organs, e.g. cancers developing. A dose of a few Gy has a reasonable likelihood of leading to a fatality in the coming days or weeks.

5.2.4   Dose coefficients

We have established that the dose accrued by an individual is dependent upon the type of radiation emitted, its energy, together with the organ of the body irradiated. Should radioactive nuclides enter the body (through inhalation, ingestion or injection), the chemical and physical form of the radioactive species will influence how it is transported and retained in the body. The radioactive nuclide may, for example, be in a gas (such as iodine) or within an *aerosol particle* that itself contains many atoms' worth of the nuclides. They may be ingested if the aerosols settle within the food chain, perhaps due to a discharge of activity to the sea and consumption by fish.

The size of an aerosol particle will influence how far the particle can travel in the air, how the particle is inhaled into the body and whether it reaches deep into the lungs (the smallest particles) or is deposited in the nasal air passages. Once within the body, there will be a natural *biological half-life* corresponding to the rate of secretion from the body. Thus, irradiation of organs can occur long after the incorporation of

Table 5.2: Example committed effective dose coefficients for adult workers for inhalation of example nuclides into the body. Data from ICRP 119 [9]. Note the large difference between ^{241}Pu and ^{240}Pu, the former is a beta emitter and the latter is an alpha emitter, which is more damaging once inside the body.

Isotope	Inhalation dose coefficient Sv Bq^{-1}
^{3}H (tritiated water vapour)	1.8×10^{-11}
^{129}I (gas)	9.6×10^{-8}
^{90}Sr (particulate)	1.5×10^{-7}
^{240}Pu (particulate)	4.7×10^{-5}
^{241}Pu (particulate)	8.5×10^{-7}

the radioactive material into the body. Nobel gases, such as krypton or xenon, will not be taken into the bloodstream due to their inert chemical nature and they only irradiate when the individual is immersed in a cloud of the gases.

The *committed dose coefficient* (d_i) is the dose received over 50 years (or from the intake age to 70 years if this is longer). The dose coefficient has units of Sv Bq^{-1} and takes into account a number of factors associated with the isotope including:

- The chemical and physical forms of the particle containing the isotope;

- How quickly it enters the bloodstream, which, if due to inhalation, depends on the chemical and physical forms and its absorption rate via the lungs;

- The radioactive half-life and the retention of the isotope in the body;

- The age group of the individual (e.g. adult, child or infant).

Example inhalation dose coefficients are given in Table 5.2.

Example: Iodine Tablets
Radioactive nuclides of iodine can be released in nuclear reactor accidents. Following inhalation, the iodine can be taken up by the thyroid gland in the body and this can lead to thyroid cancer in due course.

As a mitigating emergency measure, the taking of stable potassium iodine before exposure to the radioactive iodine will saturate the thyroid preventing the subsequent uptake of the radioactive species.

The use of iodine tablets will only protect against radioactive iodine and it will not protect against other isotopes or external radiation.

So far, we have described a dose coefficient that is utilised when radioactive particles are taken into the body. For airborne releases, there are also dose coefficients

Table 5.3: Example cloudshine effective dose coefficients for select nuclides. Dose coefficients calculated on the basis of a semi-infinite cloud and exposure to gamma radiation. Data from [10].

Isotope	Cloudshine dose coefficient $\mathrm{Sv\ Bq^{-1}\ s^{-1}\ m^3}$
$^{129}\mathrm{I}$	2.86×10^{-16}
$^{90}\mathrm{Sr}$	9.83×10^{-17}
$^{137}\mathrm{Cs}$	9.40×10^{-17}
$^{240}\mathrm{Pu}$	3.29×10^{-18}
$^{241}\mathrm{Pu}$	6.15×10^{-20}

for activity deposited upon the ground and for activity suspended in the air. The former is known as *groundshine* and the latter is known as *cloudshine*. Groundshine is calculated on the basis of 50-year exposure and is associated with chronic exposure. Cloudshine occurs from gamma radiation emanating from a plume of released activity that may surround the individual. A selected few dose coefficients are shown in Table 5.3. More discussion regarding plumes is given in Section 6.4.2.

5.2.5   Risk from radiation exposure

For lower levels of radiation exposure, there is a stochastic risk of fatality. This may manifest itself later in life such as through the development of cancer that may lead to premature fatality. Based upon studies of populations and exposure, the chance of cancer developing has been quantified as $0.055\ \mathrm{Sv^{-1}}$ for the whole population and $0.041\ \mathrm{Sv^{-1}}$ for adult workers [11] (for practicable purposes a value of $0.05\ \mathrm{Sv^{-1}}$ can be used). Should a dose to the operator of 20 mSv be calculated, the corresponding chance of cancer and hence premature fatality is $0.02\ \mathrm{Sv} \times 0.04\ \mathrm{Sv^{-1}} = 8 \times 10^{-4}$.

Above a dose of about 0.5 Gy, deterministic aspects start to come into effect. The adult *lethal dose*$_{50/60}$ (LD) value is 4 Gy, which means that 50% of otherwise healthy adults exposed to this dose will succumb to acute effects within 60 days [11]. If those so exposed survive the acute effects, there is still the potential for cancer to develop in later life.

We should note that for female radiation workers, if they are pregnant then additional controls need to be utilised to reduce their normal dose exposure. This is due to the special vulnerability to the unborn to radiation. There are also heritable effects from radiation exposure due to genetic mutations. Similarly, children should not work in radiation environments.

5.3   Principles of radiation protection

We have established that we can reduce the dose rate and hence dose from external radiation by attenuating the radiation: shielding or distance or a combination of both of these physical aspects. We can also minimise the dose by reducing the time of exposure. Finally, minimising the source term to the smallest practicable will also minimise the dose. Thus, we can establish the fundamental principles of radiation protection to be:

- Maximise shielding; and/or

- Maximise distance; and/or

- Minimise time; and/or

- Minimise source.

Ideally a plant will be designed and operated such that all of the principles are applied to their maximum extent such that the dose is reduced to ALARP. However, in the real world, there may have to be a trade-off between the principles. This can be the situation during intrusive operations when it may be necessary to trade one for the other when planning the execution of tasks. Operators inevitably have to work in radiation fields, and minimising time in these areas is always important. It may not be reasonably practicable to enhance the shielding around high dose rate items or areas. However, these radiation areas are marked with wall or floor signs reminding personnel to keep a distance or to not loiter in the area.

Not all radiation sources may be able to be removed from an area prior to entry, but reducing these as far as practicable and minimising the time in the area will help to ensure the dose accrued is ALARP. Operators in active areas will wear *electronic personal dosimeter*s (EPDS), which provide an audible feedback on the radiation level at the operator's position. This provides a real-time reminder of the radiation dose being accrued and the need to minimise such exposure through distance and time.

The time in high-radiation areas can also be reduced by ensuring operators know what they are doing and have been trained on what to do in a low radiation environment first. The operators may, for instance, use utilise long-handled tools to ensure that they are remote from the source and this may help to ensure only extremity doses are received rather than a whole-body dose. Of course, careful consideration of the time is required, because less dexterous tools may result in a longer working time. These facts should all factor into the risk assessments conducted before the work is undertaken. The *Radiation Protection Adviser* (RPA) should be involved in the planning of these tasks, the production of risk assessments and the correct use of *personal protective equipment* (PPE).

5.4 Effect of radiation on inanimate matter

It is worth a brief mention of the effect of radiation on inanimate objects. Neutron radiation is well known for giving rise to dislocation of crystal structures. This is a particular concern for graphite in reactors whereby the displacement of the atoms gives rise to stored energy in the damaged structure. This is known as *Wigner energy*. A subsequent physical shock can give rise to a rapid relaxation of the structure back to its original form, which may release sufficient heat to ignite the graphite. Semi-conductors are made from silicon with careful controlled levels of impurities. Again, crystal displacement will lead to degradation of these devices. Instrumentation does not always work well in high-radiation environments.

For all practicable purposes, gamma rays and neutrons are not attenuated by air, as it is insufficiently dense. Hence, the requirement for shielding provided by massive concrete structures around nuclear reactors and fission product waste plants. Inevitably, it is necessary to have service penetrations into the shielding, for cooling water or instrumentation. These penetrations provide routes out of the shielding for the gamma rays and neutrons. It is, therefore, necessary to design these penetrations with a *joggle* (or bend) to prevent a direct shine path through the shielding.

Finally, we note that the absorption of neutrons by certain nuclei will lead to their *activation*. Activation means that on becoming neutron rich, they form a radioactive isotope and they will subsequently decay. A well-known example is ^{59}Fe, which on receipt of a neutron will beta decay to ^{60}Co. ^{59}Fe is a component of steel and is found in reactor systems. The ^{60}Co is a significant contributor to the dose rate in the core.

For decommissioning of the reactors, this activation poses a significant hazard. One solution can be found by considering the half-life of ^{60}Co of 5.26 years, which is relatively short compared to other isotopes found in the reactor that have half-lives of thousands of years. This has given rise to the concept of a *safe store* and delayed decommissioning. By waiting over 100 years before the core is finally decommissioned, a significant reduction in dose rate will occur due to multiple half-life decay of the ^{60}Co. Moreover, after this time there is little benefit in waiting as the dose rate reaches a plateau due to the long-lived isotopes. Whether future generations appreciate being left with the waste to dispose of is anyone's guess.

5.5   Radiation detectors

Nuclear plants are equipped with a wide variety of detectors and alarm systems to monitor the environmental conditions and provide feedback to the operators. In addition, operators on the plant will have their own personal equipment that can provide instantaneous indication of dose or provide information for retrospective accountancy for dosimetry.

The use of radiation monitors and alarms is the last line of defence in a safety case due to the fact that the alarms may be there to prompt evacuation, which is mitigation resulting in the individual accruing dose. Nevertheless, it is often necessary to claim the alarms to make an adequate safety case. Therefore, this section will briefly describe some of the monitoring and alarming equipment that is installed on a plant or carried upon the person by operators. Safety assessors will need to have a reasonable understanding of the equipment typically used to detect radiation and activity, its function and role in a safety case.

It is worth noting up front that a *monitor* will solely provide indication and an operator may or may not notice the indication provided by the monitor. A monitor may also be fitted to an *alarm* system that will, visually and/or audibly, alert the operator to the defined alarm conditions being reached. For every alarm there must be a defined *alarm response*. Finally, a *sampler* will provide retrospective laboratory analysis of the conditions sampled and may be used for the demonstration of compliance, but would have no immediate role in any fault progression unless the fault progression is slow to develop and a significant dose can only be accrued over multiple sample and analysis cycles.

5.5.1 Gamma monitors

Plants that handle radioactive material that emits gamma radiation will be equipped with gamma monitors. The monitors detect the gamma radiation by a mixture of different technologies, depending on the application and the dose rates likely to be experienced. The technology includes Geiger–Mueller tubes, scintillation detectors and solid-state detectors. The physics of how these detectors work is beyond the scope of this book, but Lilley [4] provides more information.

The gamma monitors may be within a process line as part of the control system (e.g. to track the presence of radiation packages), or they may be situated throughout the accessible areas of the plant to provide protection or reassurance monitoring to the operators, as they have an alarm function. These *area gamma alarms* can be either *installed* and fixed in position on the plant or they may be *portable*. Portable monitors may be used if there are transient or intrusive operations where there may be high-radiation levels that the installed area gamma alarms might not normally detect.

A gamma monitor will have an alarm threshold (e.g. 500 μSv h^{-1}) and if this is reached, the monitor will go into alarm visually and audibly. Provided the monitor can 'see' the gamma radiation, the alarm should initiate immediately. The standard operator response to an alarm activating is to withdraw from the local area and it is usual to make-safe equipment if this can be done quickly and safely. The area gamma alarm may be relayed to a central control room and multiple monitors triggering the alarms may lead to a *building evacuation*.

Gamma monitors may also be used as part of interlock systems to prevent the opening of shield doors should there erroneously be a radiation source behind the door when entry is attempted. In this instance, the gamma monitor is part of a *gamma interlock system* and is not an area gamma alarm. A gamma interlock system is a preferable safety measure to an area gamma alarm as it will *prevent* a dose from being accrued. An area gamma alarm will prompt evacuation and will only *minimise* a dose. The gamma interlock system is higher in the safety hierarchy.

5.5.2 Installed criticality warning system

Plants that handle or process anything but trace quantities of fissile material (uranium or plutonium) are more than likely to be equipped with a *criticality warning system* (cws). A criticality may arise due to a wide range of faults. A fission event will lead to a sudden burst of gamma rays (and neutrons) that will pose a significant, likely fatal, dose to nearby personnel if the event is not shielded. There are many plants where it is not practicable to shield against a criticality due to the need for operators to handle the uranium or plutonium material that should always be maintained significantly below sub-critical limits.

Should the criticality occur in a fissile liquid, there is the likelihood of an oscillating criticality. The liquid will periodically cycle between sub-critical and critical states; heat from the criticality will cause gas bubbles that will decrease the density of fissile material, but when the bubbles decay or burst at the surface the fissile density and reactivity will increase. Thus, there may be a cyclic release of gamma rays and neutrons for many hours or days.

It is always essential that personnel evacuate from the source of the criticality as quickly as possible and this is the function of the CWS. Moreover, a criticality occurring in one building on a nuclear site will still give rise to a significant dose in other buildings not connected with the initiating event and the CWS may alert personnel across a significant fraction of the overall site.

The CWS itself consists of a number of gamma monitors that will alarm on receipt of a rapid pulse of gamma radiation. The gamma alarms may be arranged on three rings requiring detection by at least two of the rings.

When personnel evacuate in response to a CWS, they are required to move quickly. Unlike the response to other site alarms (such as a fire alarms or even activity-in-air alarms), they are not normally required to 'make-safe' their local working area, but to down tools and run. The significant, potentially fatal, radiological dose is of primary concern. The requirement for two of the gamma monitor rings to register the event is to minimise the risk of a spurious alarm, as the rapid evacuation has the potential to give rise to accidents.

The escape routes are chosen to minimise the potential for personnel moving past the likely seat of the criticality. They will assemble at a refuge point located in an area of the site where the criticality dose contours from the realistic potential seats of the criticality are sufficiently low for site workers to congregate for roll call, initial triage and so on. Some personnel may be wearing respirators and contaminated clothing (due to their work unconnected with the event). They will be kept separate to other workers to prevent contamination transfer.

Due to the importance attached to the CWS, some nuclear sites ensure that when the CWS is working there is a reassuring *clip-clop* noise to show that the CWS is operational. A cessation of the noise may be due to failure of the CWS or due to activation of gamma alarms on only one ring. Should the CWS not be operational, there will be emergency arrangements instigated, e.g. the cessation of fissile material moves.

It is essential to note that in a criticality safety case, the CWS only plays a minor role in the safety argument. Although great significance may be attached to it on plant, the CWS only provides a mitigating function. Indeed, it is likely to only provide mitigation against an oscillating criticality. The initial pulse that is sufficient to initiate the alarm may be sufficient to be fatal to the nearest workers. The principal safety argument should be based upon sound engineering, process and managerial arrangements to ensure that the plant is operated with adequate sub-critical margins and that it is unlikely that the conditions could evolve to give rise to a criticality.

5.5.3 Activity-in-air alarm

The processes associated with nuclear activities inevitably lead to the generation of aerosol that may be contaminated. The aerosol may be liquid based or solid based. It will be generated during normal operations, but fault conditions can give rise to either the generation of new aerosol or the release of existing aerosol that may have deposited on surfaces.

As an example, a spill of liquor will generate aerosol as the liquor entrains air as it falls and then there will be a splash of aerosol on impact with the ground or surfaces. A reverse ventilation flow or an explosion may lift aerosol that has accumulated or *plated-out* on ductwork or other surfaces.

The aerosol generated can then migrate to operator-accessible areas through penetrations in containment barriers or it may be released directly into operator areas. An operator handling a waste package that is dropped is an example whereby activity may be released directly.

To alert the operator that a release has occurred, particularly those unconnected to the event who may not be visually or audibly aware, *activity-in-air alarms* are installed on the plant. These systems monitor for alpha or beta activity and will go into alarm when the concentration of activity reaches the alarm trigger point. The standard response to an alarm is to withdraw from the local area. It is usual to make-safe equipment if this can be done quickly and safely. The alarming of multiple monitors may initiate a building evacuation as this is indicative of a significant release.

The activity is detected by drawing a sample of the local air across a filter from where radiation probes can detect and monitor the accumulation of activity. The siting of the monitors needs careful consideration because the activity must migrate from the point of release to the monitor point and then accumulate on the filter before the alarm trigger point can be reached.

The building ventilation flow can influence the migration patterns and for small releases of activity away from the monitor, it may not be possible to claim an effective monitoring function. Even if well sited, it may take a minute or two for activity to migrate to the alarm point. Safety cases need to factor in this activation time in the assessment of any radiological dose that takes into account evacuation in response to an alarm.

5.5.4 Stack sampler/activity-in-duct

The *cascade of ventilation flow* on a plant is from areas of low contamination potential to areas of high contamination potential. Ultimately, there will be a discharge point to the atmosphere via a stack or exhaust point. It is normal practice to sample the air flow emerging to ensure compliance with the discharge authorisations. A *stack sampler* is the means to do this and this works by drawing a representative fraction of the air flow across a sample paper. It is essential that a system introduced to detect activity does not disturb the air flow around it and the sampler must be *isokinetic*.

The sample paper will be periodically removed for laboratory analysis to determine the discharge of alpha and beta activity and if necessary, particular nuclides. A sample system of this nature is solely retrospective and cannot give any immediate indication of a fault occurring. However, a safety case may be able to make claims on a sampling system as mitigation against long-term chronic discharges. Thus, if a fault would otherwise lead to an indefinite release, it may be able to be argued that it would not progress past a repeated number of stack sampling cycles.

A stack or a ventilation duct may also be equipped with an *activity-in-duct monitor* to give real-time information in the control room. Again, this must take a representative fraction of the flow and it may alarm on a prescribed concentration level. The monitor may be situated between primary and secondary filters to detect *breakthrough* or failure of the primary filters. There may be additional monitors downstream of the filters close to the discharge point.

5.5.5   Neutron detectors

The measurement of neutron flux around a nuclear reactor provides an indication of the power output of the reactor. The more the thermal neutrons produced the more the criticality events and hence more heat generation. Neutrons are difficult to detect directly, but their absorption in the matter can give rise to secondary effects and these are utilised to provide knowledge of the flux of neutrons impinging on a detector and this can then be used to help control the reaction rate through the movement of control rods.

Neutron detectors can be based upon semiconductor technology that uses, for example, boron-coated materials that absorb neutrons. The newly activated neutron-rich isotope of boron will then decay through the emission of ionising radiation, which can be detected by the semiconductor device and provide a signal. Such a signal is proportional to the number of neutrons and cannot give an indication of the energy of the neutrons. Similarly, gas-filled detectors can be used that use scintillation technology to detect the emission of secondary radiations following the absorption of the neutrons. These can be based upon boron filled gas or even ^{3}He.

Criticality lockets

On plants that handle fissile material where there is a risk of a criticality, operators may be required to wear a *criticality locket*. This is typically a large button-sized passive monitor that may be worn around the waist on a belt or clipped to the chest. Should a criticality event occur, the strips of metal within the locket will be activated by the neutron pulse and become radioactive. Subsequent analysis of the lockets can be used to determine the dose accrued by the individual and this may help with the triage of personnel after an event. A criticality locket does not monitor neutron levels in real-time and does not provide direct feedback to the wearer.

5.5.6   Electronic personal dosimeters

Operators working on plants will wear EPDs. The EPD is typically (large) wallet sized and will be clipped to the upper body to best represent the whole-body dose position. Solid-state technology is used to detect the presence of gamma radiation.

The EPD will provide a visual digital display of dose accrued and will go into alarm if a pre-set alarm value is reached. Therefore, an EPD is useful because it can provide real-time feedback to the wearer of the dose accrued. This may be a prompt to avoid further loitering in certain areas and minimise the time-at-risk. An EPD may also be used for formal dose record monitoring to demonstrate compliance with the 20 mSv BSL(LL) and any more restrictive licensee dose limits. This can be achieved by ensuring that the chosen EPD is linked to an individual.

5.5.7 Personal air sampler

On plants that may generate contaminated aerosol, *personal air samplers* may be worn. These simply consist of a tube connected to a small fan and battery pack, which is worn by the operator. The open end of the tube is placed on the shoulder to best represent the breathing air of the operator and the fan draws a sample of the air across a filter. The filter can then be retrospectively analysed to determine the internal dose accrued by the wearer. There is often zero tolerance of internal dose to the operators.

Chapter 6

Calculation of Radiological Dose

A determination of *radiological dose* is fundamental in all nuclear safety assessments, as it provides an indication of the radiological harm that a process or a deviation from a process can give rise to. The size of the safety case and the amount of effort required to be expended is generally a function of the *harm potential* of the material. The qualitative term 'harm potential' can be a subjective concept, but broadly it relates to the ability or readiness of nuclear material to give a nuclear dose. Becquerel-for-becquerel, liquid nuclear material will have a greater harm potential than solid material due to the mobile nature of liquor and the readiness for aerosol to be generated.

The quality of a safety case should not be judged by its length, but by the safety argument with a proportionate and relevant level of detail. The safety case needs to be focused upon where the hazard is the greatest and more often than not this is where the largest doses can be accrued. Indeed, a voluminous safety case can have a detrimental effect with the reader and user, drowning in excess detail masking the safety argument. Proportionality should be a guiding principle.

This chapter will describe the processes that may be employed to calculate radiological dose to workers and the public. The transmission routes for activity or radiation can differ between the workers and the public, and this can require the use of different techniques and models. For instance, ingestion of nuclear material is not really a realistic concern for workers on the plant, as eating food and smoking are prohibited when *over the barrier*.[1] However, in addition to radioactive material in

---

[1] Over the barrier refers to the physical barrier that separates the active from the non-active side of a plant. The barrier will generally consist of a low bench onto which a person entering the active area, dressed in an overall and equipped with dosimeters, etc., will remove their shoes and swing their legs over (without touching the floor) into a pair of shoes that stay on the active side of the barrier.

On leaving, the person reverses the process followed by radiological contamination monitoring of their hands, feet and the whole body. Subsequent parts of the active plant may have further barriers that may include the use of plastic sheeting or tenting arrangements and the need for specialist personnel to enter wearing respirators or even air-fed suits.

the air, the public may be exposed to radioactive material that deposits on the ground or is released to the sea where it is taken into the food chain. Ingestion is, therefore, relevant to the public.

In calculating the radiological dose to the site workers, it is necessary to subdivide the site workers into the *local operators* and the *general site workers*. This is because the base assumptions and relevant protection to these groups may differ. Generally, the local operators will be the first to receive a dose from a given fault, simply by being the nearest to the release point.

Within this chapter, the role of safety measures in the determination of radiological dose is discussed and the concepts of *unmitigated* and *mitigated consequences* are introduced, i.e. consequences that take into account the mitigating action of safety measures. This chapter also introduces the terms *conservative* and *best-estimate*, as these are utilised in the DBA and PSA components of a safety assessment. The radiological dose is a function of *exposure time* and assumptions for how this is determined are given in this chapter.

Once these terms are introduced, it is possible to discuss the different dose models that are applicable to external radiation dose and inhalation dose. The terms *release fraction* (RF) and *decontamination factor* (DF) are introduced. A discussion of contaminated wounds is also given.

Finally, it is recognised that the calculation of radiological dose received by the public is dependent upon the dispersion and dilution of the activity in the environment. The principal methodologies utilised in dispersion models are briefly described, including the *Gaussian plume model* for airborne releases. To understand public dose, this chapter introduces the terms *critical group* and *exposure pathway*.

6.1   Role of safety measures in the calculation of radiological dose

It is the expectation that if there is a potential fault in a plant, sufficient protection will be provided to protect against the fault. Ideally, the protection will prevent the fault from progressing from the initiating event to the point of giving rise to the actual dose, i.e. the accident. These are known as *preventative safety measures* and give rise to zero radiological dose. However, many safety measures will solely reduce or *mitigate* the consequences making them less severe than they would otherwise be, but still resulting in a non-zero dose.

Generally, preventative safety measures are preferred to mitigating safety measures, but preventative safety measures may not always be reasonably practicable to provide. This situation occurs where 'hands-on' work is required such as filter changing or transporting samples where the only protection available may be the package containment layers (that may be breached on a drop), respirators and evacuation.

If we have a mitigating safety measure, then we need to consider the role of the mitigating safety function, i.e. how effective it is in reducing the dose. We therefore need to introduce the concept of the *unmitigated* and *mitigated* consequences together with the *partially* and *fully* mitigated consequences. Indeed, the starting point for any safety assessment should be the unmitigated consequences as it is these that we are generally most concerned with.

As we have noted, a preventative safety measure will, by definition, prevent the unmitigated consequence from being realised. The number of safety measures and their quality is related to the magnitude of the unmitigated consequences (see for instance the discussion of DBA in Section 7.3).

6.1.1 Unmitigated consequence

The unmitigated consequence is that which may occur without taking credit for preventative or mitigating safety measures. The calculation of the unmitigated consequence is an important step in understanding the harm potential that a fault possesses and determining just how bad it could be. The emphasis here is on 'could be', which is not the same as saying we expect the consequence to be this severe. Therefore, the safety case will demonstrate that the potential for the unmitigated consequence to be realised is sufficiently low to be both tolerable and ALARP.

The unmitigated consequence can be very high due to the calculation taking no credit for the correct functioning of any mitigating safety measures. Consequently, safety assessors should be ready to defend the consequence to engineers, plant designers and others who may (reasonably) question its validity. Remember, the safety assessment is simply trying to gauge how important any safety systems are and by how much they can/must mitigate or prevent the consequences.

The plant may contain passive features that can reduce or mitigate the consequences through their inherent physical properties, e.g. via maintaining containment or shielding. Provided these are expected to be available and not affected by the fault, the unmitigated consequences can take credit for their presence and reduce their consequences accordingly. Examples of passive features include cell structures and the building envelope. They must be identified with their role defined in the safety analysis.

6.1.2 Mitigated consequence

The mitigated consequence is that which occurs after taking credit for the action of mitigating safety measures. Note that because preventative safety measures, by definition, lead to zero dose, it is not usual to quote a mitigated (zero) consequence for the role of these safety measures. Examples of mitigating safety measures are:

1. The wearing of respirators;

2. Operator evacuation in response to an alarm;

3. Ventilation extract filters, scrubbers, etc.;

4. Ventilation extract fans.

It is useful if we can nuance our definition of mitigating safety measures and refer to *active* mitigating safety measures as opposed to *passive* mitigating safety measures.

Active mitigating safety measures rely on the equipment or personnel to physically perform a function perhaps to actively respond to the fault in order to mitigate the consequence, e.g. evacuation in response to an alarm. Active measures may be in an unrevealed failed state at the point of demand or may be unavailable.

Passive mitigating safety measures will provide their function without requiring a change of their state and an obvious example is a ventilation filter. A filter may have a dual role in normal operations and in a fault condition. It may fail to work correctly because it may not have been correctly installed leading to contaminated airflow bypassing the filter medium.

6.1.3 Partially and fully mitigated consequence

It is possible that there is more than one safety measure available. This gives rise to the concept of a *partially* and *fully mitigated* consequence. The partially mitigated consequence just considers the role of each mitigating safety measure with the fully mitigated consequence taking credit for all of them.

Example: Mishandling a Plutonium Bottle
Consider an operator handling a bagged bottle containing plutonium liquor. Should the bottle be dropped and broken on impact with the floor, there may be a release of airborne activity should the outer bag(s) be pierced. Therefore, the operator should wear a respirator whilst handling the bottle and be trained to evacuate immediately on a drop (and certainly in response to an activity-in-air alarm). The permutations of the mitigated states are shown below.

Mitigated State	Description
Unmitigated	Does not wear respirator and does not evacuate
Partially mitigated 1	Does not wear respirator, but does evacuate
Partially mitigated 2	Does wear respirator, but does not evacuate
Fully mitigated	Wears respirator and evacuates

By providing these different states, the importance of wearing the respirator and evacuating can be determined. It may actually be found that it is only by claiming credit for the respirator **and** evacuation that sufficient dose mitigation may be found (e.g. <20 mSv). With no other safety measures available, this may lead to a shortfall in the provision of protection and difficulties in making an adequate safety case. This may give rise to a search for ALARP improvements via *recommendations*.

Note that it may be able to be argued (and substantiated) that not wearing a respirator is not realistic and would be a violation. Thus, the unmitigated consequence would then account for the respirator. The evidence for this would need to be strong. It would also have to be shown that there are no credible means by which the incorrect wearing of a respirator with a substantially reduced mitigating function could occur.

6.1.4   Passive features

It is possible and reasonable to claim credit for the mitigating containment or shielding function of *passive features* even in the unmitigated consequences. This can only be done if it can reasonably be expected that the passive features will be present irrespective of the state of the plant or the fault sequence. These features are not in the 'true sense' safety measures as they do not actively respond to the fault, but they may have a significant safety role in mitigating the dose through passive means.

Should the fault sequence lead to a failure of the passive feature, then it would not be possible to claim its mitigating effect. Of course, there may be some fault sequences for which credit could be claimed and others where it could not. A cell structure may provide a containment barrier from a dropped package on the other side of it, but it would not provide containment following a seismic event if the cell structure is not seismically qualified. Examples of such passive features include:

- Passive knockout of particulate traversing through the length of ventilation ductwork;

- The multiple containment layers of nuclear packages;

- Cell containment or bulk shielding structures;

- Gloveboxes (excluding gloves and posting ports);

- Room walls and doorways;

- Building outer fabric.

It is often found that passive features operate in conjunction with an active mitigating safety measure, which enhances the DF[2] solely provided by the feature. We cannot take credit for the active component in the unmitigated consequence.

A good example of the role of active and passive components is the DF provided by a cell containment structure or a glovebox. The cell or glovebox is connected to an extract system, which ensures that the air in the cell or glovebox is at a lower pressure than the operating area. This results in the cascade of airflow from the area of lowest contamination potential (operating area) to the area of highest contamination potential, which is often the cell or glovebox. On its own, the cell or glovebox will provide a barrier to activity migration, but this will be even better if the activity has to migrate 'against the direction of the wind' induced by the ventilation system.

However, we can reasonably consider a ventilation system (which is an active mitigating system) connected to a glovebox to be failed, we cannot reasonably expect a plutonium sample to be manipulated outside of a glovebox. This would not be a mistake, but a clear violation of standard working practice. We can also consider the

---

[2] The DF is often given as the ratio of activity concentration on one side of the system to that on the other. It can also refer to the absolute (mass) fraction passing across the system; e.g. if a drum lid provides a mass DF of 10 on a drum drop, then $\frac{1}{10}$th of the drum mass will escape containment.

sample being manipulated in a glovebox that has a failed glove. A glove is a maintainable item and can be damaged, but if this occurs, we would still take credit for the overall containment structure of the glovebox even if only a reduced DF could be justified in the particular fault sequence.

Clearly, failure to take into account the passive features can result in significantly higher unmitigated doses. This would then feed into the DBA and PSA, which then leads to more onerous demands being placed upon the provision of safety measures. These may not be reasonably practicable to provide and/or may place significant operational and maintenance burdens on plant personnel.

Example: Loss of Containment of a Vessel

Let us consider a *well-sealed* cell that contains process vessels. A well–sealed cell ensures that the gaps around the service lines that penetrate into the cell are sealed to minimise the adventitious pathways from the cell to the operating areas. The number of penetrations and their relative sizes are small such that they offer a small fractional surface area compared to the interior surface area of the cell.

A loss of containment from the vessels will lead to a release of aerosol into the cell from where activity may penetrate the operating area via any residual adventitious openings in the cell structure. The fraction of the material made airborne is known as the RF. Under normal operations, the cell is connected to a ventilation system that maintains the cell under a depression with respect to the operating areas. Air cascades into the cell from the operating area via the adventitious openings. The permutations of the mitigated states are shown below.

Mitigated State	Cell Extract	Evacuation
Unmitigated	N	N
Partially mitigated 1	Y	N
Partially mitigated 2	N	Y
Fully mitigated	Y	Possible

Each mitigated state should be calculated within the safety case. It is probable that with the extract operational there would be no significant airborne release to the operating area and evacuation (in response to an activity-in-air alarm) would not be required.

Standard plant practice may be to withdraw on loss of extract irrespective of whether there had been a release. There would then be subsequent controlled re-entry with health physics and potential respirator wearing.

6.2   Conservative and best-estimate

We have discussed the terms *unmitigated* and *mitigated* with respect to radiological consequence or dose. We now need to introduce the terms *conservative* and *best-estimate* as they also apply to radiological dose. In simple terms, a conservative dose errs on the side of caution and bounds uncertainty with sufficient pessimism to ensure that the calculated dose will exceed what could be accrued in reality. A best-estimate dose uses as accurate information as possible to reflect what is expected to happen. A conservative dose will always be larger than a best-estimate dose.

DBA tends to utilise conservative doses whilst PSA tends to utilise best-estimate doses unless conservatism is required due to significant uncertainty. Sometimes conservative doses are used for PSA as this provides for simplification, but potentially at the expense of more onerous risk calculations.

It is fair to say that the terms *conservative* and *best-estimate* can cause confusion and may not always be calculated appropriately. It is very easy to develop a release model that has a conservative dose. We can conservatively set all RFs and DFs to 1 and assume an infinite residence time. If this shows a trivial dose, then we could say the conservatism is appropriate as we have proved the fault is not one of concern.

However, an over-conservatism may inflate a trivial dose to an onerous one that requires more safety measures of a higher quality than warranted. Conversely, a consequence that is not adequately conservatively assessed may undercalculate the true consequence and leave a deficiency in the provision of safety measures. There is a balance to be struck in applying the degree of conservatism to utilise.

It is worth highlighting that when a radiological dose is calculated, it is generally of the form

$$\text{dose} = \text{activity} \times \text{release fraction} \times \text{decontamination factor} \times \ ....$$

and if there are conservatisms in every term they are multiplied together. A factor of 10 conservatism in each term will give a dose that is conservative by a factor of 1000 just from the three terms above! Is this now a realistic or credible consequence?

6.3 Dose calculation: workers

6.3.1 Distinction between local operators and general site workers

Generically, this book refers to the *workers* as the wider workforce or personnel who work at nuclear plants. However, in assessing radiological doses to the workforce, it is necessary to distinguish between the local operators and the wider general site workers. We can define:

- Local operators (for brevity we will now drop 'local') as being the personnel who operate the plant and who are likely to be the closest to the point of activity release or loss of shielding. Operators may even be involved in the initiating event, e.g. dropping a radiological package and may be directly aware that a fault has occurred;

- General site workers (for brevity we will now drop 'general') are the personnel who are not in the immediate vicinity of the release or loss of shielding and are not connected with the plant operation that leads to the fault, e.g. site workers in an adjacent plant room. Site workers may even be within different buildings on the site.

Site workers will be unaware that a fault has occurred unless the release is accompanied by significant physical effects (e.g. smoke and fumes, explosion or toxic gas). For both operators and site workers, an alarm system may alert them to a release of radioactive material or loss of shielding. For a significant release, this will almost certainly instigate a *site emergency* in which personnel are required to seek shelter in the closest buildings. Conversely, if a criticality has occurred, the workers are required to leave the relevant buildings as quickly as possible by designated escape routes to assemble at the designated criticality muster point (see Section 5.5.2).

Due to their proximity to the point of release or loss of shielding, the dose to the operators is likely to be significantly larger than the dose to site workers. A combination of increased distance (e.g. due to inverse square law) and intervening structures that provide containment barriers or shielding will ensure that the dose to site workers is naturally reduced. There are two important aspects to consider that may affect this statement.

Firstly, in the absence of taking credit for any alarm system, the exposure duration of site workers may be longer than that of the operators. The operators are the most likely to have a range of direct indications to evacuate (e.g. they see the fault occurring and may also hear it, etc.). If the fault is very significant, obvious and possesses significant and immediate non-nuclear consequences if an operator were to remain, it may be possible to justify a short evacuation time.

Examples of faults where there may be obvious and overwhelming drivers to evacuate may include a flask drop and the spillage of its contents or the confrontation with a fire and/or smoke where the urge to evacuate may be over-whelming (though there may also be an urge to investigate and/or tackle the fire so this does not always hold true). However, for the majority of faults, the unmitigated consequence should take no account for evacuation and should be based upon the natural residence time at the working location. In practice, unless a very short evacuation time is justified for the operators, it is generally found that the dose to the operators will be larger than that received by other site workers.

Secondly, there are some faults that may lead to releases of activity via vessel ventilation systems that do not lead to a release within the plant operating area. In this instance, the release will be via the stack and there will be no dose to an operator on the plant where the fault occurred. The dose to site workers may then be determined based upon the release of a *stack plume* and atmospheric dispersion (see Section 6.4.2). It may actually be determined that the stack and subsequent release are sufficiently high that the plume does not reach the ground within the boundary of the site. Hence, the only dose is to the public.

Within a safety case, it is generally necessary to provide a calculation of the doses to the site workers and to the operators. In many scenarios it may be possible to provide a simple justification that the site worker consequence is bound by (smaller than) that of the operators without further calculation. Additionally, the safety measures that protect one set of workers may sufficiently protect the other set of workers. It is not necessary to clog up a safety assessment with many different explicit dose calculations if some are clearly trivial.

6.3.2   Total worker dose

A fault may give rise to one or more of a:

- Release of airborne activity, which is inhaled by the workers leading to an inhalation dose ($dose_{inhal}$);

- Loss of shielding (or criticality) leading to enhanced external radiation levels at the worker's location leading to an external dose ($dose_{ext}$);

- Cut, abrasion, burn or puncture of an operator's skin such that contamination penetrates into the body, leading to a contaminated wound dose ($dose_{cw}$).

The total dose ($dose_{total}$) to the worker is simply the sum of these, i.e.

$$dose_{total} = dose_{inhal} + dose_{ext} + dose_{cw}. \qquad (6.1)$$

We noted above that ingestion is not normally relevant for workers. However, should there be a mechanism to splash bulk liquor onto an operator's face, there may be an involuntary ingestion of the liquor and ingestion would be an additional term used in Eq. 6.1.

It is often found that a particular fault will only give rise to one or two mechanisms for dose and Eq. 6.1 would be used accordingly. Contaminated wounds are only a concern to the operator. The methodologies used to calculate each term will be described in the coming sections.

Example: Consequence Approach for a Gamma Plant
A plant handles and stores containers within which is solid encapsulated nuclear waste. The waste emits significant quantities of gamma radiation. There are very low or trivial levels of contamination on the plant. The containers are maintained behind bulk shielding at all times and some of this shielding will include shield doors to enable access to container lifting equipment.

There are faults associated with the shield doors such that an incorrect shield door opening sequence could occur leading to an operator being exposed to an unshielded container. Therefore, for this fault whilst there is a significant external radiation hazard from an incorrect shield door opening sequence, there would be no concern with respect to contamination release and inhalation or a contaminated wound occurrence.

Example: Consequence Approach for a Plutonium Plant
A plant undertakes experiments on plutonium material that is handled in a glovebox. Plutonium presents a significant inhalation hazard and contaminated wound hazard. However, plutonium does not offer a significant hazard with respect to external radiation and there is no shielding around the glovebox.

In this example, if an item of glovebox equipment could fail such that it coincidentally leads to an energetic release of powder into the glovebox internal volume and damages a glove, it could breach the high-integrity glovebox containment barrier.

The event could also coincidentally cut and contaminate the operator's hands. The operator may therefore receive a significant contaminated wound and an inhalation dose. Due to the lack of shielding, there are no faults associated with external radiation.

6.3.3   Exposure duration

Both internal and external dose models give rise to a dose that is a function of exposure duration, i.e. how long a worker is present in the released airborne activity or the radiation shine path. To determine the time of exposure, we need to take into account:

- Whether the fault is obviously revealed or not;

- The working pattern and natural end to the exposure duration;

- On revelation, if there is any incentive for operators to correct the fault;

- Whether there is any potential for the fault to simultaneously incapacitate the operator and inhibit evacuation;

- The function of any alarms.

Conservative and best-estimate exposure durations can also be utilised as appropriate in line with the requirements of DBA and PSA. We will explore some of the aspects influencing exposure duration below.

The working pattern and natural end

To prevent the ingestion of contamination, an operator working across the barrier on plant cannot eat or drink. Typically, a working time of two hours can be assumed for the general working period before the operator leaves the active area for refreshment and so on. Operators crossing the barrier will use frisk probes and installed monitors to detect any contamination upon their body or clothing. Thus, if they were to be unknowingly contaminated from a release of airborne activity, this should reasonably be detected, prompting investigation and decontamination. A licensee will normally provide guidance on what the maximum exposure duration should be.

Frisk probes and installed monitors would not detect exposure to external radiation. However, even without accounting for time on the clean side of the barrier, operators would not solely reside for the full working duration in one high-radiation location on plant. Their duties would take them to different places and they would in all likelihood be expected to go to a plant supervisor's office, or a permit office, or a health physics office during the execution of their duties on plant. Each of these locations would be in a different dose rate area. Each time they return to their working location, there is a fresh opportunity to stop, take note and inspect the working area to notice something untoward. Consequently, two hours can again be considered a reasonable upper bound for exposure time to high-radiation levels.

Some specific activities on a plant may only take a few minutes. For example, exporting a sample through a shielded posting port may take a couple of minutes to do. The potential exposure duration close to the open shield port may reasonably be conservatively bound by five to ten minutes. Glovebox operations may be conducted for 15–20 minutes for which a bounding conservative 30 minutes may be taken, for exposure close to the glovebox. The default assumption of a full two-hour working period may be overly conservative in these situations. The best-estimate consequences can use the expected working times.

Operators further away or other site workers not connected with the operation may not be so time bound. Their exposure should not be constrained by the task duration, but default to the maximum conservative value, which we are taking to be two hours here. These workers should experience the dose rate or activity concentration at their location. Thus, in assessing the dose to operators and other workers, there is a trade-off between:

1. A close working location in a higher activity/radiation environment and shorter exposure time;

2. A more distant location, but in a lower activity/radiation environment for a longer time.

For a simple dose model, we may expect the dose to be linear with time, i.e. double the time and double the dose. A simple dose model may suggest that activity concentration decreases with the cube root of distance, as there is a bigger volume into which activity must be dispersed (volume is length × depth × width). External radiation may decrease by the square of the distance, as given by the inverse square law (see Section 5.1.2). Consequently, the dose for the local operator is likely to be bound to that of the more distant worker. Both should be determined for completeness, particularly when noting that the protection for the local operator and site worker may be different.

Alarms

An alarm, whether an activity-in-air alarm or an area gamma alarm, is a mitigating system. Therefore, credit for its correct function should never be taken in the calculation of the unmitigated dose. The unmitigated dose should, therefore, be dependent upon the natural end to the exposure duration as discussed above. In contrast, the mitigated dose can take credit for the correct function of the alarm. There are, however, important caveats that must be remembered that are now discussed.

Area gamma alarm
For an area gamma alarm, we must firstly be confident that the detector is in the shine path of the radiation field. Secondly, we must also be confident that the dose rate at the detector is sufficient to trigger the alarm. Both of these may not necessarily be given.

Firstly, if there is a highly collimated beam, an area gamma monitor may not be suitably located and any scattered radiation may not be sufficient to enable the monitor to go into alarm. Thus, a safety case must be mindful of non-isotropic radiation.

Secondly, a gamma monitor may be located in a location that 'sees' a relatively low-dose rate that is below the trigger level of the alarm. This could be due to the distance from the source and/or the presence of intervening structures. Moreover, the plant may sometimes handle lower-emitting sources and the alarm may have been calibrated for more significant radiation sources. The safety assessment must consider the range of sources that could be of concern and ensure, by working backwards, that the gamma monitor will alarm at the location where operators are to be located if the alarm is being claimed. This issue is also true for gamma monitors used in gamma interlock systems. For a plant handling miscellaneous radiation sources, in particular, care must be taken.

Assuming that we are confident that the detector is in the shine path and will be triggered, we would expect the alarm to initiate immediately as gamma radiation will travel at the speed of light (a lazy 3×10^8 m s^{-1}!). Thus, provided we are confident that an operator can hear (and possibly also see) the alarm, the mitigated dose can then take credit for rapid evacuation provided there are no physical impediments to withdrawal. A dose duration of 30 s may be justifiable in this instance, but this will be dependent upon the specifics of the working environment.

On the plant and across the barrier, operators will also generally wear EPDs. These are placed on the torso and will provide an audible signal on detection of radiation. They can be used for local reassurance monitoring and will also alert the operator if there is an elevated radiation field. The EPDs support the provision of defence-in-depth and may provide an additional mitigating prompt to evacuate. However, EPDs are less easy to substantiate (see Section 10) as they are portable, can be dropped and damaged, may have a flat battery, not be switched on or even be forgotten to be worn. Therefore, they would normally not be relied upon as the sole means of prompting evacuation.

Activity-in-air alarm
An activity-in-air alarm will draw activity across a sample filter and then use a radiation probe to detect the activity on the filter. It therefore requires activity to migrate to the filter, which will obviously take a period of time. Moreover, the detector may well be positioned such that the operator is exposed before the activity reaches the detector. Ideally, we would hope that the monitors are positioned close to the working area, but on large plants where a release could come from many different places this may not be practicable.

Even when activity is drawn across the filter, it will take time for the activity to build up to the point where the alarm sounds. Overall, we might expect operator exposure of at least one minute before the operator is alerted plus time to evacuate, again depending upon the specifics of the environment. Immediate sounding of an alarm should never be assumed following an activity release. It is not unheard of for engineers to not substantiate alarms to function because of the difficulty in substantiating that activity would migrate to the detector. The ability of activity to reach the detector can be influenced by bulk air movements in the plant, such as those induced by ventilation systems.

Operator incapacitation

Operator incapacitation can be a tricky subject and it is fair to say some assessors have differing views on this. Firstly, it is worth stating that the dead cannot receive a meaningful effective dose measured in sieverts, as there is no biological impact of radiation on the organs within a corpse.[3] It is a meaningless concept when the casualty is dead directly from the industrial hazard aspect of the fault. However, this has not stopped safety cases assessing doses to operators who have fallen down lift shafts, been next to large explosions, effectively hit by planes or immersed in clouds of corrosive and toxic gas. It is sometimes said, 'If they just happen to survive, we need to know what their dose might be'. This can lead to very high and unrealistic doses. In such situations there is clearly a need to manage a significant hazard that is not related to radiological issues.

When there is a significant industrial hazard that may also release radioactivity, one option is that the industrial hazard should be recognised as the principal hazard of concern and the safety case should recognise this. There is likely to be legislation or RGP for the management of these hazards, and the safety case should draw attention to how these hazards are being managed to reduce the risk to ALARP. It does not necessarily need to get bogged down in lots of detail on how the industrial hazard is managed. It is this industrial hazard management that prevents the catastrophic failure that will also prevent a release and exposure to other workers and the public. The licensee should provide advice on the approach to be taken.

If it is a reasonable assumption that an operator would be killed by the industrial hazard, then focus the consequence assessment on the other workers in the wider environment. These workers may not be directly involved in the catastrophic failure or may have a reasonable chance to escape the direct effects of the industrial hazard and may be around to accrue a radiological dose. Indeed, it may actually be found that these workers may still receive a 'significant' dose that requires safety measures to adequately manage the risk. Therefore, the focus on them does not do away with the search for lines of protection the provision of defence-in-depth and so on.

In doing this, let us remember that radiological risk, in the true sense, is the product of frequency and consequence. For an operator to have survived the significant industrial hazard and receive a radiological dose, this frequency (which can be a best-estimate value) should factor in the very small likelihood that the industrial hazard was survivable. Thus, their radiological risk would be suppressed compared to that of the other workers, but their industrial hazard risk will obviously be much greater.

Not all industrial hazards will lead to operator fatality. The industrial hazard that also leads to the activity release/radiation exposure may reasonably lead to an impairment to evacuation. For example, there may be disorientation or even the trapping of an operator with no viable escape route. In these cases, it is not possible to define

---

[3] Strictly, we could say a corpse, just like any inanimate object, can still receive a dose measured in gray as this is simply energy absorbed per unit mass.

a specific time of exposure. It is better to determine the time to breach thresholds (e.g. 20 mSv or 1 Sv) and determine the credibility of these being exceeded given the constraints: the revealing of the fault to others and any intervention by emergency services. This is an area where the safety assessor should seek advice from others, particularly human factors assessors.

6.3.4   External radiation dose

The whole-body dose accrued by a worker in a constant external radiation field is linear with time t and is a function of the dose rate d_p at location p. Thus, the dose is simply given by

$$\text{dose}_{\text{ext}} = d_p t. \tag{6.2}$$

The dose rate can be determined by radiation calculations and the unmitigated and mitigated consequences can be determined by suitable use of exposure time, as discussed above. The safety case will justify the chosen exposure location, which may include consideration of conservative and best-estimate positions of the worker with respect to the radiation source. It may be determined that on a best-estimate basis, the fault only makes it possible to accrue an extremity dose rather than a whole-body dose. It is conservative to assume whole-body exposure.

Radiation sources may be well-defined physical sources such as unshielded containers. A spill of liquor may give rise to a pool of liquor on the floor that would irradiate the local area. A spill may also be directly onto an operator giving rise to irradiation from contamination on the clothes or skin. In this instance, there may be a beta component to consider.

A criticality will give rise to an initial burst of gamma radiation and neutrons. A review of accidental criticality accidents [12] shows that criticality events have led to fatal operator doses (>1 Gy). Criticality assessors can make use of standard look-ups for the dose to operators from a given number of fissions. The dose to the other site workers (or public) further afield can be simply calculated by assuming the inverse square law and significant structures that provide shielding can be included in a more complex dose model if required. This is undertaken when modelling contours of dose from a criticality event to determine evacuation zones, muster areas and escape routes and to determine if there is a significant criticality risk off-site.

6.3.5   Inhalation dose

The inhalation dose to a worker is determined on the basis that the operator is immersed within a cloud of activity. At the operator's location p, the cloud has an instantaneous concentration at time t of $c_{t,p}$. The operator will breathe in a volume of air at a rate determined by their *breathing rate B*. The operator will then be resident in the cloud until it either passes/settles or the operator withdraws.

It is recognised that, with time, the concentration may change as the activity migrates to and then past the operator. To account for this change, a concept known as the *time-integrated concentration* is used, which we will give by the term C_p at position p. The instantaneous concentration has units of Bq m^{-3} and the time-integrated concentration has units of Bq m^{-3} s. In simple terms, the time-integrated concentration can be considered to be the sum of the concentration (that may change) over a period of time. The inhalation dose is then given by

$$\text{dose}_{\text{inh}} = C_{\text{p}}BD, \tag{6.3}$$

where D is the dose conversion factor given in units Sv Bq^{-1}. As a check, the units of Eq. 6.3 are

$$\text{Sv} = (\text{Bq m}^{-3} \text{ s}) (\text{m}^3 \text{ s}^{-1}) (\text{Sv Bq}^{-1}) = \text{Sv}. \tag{6.4}$$

The fingerprint would be used to determine how many becquerels of each isotope are present in the unit volume or mass. The dose conversion factor would be given in terms of Sv ml^{-1} or Sv mg^{-1} of the radioactive solid or liquid. For dispersed activity-in-air, the concentration would then be given in terms of mg m^{-3} or ml m^{-3} in which the m^{-3} refers to a volume of air. This approach is convenient because a fault is often analysed in terms of a fraction of respirable material released as aerosol, i.e. a respirable RF.

As an example of the above approach, should liquor be lost from a vessel, whilst all of the liquor may be lost, only a fraction will be made airborne as a respirable aerosol. This will be based upon the initial splash of the liquor and potentially a chronic release due to the influence of air flow across the surface. The value of any RF in this example will be small in comparison to the overall volume of liquor and may be of the order of 10^{-6} or smaller.

The breathing rate within Eq. 6.3 is related to the individual (adult, child, etc.) and the type of work undertaken. A value of 1.2 m^3 h^{-1}, which equates to 3.3 × 10^{-4} m^3 s^{-1}, is given in ICRP 119 [9] for average workers. The dose conversion factors for individual isotopes can be found in ICRP documents. The selection of appropriate dose conversion factors can be a specialist area and a nuclear site licensee will provide look-up tables for common isotopes for use in their dose calculations.

To put the above into practice, a number of models have been derived in the industry to calculate doses for the workers. The key aspect in the models is the determination of the time-integrated concentration C_{p}. Two models are frequently utilised which will subsequently be described and these are:

- Expanding cloud model;

- Fixed concentration model.

We will also describe a simple hybrid model that utilises aspects of both models.

In determining the time-integrated concentration in a model, it is necessary to know how much activity has been released. We have introduced the term *release fraction* and now mention again the DF. The DF is the fraction of material removed by a containment barrier. This reduction may be in terms of an absolute reduction, if the DF is a *mass* DF, or in terms of concentration if the DF is a *concentration* DF. Examples of a containment barrier include a wall or cell structure, multiple package layers or even the filter within a respirator.

If A_i is the initial pre-fault activity, then the total respirable aerosol suspended in the air and available for inhalation A_r is

$$A_r = \frac{A_i(\text{RF})}{(\text{DF})}.$$ (6.5)

In this context, the DF is a mass DF, i.e. an absolute reduction in activity. Licensees should provide guidance on RFs and DFs and their use. RFs can be found in a number of open sources including from the US Department of Energy (DOE) [13].

Finally, we note that there are other aspects that can influence the inhalation dose from released activity. Over time, aerosols will settle and plate-out onto surfaces and be unavailable for inhalation (unless subsequently resuspended).

Expanding cloud model

A commonly used model for releases within a building is the *expanding cloud* model in which the released activity is uniformly constrained within an expanding hemispherical cloud of radius r and volume $\frac{2\pi r^3}{3}$. The cloud expands from the release point, engulfs the position of the operator and continues to expand until it reaches the volume of the room. At this point, the concentration is then assumed to remain constant. However, if room air changes are accounted for, the concentration will then decrease with time.

The model is appropriate for scenarios where a sudden release of activity occurs. Typical examples include a dropped package and release of its contents or a failure of a tank leading to a short-term splash release. A fraction of the inventory, the RF, will then be made airborne and will diffuse through the room with speed u.

At time t the released activity will reach a distance r from the release point (the centre of the expanding hemisphere). The instantaneous concentration at distance r from the release point is a function of time and for a unit release of activity is given by

$$c_{t,r} = \frac{3}{2\pi (ut)^3},$$ (6.6)

where we have replaced r for ut. The dispersion of the particles and the expansion of the hemisphere will reach the operator at time $t_1 = \frac{r_1}{u}$ and expansion will continue until the room volume V is reached at time t_2. For simplicity, the room is taken as a larger hemisphere and t_2 is given by

$$t_2 = \left(\frac{3V}{2\pi}\right)^{\frac{1}{3}} \frac{1}{u}.$$ (6.7)

Between t_1 and t_2 the time-integrated concentration is given by

$$C_r = \int_{t_1}^{t_2} c_{t,r} \, dt.$$ (6.8)

Resolving the integration with Eq. 6.6 for $c_{t,r}$ gives

$$C_r = \frac{3}{4\pi u^3 (t_1^2 - t_2^2)}.$$ (6.9)

At time t_2 the concentration will remain constant and the dose becomes linear with time. It is normal for there to be some rate of air change either through natural ventilation or through the action of an extract system. It is conservative and appropriate for an unmitigated consequence to take no account of an extract system. We will just note that if air changes are accounted for, the concentration will decrease exponentially with time, i.e.

$$c_t = c_{t_2} \exp(-\sigma (t - t_2)),\tag{6.10}$$

where σ is the air change rate. We will leave it as an exercise to the reader to integrate Eq. 6.10 to provide the time-integrated concentration component following the filling of the room.

Fixed concentration model

This model assumes that the initial pre-fault activity A_i is subject to a release mechanism that instantly suspends a fraction of the activity into a given volume V. The fraction released is the RF and the suspended activity remains at a constant concentration c that is given by

$$c = \frac{A_i(\text{RF})}{V(\text{DF})},\tag{6.11}$$

where the DF is a mass DF that affects the initial release prior to filling volume V. The dose to the operator will then be linear with time t. Thus, the time-integrated concentration C is simply

$$C = ct = \frac{A_i(\text{RF})t}{V(\text{DF})}.\tag{6.12}$$

In this model, the dose is not explicitly dependent upon the distance of the operator to the release point. The volume could be taken to be that immediately around the operator, i.e. the local *breathing volume* from where the air is drawn. It is not unreasonable to consider the local breathing volume to be a cube focused on the operator with dimensions of 2 m × 2 m × 2 m, i.e. 8 m^3. This will be conservative if there is no account for a wider dispersion out of the breathing volume or the time taken for activity to reach the breathing volume. In many situations, the exact release point in the plant may be unclear and this model assumes that the operator is adjacent to it. A less conservative model would base the volume on the distance of the operator to the release point with the activity dispersed in a volume centred on the release point with the volume being a cube or hemisphere.

A fixed concentration model is used when the release of activity is into a volume that is separated from the operator by a containment barrier. If there is a containment barrier, then a concentration DF should be applied to Eq. 6.12.

As an example, process equipment may be situated in a cell from which operators are excluded. If there is a release from the process equipment; e.g. due to a ruptured pipe, it may be expected that the activity will firstly fill the cell volume prior to diffusing out of the cell via adventitious openings to the areas where operators have access. The wall of the cell will provide a DF between the *in-cell* and *out-cell* areas, as the wall will resist the diffusion of activity. Thus, the concentration in the out-cell areas c_{out} will be a fraction of that in the cell c_{in} with the fraction being the DF. Therefore, the out-cell concentration is simply

$$c_{out} = \frac{c_{in}}{(DF)}.$$
$\qquad\qquad\qquad\qquad\qquad\qquad\qquad$ (6.13)

The same approach can be adopted for releases occurring in one room and workers being situated in an adjacent room with activity migrating via doorways and so on.

Example: Mishandling Waste Package
Consider an operator handling a waste package in a laboratory. The operator may be required to wear a respirator during this operation, and the doors to the laboratory will normally be closed. Should the operator drop the package, it may break leading to a release of activity should the bottle's over-bagging be pierced. The activity will be released into the local volume around the operator from where it will then expand to fill the volume of the room and beyond. We will not discuss the merits or ALARPness of this operation here.

It may be argued that the event is visually obvious to the operator and that given core training, evacuation would be expected to occur rapidly. However, it may be conservative, in the unmitigated consequence analysis, to assume no evacuation or the wearing of a respirator. Both evacuation and the wearing of a respirator are mitigating safety measures and should not be accounted for in our initial unmitigated consequence calculation. The unmitigated consequence will then assume the maximum residence time in the room in question, which in this room can be justified at 30 min.

One partially mitigated dose scenario would assume the wearing of a respirator for which a DF = 100 can be justified. The other partially mitigated scenario would assume no respirator but prompt evacuation.

What about other site workers who may be situated outside of the laboratory? Unless alerted by alarms, they will clearly have no indication that a fault has occurred. Activity will fill the laboratory prior to migrating outside the room into the adjacent areas. Thus, we would expect to use Eq. 6.13 modified by the concentration DF appropriate to a room with a door set (e.g. DF of 10).

The unmitigated consequence to the other workers may again assume a time of two hours, but it may be able to justify a mitigated consequence of perhaps five minutes due to the evacuation in response to the activation of an activity-in-air alarm. These alarms will not necessarily alarm instantaneously as activity will have to migrate to the monitors and at least one minute should be assumed for this.

This example shows the importance of at least some consideration of other workers outside the room where the fault occurs due to their lack of direct notification. They will not be routinely wearing respirators and their sole protection is provided by their distance, the passive filtration of any barriers and an alarm system. It may be found during detailed analysis that this does not provide sufficient protection to adequately mitigate their risk.

A Useful Approach

It is often convenient and conservative to consider the *maximum sustainable concentration* of respirable aerosol that can be suspended in the air within a cell or a building. A bounding value of 10 mg m^{-3} is given in Sutter *et al.* [14], which is associated with fog or mist. A larger mass density cannot generally be supported by the air and will settle relatively quickly before the aerosol can migrate to where the operator is likely to be present. This is especially true if the aerosol has to traverse through containment barriers that will provide resistance to the migration of activity. Using the sustained aerosol concentration, the operator dose is linear with time. Explosions or energetic events may lead to larger concentrations being suspended for a few minutes, and Selby *et al.* [15] suggest a bounding value of 100 mg m^{-3}.

Simple expanding model

A simple model that includes aspects of the expanding cloud and the fixed concentration model is sometimes used. Let us suppose that if there is a release of activity A, then it is into a local volume surrounding the operator (this value is taken to include all RFs and DFs). Again, for the sake of argument, we take a reasonable approximation that this is into the local breathing volume of 8 m^3 and this gives an initial concentration of $\frac{A}{8}$ Bq m^{-3}. We can then determine the dose as a linear function of an initial time, say 30 s.

After this initial period, we simply assume that the activity has dispersed into a larger volume: the volume of the room. Let us assume that the room is relatively small and has a volume of 100 m^3. Thus, the concentration in the larger volume is now $\frac{A}{100}$ Bq m^{-3}, and the time-integrated concentration is then the sum of the two components, i.e.

$$C = A \, \mathrm{Bq}\left(\frac{30 \text{ s}}{8 \text{ m}^3} + \frac{n30 \text{ s}}{100 \text{ m}^3} \right), \qquad (6.14)$$

where n is the number of 'blocks' of 30 s assumed for our maximum chosen residence time.

6.3.6 Contaminated wounds

Contaminated wounds are only a concern for operators engaged in hands-on work in contaminated areas. Decommissioning operations are one area where there is the potential for contaminated wounds due to the use of cutting equipment in active areas. Gloveboxes are another area where care must be taken to avoid contaminated wounds. Gloveboxes are used where there is a significant contamination hazard and a high level of containment must be made. A puncture by a sharp through a glove can inject sufficient activity into the operator to give rise to a large, potentially fatal, dose. This is of particular concern should the glovebox contain plutonium, for instance.

Calculating the radiological dose from a contaminated wound is fraught with difficulty. The dose is dependent upon the:

1. Size of the wound (cm^2 for surface grazes and burns or cm^3 for puncture wounds), V;

2. DF provided by any clothing (worn by default or as PPE), F_c;

3. Fraction of the residual activity absorbed into the blood stream, F_a.

For a particular isotope surface contamination of activity level A_i (Bq cm^{-2}) or activity within an injected volume (Bq cm^{-3}), the contaminated wound dose is given by

$$\text{Dose} = \sum_{\text{Isotopes}} A_i V F_c F_a d_i, \qquad (6.15)$$

where d_i is the wound internal dose factor (Sv Bq^{-1}) for isotope i. We should reflect that determining the size of the wound can be difficult to do, as too is the determination of fraction absorbed into the blood stream, for instance, how much rolls off the body is removed by clothing, absorbed into the wound and then transferred into the blood and taken into the body.

For many nuclides, particularly those that require glovebox work, Eq. 6.15 will quickly give rise to significant doses $\gg$Sv where acute effects will be relevant. The absolute numerical value of the dose becomes arguably irrelevant. Puncture wounds, for instance, do occur from time-to-time and this is not a theoretical hazard. Prosecutions have occurred in the UK due to actual wounding events.[4]

Not all licensees explicitly calculate the dose from contaminated wounds, particularly when they are expected to be significant. Rather than focusing on the actual dose, the emphasis must be upon the demonstration that the risks have been adequately controlled to minimise this hazard. Briefly, we note that the emphasis must be on:

- Negating the need for hands-on work;

- Reducing the inventory;

- Removing sharps and items that can puncture—sharps audit and visual inspections;

- Management and training—risk assessment and safe system of work;

- Finally, adequate PPE such as the use of handled tools and puncture/cut resistant gloves.

As always, reference must always be made to a site's own methodology for the calculation of contaminated wounds (or not). More detail about the approaches that can be adopted for contaminated wounds, including their treatment, is provided by the National Council on Radiation Protection and Measurements (NCRP) [16].

A contaminated wound is almost certainly going to be a revealed fault that will require some degree of medical attention and this is self-evident if there is a painful

---

[4]Sellafield Limited was prosecuted and fined £380,000 plus costs following a glovebox puncture wound incident that occurred in 2017. The operator was injured whilst cleaning a corroded alarm probe within a plutonium glovebox leading to an estimated contaminated wound dose of >100 mSv.

injury. Operators in active areas are well aware of the hazards posed by contaminated wounds and the need to seek urgent medical attention for their own preservation should they occur. Failing to seek such attention is very unlikely. This is backed up by noting that the standard approach when leaving an active area is to utilise frisk probes and installed monitors; these should detect activity within a wound and on the body.

6.4   Dose calculation: public

During normal site operations, the public may receive a dose due to radioactive discharges to the atmosphere or water courses (seas, lakes and rivers). They may also receive a gamma or neutron radiation dose either from a direct line of sight to the bulk sources or from scattered radiation from interaction of upwards travelling radiation with the air (known as *skyshine*).

Should a fault arise and there is a discharge of radioactivity or an increase in gamma or neutron radiation, there will be an increased dose to the public. The methodology for the calculation of the public dose is essentially the same, whether it is due to normal operations or fault conditions, but there are some subtle differences that we will explore in this section. The normal operational dose will be due to chronic exposure, whilst a dose from a fault condition would generally be expected to be of a more limited duration.

When considering the dose to the public, it is also necessary to consider radioactivity that enters the food chain. This necessitates the consideration of ingestion of the radioactive material.

6.4.1   Critical group

For a given route of radiological public exposure, it is necessary to define the *critical group*, which is the person(s) most exposed to the event. In determining the critical group, account of the nuclides released and their exposure pathway can be taken and it may be that an adult or child or infant is at most risk. It is for a licensee to determine and justify their selection of the critical group.

For an airborne discharge or exposure to external radiation, the critical group is likely to include persons living closest to the *site fence* or a person within a public building that is routinely occupied adjacent to the site, i.e. the *closest point of habitation*. Sometimes, the site fence itself is often used as the reference point rather than such a point of habitation. The selection of the site fence is conservative and it is the closest point to the site that a member of the public can reasonably be. It is worth noting that many nuclear sites are remote and public residence at the site fence is expected to not be a routine event. Thus, the selection of the site fence may be overly conservative and the selection of a permanently inhabited building further away may be more appropriate. 'Primrose Cottage' may have the unfortunate claim to be the location for the reference dose calculations (it is unlikely that the residents know this).

Some site discharges will be via pipes to lakes, rivers, estuaries or the sea, i.e. aquatic or marine environments. Under fault conditions, an erroneous discharge could occur in the same manner as an aerial discharge leading to higher levels of activity in these environments.

For a release to the aquatic or marine environments, the critical group will take into account the deposition of activity on the beaches and the beaches' potential public occupation, together with those individuals that may consume fish or shellfish, for instance. One infamous example was the finding of fuel particles on the beaches around Dounreay in the UK that posed a hazard to beach dwellers.

6.4.2   Atmospheric dispersion

Particulate-based activity (aerosols) made airborne in a plant will generally largely settle within the confines of the plant envelope, but a fraction of the smallest of the particles may escape from the building fabric and be released to the atmosphere. The release of aerosols contrasts with gases that would generally be expected to be fully released from a plant over time with exceptions including:

1. Fission product noble gases that have short half-lives—an example being ^{135}Xe with a half-life of nine hours;

2. Reactive gases—an example being uranium hexafluoride that will react to form uranium oxide particles and (non-radioactive, but very toxic) hydrogen fluoride gas.

Should the activity be released to a plant's ventilation system, it will be discharged to the atmosphere from a discharge point at a particular height. The discharge point may be >100 m above ground level for the tallest of *discharge stacks*. When a discharge is via a stack, the plume may not reach the ground for hundreds of metres and this may lead to a different critical group than that associated with a *ground level* release. The *effective release height* of the stack takes into account the actual stack height, the exit velocity of the material, its density (buoyancy) and atmospheric stability.

The activity released in this manner will mix in the atmosphere and will be dispersed by random turbulent and diffusion motion, natural buoyancy and the action of the wind blowing across the discharge point. Atmospheric models have been developed to determine how the concentration in the atmosphere changes with time following a release at a given point of interest. Atmospheric models in use in the nuclear industry include those that consider the plume to have a *Gaussian distribution* in the lateral dimensions. From the derivation published in [17], a basic Gaussian plume model giving steady-state concentration C at location x, y, z is of the form

$$C_{(x,y,z)} = \frac{Q}{2 \pi u \, \sigma_y \sigma_z} \exp[-(y - y')^2 / 2\sigma_y^2]$$

$$\{\exp[-(z - H)^2 / 2\sigma_z^2] + \exp[-(z + H)^2 / 2\sigma_z^2]\}, \qquad (6.16)$$

where x, y, z is a point, downwind of a point source (x', y'), at effective height H and constant emission rate Q, reflected from the ground and under the influence of a constant wind speed u and standard deviations in concentrations σ_y and σ_z in the crosswind and vertical directions (both dependent upon position $x - x'$). Equation 6.16 shows that with increasing wind speed, the concentration at any one point is reduced.

A simple modification to the Gaussian plume involves the consideration of radioactive decay. The concentration of a particular nuclide released from a stack into the plume, at a given point of distance x on the axial line, is modified by a factor $\exp[-\lambda \frac{x}{u}]$, where λ is the radioactive decay constant. Added radioactive complication can be factored in by considering the radioactive growth of daughter products *into* the plume. Clearly, for nuclides of long half-life in comparison to the time taken to traverse the distance, the modification is insignificant; it can be important for the consideration of very short-lived fission products following a criticality, for instance.

The atmospheric dispersion models used in industry can become increasingly involved and be used to generate sets of time-integrated concentration curves. These curves are a function of parameters: distance, weather conditions (including temperature inversions that can inhibit upwards vertical motion), surface roughness, release height, deposition and ground impact rates, radioactive decay (as just described) and the release duration. Therefore, the models can become very complex and encompass modified Gaussian plumes for which their detailed description is far beyond the scope of this book. One early model that has been extensively utilised in the UK is the National Radiological Protection Board (NRPB) model known as R-91 [18]. Whilst the model is old it is still used in the industry to form the basis of many dispersion calculations.

It is found that individual licensees will churn through the numbers for their site based upon their adopted model and produce look-up tables for general use to determine public doses for a given release of nuclide and assumed atmospheric conditions, dose point of interest and so on. This will enable the determination of conservative and best-estimate calculations to be undertaken. For instance, conservative calculations will utilise the appropriate weather conditions that tend to minimise vertical development of the plume to maximise its concentration on the ground. If there is a release in general plant areas, it is generally conservative to assume a ground-level release for public dose calculation. Mitigation would be via a stack discharge at height, which itself may feature further mitigation from ventilation clean-up systems such as filters.

It is important to stress that slightly different approaches need to be adopted for short-term releases and long-term releases. A short-term release will occur as an initial 'puff' release of activity from an accident, such as from a burst or dropped package. A long-term release is generally relevant for normal operations where there is a continuous release of activity via a stack. A long-term release may also be relevant following an accident that has a component of a continuous release. The consideration of a long-term release should factor in changes in the wind direction over time and the use of more average weather characteristics. The critical group may differ for such a release as continued residence at the site fence, for instance, would not be credible.

The limitation of any dispersion model needs to be understood. For instance, the use of models that are suitable for distances of hundreds of metres to tens of kilometres would not be suitable for modelling dispersion over geographical distances. This is due to the simplifications in the model such as constant wind speeds and weather conditions, which we all know change over distance and time. Releases close to large buildings may also be subject to *near wake* effects due to building-induced turbulent flows that affect the dispersion of activity. These effects can become complex, will be site specific and will modify the concentration values close to the building. Site licensees will determine the applicability of the near-wake models to use.

6.4.3 Marine dispersion

Many nuclear plants are sited close to natural masses of water, i.e. rivers, lakes, estuaries or the seas. This is to provide a large source of cooling water and heat sink, but it also offers a route for liquid discharges to occur. As with aerial discharges, there are stringent requirements to ensure that such environmental discharges are minimised as far as practicable and that BAT/BPM are employed.

Nevertheless, discharges do occur on a routine basis. Where there is a normal discharge, there is more than likely to be a fault condition whereby excess activity can be erroneously discharged via this route. Example faults include:

- Mis-sentencing of a radioactive substance to the wrong disposal route; or

- Failure of the normal effluent clean-up or abatement systems prior to discharge; or

- Breakthrough of activity from a primary circuit to a secondary circuit.

The movement of the radioactivity will be influenced by many factors including the rates of sedimentation, terrain features, currents and large-scale movement of bodies of water. The public may subsequently accrue a dose from this activity via a number of pathways. These pathways are determined by where the radioactivity is transferred to and the public 'use' of the associated water, its environment or aquatic life present there and its interaction with the population. For example, radioactivity settling in sediment can lead to an external radiation hazard to persons close to a river bank or seashore. River water may be piped to homes for washing or drinking, fish and seaweed and so on may be food sources for the public. If these are contaminated, then there will be ingestion of radioactivity.

To model the movement of radioactivity in these environments, marine dispersion models have been developed. These utilise *compartments* where the activity in each compartment can be calculated and the rates of activity transfer from one compartment to the next are also determined, representing the dispersion or dilution of the activity through the wider environment. The compartments can be sized and numbered appropriately to consider the movement of this activity on continental scales.

An example marine dispersion methodology was developed and described by the then European Commission in their report [19]. The methodology is known as Consequences of Releases to the Environment: Assessment Methodology (CREAM) and has subsequently been incorporated in commercially available computer software. At the core of the methodology is the consideration of the rate of change of activity A with time t in compartment i, i.e. $\frac{dA_i}{dt}$. This is related to the activity at that time in compartment i and will be influenced by activity transfer to/from adjacent compartment j and the original nuclear plant source discharge rate Q_i into compartment i. Therefore, the rate of change of activity is given by

$$\frac{dA_i}{dt} = \sum_{j=1}^{n} k_{ji}A_j - \sum_{j=1}^{n} k_{ij}A_i + Q_i - k_i A_i, \qquad (6.17)$$

where k_{ji} and k_{ij} are the rates of transfer between compartments i and j, k_i is the effective loss rate within compartment i (such as radioactive decay) and n is the number of compartments in the model. It is worth noting that stripping out the first three terms in the model leads to $\frac{dA_i}{dt} = -k_i A_i$, which is of the same form as the radioactive decay equation (Eq. 4.1). This represents a static situation where there is no physical activity transfer into or out of the compartment other than an exponential loss mechanism within the compartment. This loss may be radioactive decay, sedimentation and so on.

Equation 6.17 determines the rate of change activity in a particular compartment and its integration will give the time integral to the activity. With this information, it is then a matter of determining the transfer of this activity into the various pathways. The concentration of activity can be determined in a compartment simply by dividing its volume. With this concentration, it is possible to determine how much activity is transferred into the relevant pathways and from there the public dose. The detailed methodology of this process and the equations are provided in [19] and are beyond the scope of this book.

Part III

SAFETY CASE PROCESSES

Chapter 7

Introduction to Hazard and Fault Analysis

This chapter provides an introduction to *hazard and fault analysis*, which are significant components of any safety case. The analysis involves understanding how the hazards and faults progress through the *fault transient* or the *fault sequence progression*. The hazard and fault identification process is one of the key early steps in producing a safety case and the generic term HAZID is used to describe this. The HAZID must be a robust, logical and structured process that can maintain auditability to source documents. This is sometimes known as the *golden thread* and it is the auditable link between the fault identification and assessment to claims on protection.

There are a number of processes that are used for HAZID, but the principal mechanism is the HAZOP study. This chapter describes the HAZOP process and how different types of HAZOP can be tailored to the design stages described in Section 3.2. HAZOP can be a powerful tool that can identify operability issues as well as hazards/faults. The technique is used in a wide range of high hazard industries not just the nuclear industry.

Following the conducting of a HAZOP, there will be a need to consolidation, rationalisation and sentencing of the identified hazards and faults. We should recap that a hazard is an intrinsic property of something that can do harm whilst a fault is a failure of something to do what it is meant to do. Both terms are used interchangeably, but there is a strict difference. External hazards, for instance, can include seismic events that essentially can give rise to faults, e.g. failure of a building structure. A crane may pose a hazard to nuclear plant, whilst a drop onto the plant due to rope failure is a fault. The consolidation will lead to the generation of a *fault list*, which forms the basis of any subsequent hazard analysis. Each fault should have a unique reference number for traceability.

Once faults have been identified their combining into *fault sequence group*s (FSGs) is an essential stage in the process. The use of FSGs ensures that there is a manageable list of faults to assess. Each FSG will determine how the fault sequence develops, the consequences, the protection required and the risk that the sequence may pose. Again each FSG should have a unique reference number and a clear link to the individual fault reference numbers in the fault list.

In order to understand how faults may affect a plant, it is necessary to understand how the plant should operate during *normal operations*. Therefore, this chapter explains the importance of defining the *scope* of a safety case and how this may be documented. The scope of the safety case may be an important component in defining the *envelope of normal operations*. The SOE and the *safe envelope* are introduced and the relationship to the envelope of normal operations is given by a worked example. The derivation of *limits and conditions* within the safety case is an important component in defining the SOE and this is also discussed in this chapter.

It must be recognised that not all faults that may arise within a plant are as severe as others; i.e. there will be a spectrum of consequences. In addition, there will be a spectrum of IEFs; some faults may reasonably be expected to occur in the plant's lifetime, whilst others may be so unlikely as to present no significant risk. These factors will influence what is included within the *design basis* and those that are *beyond the design basis*. The role of PSA is introduced, but the mechanics for doing this is deferred to Section 8.

7.1 Fault identification and sentencing

This section focuses on the identification of faults via HAZOP and then the sentencing of the faults. The HAZOP was developed several decades ago and was originally used in the chemical process industry having been developed from 'what-if' studies. HAZOP has since been extensively used in the nuclear industry and is without doubt the 'go-to' process for fault identification. So what is a HAZOP? Well let's first break down the name:

- HAZ for hazard—identification of hazards (for which we can interchangeably also read across faults);

- OP for operability—identification of issues that may affect how operations are conducted, but without a safety concern.

For the safety case, we are obviously primarily interested in the hazard and fault identification component of the HAZOP. However, if we are embedded in a design project for a new plant or process, the project as a whole will be interested in the operability of the plant. The operability will include consideration of issues such as:

- Whether the process works;

- Process control and instrumentation;

- Position and types of valves, pipework and vessels;

- Sequencing;

- Layout.

Operability is an important aspect—it is not enough for us to simply design a 'safe' plant if it is not efficient, or simple or intuitive for the operators to operate or maintainers to maintain. After all, a truly safe plant is one that does not operate. Failing to take into account the needs of plant personnel can lead to divisions and the development of a 'them and us' culture. This is not healthy and will not get the best results for all concerned. Too many impracticable safety cases have been imposed on a plant in the past that have been difficult to follow and made it difficult to operate. If plant operators do not understand why a restriction is in place and this affects efficient operation, then the safety case process has failed.

A HAZOP utilises a mixed team to systematically step-by-step review the process or plant design that is represented on a series of drawings or written sequences, such as *method statements* or OIS. *Guidewords* are utilised to tease out the deviations and identify the hazards and operability issues. It must be remembered that whilst the safety case is interested in the nuclear hazard aspects, a design project will be interested in all hazards and the operability issues. This will require a rounded team attendance and there may be aspects of a plant where there would be no nuclear hazard, but potentially significant industrial or environmental hazards. The appropriate discipline safety assessors should be in attendance.

A HAZOP works best with a mixed team loosely numbering between six and a dozen members. Two members will be taken by the chair and secretary and with at least one of each from safety, process, plant and engineering that will be a minimum of six. Too few members and there will be too little interaction to bounce ideas between the members and possibly too little knowledge brought to the meeting. However, too many members will inevitably lead to difficulties in controlling the meeting; some members may not contribute whilst others may dominate. Keeping numbers down can be difficult if a contracting organisation sends a representative from each discipline that is then supplemented by the equivalent from the licensee organisation, which will more or less double the numbers. This is unavoidable and will require a good chair.

7.1.1 HAZOP stages

During a design project, good industry practice places an emphasis on early stage understanding of the hazards that may be present in the design. This enables early development of the correct HMS, the demonstration of ALARP and the minimisation of project risk by not progressing with solutions that do not provide for adequate safety. The staged HAZOP process can help with this. Three stages of HAZOP are described that align with the different design phases that we have defined in Section 3.2. Remember that different organisations and licensees have different definitions of these phases and what they involve so this is a generic description.

HAZOP 0

A HAZOP 0 is sometimes undertaken in the earliest stages of a major new build/process project during the concept design phase (see Section 3.2). The purpose of the study is to allow an early safety review of the proposal to ensure that safety principles are adopted at the earliest stage. The principal aim of the study is to identify and consider an HMS against the identified hazards associated with the process with the ideal aim of eliminating them entirely.

The study team should examine the inventory, materials and principal process operations to determine the principal hazards inherent in the process, inventory or material handled. The input into a HAZOP 0 may include:

- Inputs (feeds), outputs (products) and intermediate products;

- Principal process or mechanical handling stages;

- Inventory;

- Nature of control.

The output of the study is the generation of an HMS that can be applied against each hazard. These can then be developed and optioneered and progressed through the design process as discussed in Section 3.2.

HAZOP 1

During the preliminary design phase of a project, a HAZOP 1 is normally undertaken and will be a follow-on activity from the HAZOP 0. For the given design solution that has been developed, the HAZOP 1 enables the hazards to be identified together with any significant operability issues. For the HAZOP to work, there must be an outline design commensurate with the information available at this design phase and the information known.

Typical documents subject to a HAZOP 1 would be the PFDs and/or the MFDs for process and mechanical aspects of the plant operation. A GA showing the layout of principal areas of the plant can also be useful and feed into the HAZOP. The information known to the HAZOP team should include the items required for HAZOP 0, but these should be known in more detail or with greater confidence and clarity due to the design development that will have been undertaken.

If the design solution is for an installation or decommissioning activity, then a HAZOP 1 of an outline method statement can be useful. The outline method statement will identify the principal tasks to be undertaken and the HAZOP will identify the hazards and operability issues associated with these.

HAZOP 2

A HAZOP 2 normally follows on from HAZOP 1 during the detailed design phase of a project. The HAZOP provides a systematic review of the plant and can include construction and commissioning activities. A HAZOP 2 should be conducted on what is believed to be the final design in terms of process. Therefore, before undertaking such a HAZOP, a *design review* should have been undertaken to confirm that:

1. Correct HMS has been applied and hazards and faults have been eliminated as far as reasonably practicable;

2. Design works from a process perspective;

3. Design delivers customer requirements.

Consequently, if the HAZOP degenerates into questions of fundamental design rather than just tweaks, the HAZOP has been called too early. Where major changes to the design are required these will be given as *actions*, but the HAZOP will struggle to correctly identify the faults or operability issues if there are too many changes to the design that are required. If this happens, re-HAZOP will be necessary after the final design is agreed.

7.1.2 Mechanics of HAZOP

Irrespective of the type of HAZOP, the fundamental approach is the same. The drawing or method statement and so on would be broken down into a series of *nodes* and to each node a selection of *properties* and for HAZOP 2, *keywords* are applied. The nodes represent logical processes or drawing steps, which could be a single vessel or pipe or a logical collection of these. Too many nodes will lead to a very long HAZOP process, but too few may make the selection of items too disparate to apply the properties and keywords. For HAZOP 2 it is the combination of the properties and keywords that give rise to the *deviations*, i.e.

$$\text{Deviation} \; = \; \text{Property} \; + \; \text{Keyword.}$$

The properties applied may differ between the different types of HAZOP and examples are shown in Tables 7.1 and 7.2. HAZOP 0/1 is more focused towards hazards/issues whilst a HAZOP 2 is more focused towards faults, e.g. late, early, and reverse and so on.

Following the HAZOP, a set of minutes will be produced and issued (the minutes can also be agreed upon at the meeting if they are displayed for all to see). The actions will be resolved and fed back to the HAZOP team for review.

Table 7.1: Example HAZOP 0/1 properties.

Property	
External/internal dose	Shielding
Criticality	Containment
Ventilation	Fire/explosion
Maintenance	Services
Effluents	Corrosion
Weather	Seismic
Impact	Reaction

Table 7.2: Example HAZOP 2 keywords. The first group is for a process plant, e.g. the movement of gases or liquids through pipes and vessels, and the second group is for a mechanical handling plant, e.g. the movement of solid waste containers. For a given property all the keywords are cycled and applied as appropriate.

Process		Mechanical handling	
Property	**Keyword**	**Property**	**Keyword**
Flow	More/less	Movement	None
Temperature	None	Speed	Too much/too little
Pressure	Part of/as well as	Acceleration	As well
Concentration	Reverse	Direction	Reverse
Level	Early/late	Distance	Early/late
Radiation	Other	-	Other
Viscosity	-	-	-

7.1.3   Fault list

Once identified, the hazards and faults must all be assessed to determine the risk to the public and workers. However, the raw HAZOP files will contain all manners of identified deviations of which only a fraction will be true radiological hazards and faults. For instance, a HAZOP may identify:

1. Actual faults that we are interested in (initiating events in their own right);

2. Operability issues such as a reduction in throughput, but not a fault leading to a hazardous situation;

3. Problems in the design or process that require actions to change the plant or process;

4. Comments on the drawings due to drafting errors;

5. Faults or hazards that do not pose a radiological consequence, e.g. a release of a toxic non-radioactive gas that has no nuclear domino impact;

6. Failure of safety measures.

Taking the above list, item (1) is clearly of direct interest for a radiological assessment. We may also note that item (5) may be of interest for a non-radiological assessment as it is generally necessary to provide confidence that these faults are adequately managed. Moreover, there may be domino effects such that a release of a toxic gas may, for example, affect an operator who may then drop a radiological package leading to a release. As another example, a pressurised gas vessel may pose a direct hazard to workers nearby should it energetically rupture. A pressurised system may also pose a hazard to gloveboxes or other vulnerable containment in which radioactive material may be stored in close proximity.

Item (6) refers to a failure of a safety measure. However, the failure of a safety measure does not initiate a fault that would lead to a radiological consequence, it is solely a degradation of protection that may be claimed against a genuine initiating event. Thus, it should not be carried forward for further assessment as an initiating event, but is useful to note as a potential unrevealed failure mode.

Finally, it is worth noting that not all HAZOPs produce very good minutes of the meeting. It can be difficult to interpret what was meant when the HAZOP was undertaken. Even for a moderately sized and complex plant, there may be hundreds of HAZOP-derived deviations, let alone those identified from other sources. In the raw state these can be unwieldy and unmanageable, and as we note, only a fraction of the deviations are true initiating faults that we will be interested in.

To simplify matters, the usual approach is to produce a *fault list*. The fault list is an intermediate bridging document between the original fault identification documents (HAZOP record, etc.) and the subsequent hazard assessments (radiological, criticality, non-radiological, etc.). The fault list will justify which deviations are taken forward for assessment and in which document and which are not. It is, therefore, a vital link in the audit trail and will need to be thoroughly checked for less important faults being lost.

The fault list should not be confused with the *fault schedule* for which the latter summarises the faults, doses and protection. The fault schedule is discussed in Section 7.8.

In terms of fault list structure, each HAZOP deviation can be individually extracted and a commentary and forward reference assigned or the justification for the screening out of the deviation. By its nature, a fault list lends itself to a tabular style document that should be preceded with an introduction, scope of the document and so on, together with a reference list of the fault identification source documents, e.g. the HAZOP minutes. Given its potential length, a spreadsheet is often a preferable format for producing a fault list and this provides an easy way to filter the faults, e.g. those screened out or those of a criticality nature. It cannot be overly stressed that every source deviation must be accounted for to ensure that the audit trail is complete.

7.1.4 Initiating events

The fault identification process will identify a wide range of faults associated with, for example, process equipment. A simple example is a valve that may be closed when it should be open. Open is the normal state and closed is the fault condition. The HAZOP may or may not have established the reason for the valve to be closed, but the closed valve has clearly been flagged as a fault condition. If the valve is a manual valve, it may be erroneously closed because of operator errors. If it is a control valve, it may be closed because:

- An input sensor to the control system has given an incorrect signal;
- The control system is in error;
- The valve actuator has failed.

So, in reality, we have one fault of an erroneous closure of the valve and three different initiating events leading to it. From this we can see that the initiating event is the first thing that goes wrong and it is the start of the fault progression. Further than that, we define an initiating event as the initial failure that, if uncorrected by the correct actioning of safety measures, will lead to an unacceptable consequence. This unacceptable consequence could be an environmental discharge, an operability problem, a radiological consequence or a combination of all of these or even other consequences. Within the safety case, we will primarily be concerned with the radiological consequence.

7.1.5 Fault sequence groups

As we have noted, it is quite possible that even for a moderately sized plant, there may be hundreds of different faults identified. We can state now that, in general, it is not realistically practicable to assess each of these faults individually. If we did assess every fault individually, the safety case would be so vast that it would not be possible to take it all in or see the wood for the trees.

Fortunately, it is possible to group up faults and simplify and shorten the overall assessment without compromising the robustness of the safety case. Following the compiling of the fault list and the start of the assessment, one of the first tasks is to group the faults into a select number of FSGs. An FSG will include similar initiators that call upon the same safety measures to prevent or mitigate the consequences from arising. We may call this a *common demand event*.

7.2 Envelopes of operation

It is given that a plant must always operate in a safe manner. There will be safety measures to prevent deviations or faults from progressing to the point of being unsafe with a release or an accident likely to occur. We can ask ourselves what is the relationship between what is considered to be 'safe' and 'unsafe'? To answer this question, we need to consider:

1. The scope of the plant and the envelope of normal operations;

2. The SOE and the safe envelope.

Envelope of normal operations

Every safety case is based upon a set of assumptions and the safety case would be undermined if these assumptions were found to be incorrect. It is clearly important that the *scope* or *basis of assessment* of the safety case is clearly documented. This may be written in a standalone scope document and this would form part of the audit trail of the safety case or relevant parts of it may be written in safety case documents. It may be identified that certain aspects of the scope are important and that the safety case is sensitive to changes in a parameter or condition associated with normal operations. For example, if it is assumed that the safety case has assessed the handling only of uranium-based material, then there is no justification for the handling of plutonium-based material. The safety case may well consider the erroneous receipt of plutonium-based material, but the day-to-day handling of it is excluded.

A plant will operate in a normal envelope of process parameters as prescribed by its design, both physical and operational. The envelope could include aspects such as:

- The actual operations undertaken;

- Process temperatures and pressures;

- Heat generation rates and removal;

- Inventory, including absolute becquerels and fingerprint;

- Liquor levels;

- Chemical composition;

- Throughput.

There may also be other more mechanical aspects that provide an envelope of normal operations, which may include:

- Item masses;

- Number of mechanical handling events;

- Nature of containers or overpacking;

- Position of cranes, lifting heights and lifting arcs;

- Number of cell entries.

Parameters or *limits* and *conditions* may need to be formally written down and may be specified as *operating assumptions* (OAs) or even ORs.[1]

In specifying any envelope of normal operations, there should be an adequate margin to encompass potential deviations and avoid the need for future safety case modifications to justify an increase. For example, if it is assumed that 10 operations may be undertaken everyday, then this may be fine if the real number expected is only seven. Conversely, there is little point assuming 10 if only one operation is undertaken every other day. The value used may feed directly into the calculation of the plant risk and a 20-fold over-estimation may make the difference between being above the BSO and being comfortably below it.

---

[1] It is fair to say that within the UK there is a wide spectrum of what constitutes an OR, which are derived from the requirements of LC 23 and the specifications of limits and conditions. We will not be drawn into any debate in this book. What is important is that where they are important, limits and conditions need to be written down, communicated and complied with and it may be inferred that by the nature of the name, ORs are important.

Safe operating envelope

The plant should operate within the envelope of normal operations as defined above with this maintained by the control system (whether it be an operator or computer system). Occasionally, faults may arise and the plant may deviate from where it should be maintained. For example, the temperature of a process may rise above the value it should be maintained at, perhaps due to a faulty heating system. If a deviation has a safety implication, then the relevant safety measures should act to terminate the deviation and prevent the fault from progressing to a radiological consequence. The safety measures will act within an envelope, potentially with a margin, that we may define as the SOE. The plant is still 'safe' within this envelope, but we are within the region where the safety measures operate. In our temperature example, a temperature sensor may detect the temperature deviation and isolate the power at $+10\,°\mathrm{C}$ from the maximum normal temperature.

The positive action of a safety measure should be communicated directly to the operators with the process stopped, investigated and corrected. It is not normal practice for the safety measure to 're-set' and enable the process to restart should the deviation disappear. In our example, if there is overheating due to a heater failure (potentially due to its control circuit), a high-temperature trip would detect the overheating and isolate the power supply to the heater. The trip should only be cleared when:

1. The trip conditions have disappeared (the temperature falls below the trip value);

2. The operator actively instigates a reset after appropriate investigation, repair and so on.

Good design would see adequate margin between the envelope of normal operations and the SOE. This margin will minimise the number of excursions that may lead to a plant trip through the action of the safety measures—with a bigger margin there is more likelihood for self-correction by the control system or the operators.

The limits and conditions associated with the SOE are important and we can define the following:

Limit: The maximum justified state of operations within the SOE, which will typically have a numerical value, such as a limit on temperature, mass, volume or becquerels.

Condition: The circumstances necessary to keep operations within the SOE, such as the physical properties or nature of material processed, shielding and containment and the checks and safety measures available.

To ensure that the plant can be maintained within the SOE, it is essential that the safety measures that protect against the fault are identified and are available. A level of importance must be attached to these safety measures and each licensee will determine their designations. For example, important procedures may be termed OIs and important items of equipment may be termed *safety features* (SFs) for passive items (walls, doors, flasks, etc.) or *safety mechanisms* (SMs) for active safety measures (alarms, trips, interlocks, etc.). The exact names do not matter only that, its importance to safety is understood by all concerned.

It must be recognised that, from time-to-time, safety measures may be unavailable due to *examination, maintenance, inspection and testing* (EMIT). To ensure that the potential for the SOE to be breached (should there be a fault) does not arise during this planned *outage time*, the plant's documentation must define what the *substitution* or *action-on-failure* arrangements are. Action-on-failure occurs when a safety measure fails in a manner that reveals the failure. The operational arrangements when safety measures are unavailable may differ and may include:

- Substitute the unavailable safety measure for another safety measure that can deliver the same safety function and continue with the normal operations;

- Cease the relevant normal operations, thus eliminating the potential for the relevant fault to initiate or progress to an unprotected harmful state;

- Continue for a defined period of time without the safety measure until it is re-turned to service or the process completes.

The last option mentioned above represents a *time-at-risk* argument and is the least preferable. It should only be utilised if other options are not available. If it is chosen it will need to be carefully justified on ALARP grounds, and there may need to be an increased regime of surveillance to try and ensure that an initiating fault can be detected or mitigated against. It is an option that may need to be deployed if a process is underway that may introduce other hazards if not completed.

Example: Action-on-Failure

The over-raise protection system on a crane is identified to be failed part way through a lift. The system is safety related and ensures that the SOE cannot be breached. The operator could either stop the lift and wait for the system to be repaired or continue the lift. Stopping the lift would lead to a suspended load, which is hazardous. Continuing with the lift would be the safer option, but subsequent lifts would not be undertaken until the system was repaired.

Example: Substitution

A gamma interlock system that prevents operators entering a cell if radiation levels are high is unavailable due to repair. Cell entry is infrequent and entry is not urgent. Entry should be prohibited until it is returned to service. However, if it is essential that an entry is made, a substitute system may be justified that may comprise a mixture of enhanced supervisor checks that the area is clear of radiation sources accompanied by enhanced health physics radiation checks on cell entry (health physics checks are standard practice, but their importance during this operation may be emphasised).

Safe envelope

The safe envelope is essentially the transition between 'safe' and 'unsafe' conditions, and it is beyond the envelope of normal operations and the SOE. It may also be referred to as the *safety limit* and there may be a step change in conditions. In our example, the safe envelope may be the point (or close to it) at which the overheating leads to melting of the substance or combustion.

For a conservative design, we may expect a margin between the SOE and the safe envelope. However, if the SOE is breached, there may be no practicable safeguards to prevent eventual breaching of the safe envelope. Breaching of the safe envelope may require the instigation of recovery or emergency arrangements to minimise the potential consequences.

Example: Vessel Containing Liquor

An easy example that shows the position of the normal envelope, the SOE and the safety limit is with a vessel. The vessel has a normal envelope with lower and upper liquor levels. Liquor may be transferred into the vessel and the control system will ensure that it is maintained with lower and upper levels, L_L and L_U. A schematic is shown in Fig. 7.1.

Whilst the safety analysis shows that there is no concern with regard to too low a level, there is a concern with respect to too much liquor. This can lead to an overflow of the vessel as there is an opening in the top of the vessel with a pipe to the cell bund. Therefore, there is a high-level trip to isolate incoming transfer if the liquor level reaches high level L_H and even a second trip at the high-high level L_{HH}, with the SOE defined by the high-high level. The safe envelope is the level just before liquor would reach the overflow level and be lost from the vessel.

With a good design, this should not necessarily lead to significant consequences. There should be secondary containment with liquor detection and the ability to recover the liquor to another vessel. If the liquor is fissile, the geometry of the secondary containment should ensure that a critical arrangement cannot occur, but this is not always found to be true on older plants.

7.3   Design basis and beyond design basis

The safety case will consider a range of hazards and faults that may give rise to a radiological consequence. There needs to be a rationalisation of the hazards and faults such that those that truly pose trivial risk without reliance on safety measures are screened from analysis. This gives rise to the concept of the *design basis* and *beyond the design basis* (BDB), which we can define as:

Design basis: The conditions of the plant or the events (hazards or faults) that may occur within it for which design provision is provided for to ensure that the plant can withstand the conditions or events through the action of safety measures.

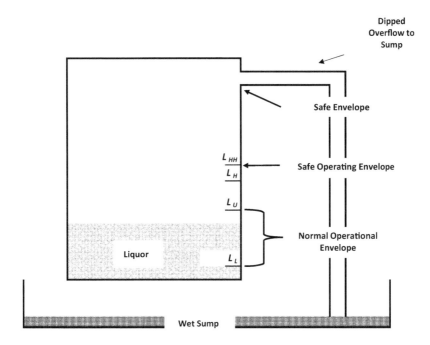

Figure 7.1: Schematic vessel showing the relationship between the normal operational envelope, the SOE and the safe envelope. Liquor is transferred to the vessel by steam ejectors or pumps (not shown). A real vessel would also have connections to the vessel ventilation system and instrumentation (also not shown).

The vessel has an overflow to a bund that is maintained wet to ensure a seal and prevent the migration of aerosol from the vessel ullage to the cell environment in which the vessel is situated. The normal operational envelope is defined by the upper and lower levels L_U and L_L. There are two high-level trips: one high and the other high-high, L_H and L_{HH} for which the SOE is defined as just above the L_{HH} level. The safe envelope is defined to be just below the overflow level.

Beyond design basis: The conditions of the plant or the events (hazards or faults) that may occur for which design provision is not provided for, but for which there may be emergency arrangements to mitigate the effects.

7.3.1   Design basis analysis

With safety input from the concept stage onwards, the plant design aims to accommodate all but the most remote faults (in terms of frequency) that may give rise to a radiological consequence. Such faults are termed 'within the design basis' and DBA is an important part of the safety case that demonstrates the robustness and *fault tolerance* of the plant. In simple terms, if such a fault occurs, the plant should be able to cope with the event and prevent significant consequences from arising. It is sometimes known as a *deterministic assessment*.

The use of DBA is complementary to PSA in understanding the adequacy of a plant design, but the approach is very different. DBA is not about risk, but successful application of DBA may subsequently help in making an adequate risk case. The robustness of the safety measures allocated during DBA will influence the risk process.

At the heart of DBA is an understanding of the nature of the events that may affect a plant in terms of the unmitigated consequences and the IEFs. The faults within the design basis are taken to be those that may lead to significant radiological consequences **and** have IEFs above defined thresholds. It is important to stress that the focus in DBA is on the IEF rather than the top event frequency as the former takes no account of the action of safety measures. The safety measures may then be identified and required to protect against the initiating events. The consequences must be unmitigated because mitigation is treated as a potential safety measure. DBA, therefore, is based upon how bad the initiating event could be and what must be protected against.

The broad principle in the UK is that DBA applies to faults that can give rise to the doses exceeding the BSL(LLs) of 20 mSv (workers) and 1 mSv (public) (see Table 2.1) provided the IEF is $> 10^{-3}$ y^{-1}. The cut-off value of 10^{-3} y^{-1} ensures that the design has provision for safety measures where there is a reasonable chance of a BSL(LL) being breached over the plant lifetime. As the consequences subsequently increase, the IEF for DBA applicability decreases. There is a lower cut-off value of 10^{-5} y^{-1}. For natural hazards, a general cut-off of 10^{-4} y^{-1} is taken—below this value there is significant uncertainty in the extrapolation of data to such infrequent events. Beyond the lower IEF, cut-off is the region where beyond design basis assessment may be undertaken.

When applying DBA, consequences are determined on a conservative basis, though IEFs can be undertaken on a best-estimate basis. The relationships between consequences and IEFs are best illustrated by the use of a 'staircase' diagram as shown in Fig. 7.2.

It is an expectation that sufficient safety measures be included in the plant design to prevent (or, of least preference, mitigate) the faults that are in the DBA region. If the safety measures prevent the progression of the fault, then there will be no consequence. However, if the safety measures are mitigators, BSOs for the mitigated doses are given in the ONR SAPs [1] of 0.1 mSv (workers) and 0.01 mSv (public). The safety measures that are designated for DBA would operate within the SOE of the plant.

For faults outside of the DBA region, safety measures may not need to be provided as the faults fall outside of the design basis. This helps to ensure proportionality and is intended to help ensure that protection is focused where it will be of most benefit. It will be the role of the PSA to demonstrate that for the faults that fall outside of the design basis, there is still adequate protection to ensure a tolerable and ALARP level of risk. Safety measures may still be required on a *risk-informed basis*.

When considering the type and range of safety measures designated to satisfy DBA, they must be demonstrably independent of the initiating event. This gives rise to design aspects such as *separation* or *segregation* of control and protection, which should help protect against a single fault or cause giving rise to both loss of control and protection. The single fault or cause is known as a *common cause failure* (CCF). The provision of *diversity* between control and protection may also assist in ensuring the

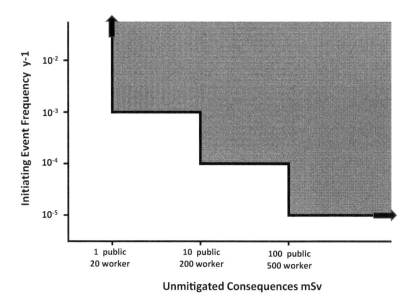

Figure 7.2: Design basis analysis showing the shaded region where DBA applies for man-made faults. Within the shaded region, safety measures are expected to be provided to ensure that the plant is tolerant to the fault and prevent realisation of the consequence. Adapted from the ONR SAPS [1].

potential for CCF is minimised. CCF, segregation and diversity are discussed further in Section 8.3.

If we reflect on the SOE discussed in the previous section, to ensure that there is provision to satisfy DBA and remain within the SOE, there must be:

1. Substitution arrangements specified to ensure that there are sufficient safety measures available when a safety measure is knowingly unavailable, i.e. during EMIT;

2. The provision of a second safety measure to protect against unrevealed failure in a safety measure.

Item 2 mentioned above provides *tolerance to single failure*; i.e. no single random failure will lead to a failure to deliver the overall safety function or protection. With items 1 and 2 together, it may be necessary for a design to include additional safety measures to enable substitution for *planned* maintenance if there is a desire to continue with operations when a safety measure is unavailable due to EMIT.

Within the UK, the licensees will determine their own DBA criteria in terms of IEFs and consequences and they may produce their own versions of Fig. 7.2. The licensees will specify the number of safety measures expected as a function of position within the figure and determine their own approach to being tolerant to single failure.

Low consequence

Formally, DBA does not apply to faults that have an unmitigated conservative consequence below the thresholds of 20 mSv (workers) and 1 mSv (public). However, it
is generally recognised that DBA leaves a little bit of a gap in the provision of protection, potentially for 'frequent' faults that may lead to consequences up to the two dose
thresholds. A *low consequence region* is specified that also requires provision of a safety
measure unless it can be demonstrated that the risk in this region is negligible. This
demonstration may be via reference to an explicitly low IEF and/or low best-estimate
consequence.

Licensees utilise different cut-off values for the low consequence region, but a conservative lower value of 2 mSv is typical for workers and 0.1 mSv is typical for the
public. Below these values, the dose may be deemed to become comparable to the
dose received during normal operations and the provision of explicit safety measures
may become disproportionate. It may also become difficult to distinguish between a
fault and normal operations and there will be established techniques that are normally
deployed on a plant to minimise dose from normal operations.

Example: Demonstration of 'Low Consequence' Risk
Let us assume that for the workers the low consequence region only extends down to
an unmitigated conservative consequence of 2 mSv (2×10^{-3} Sv). There is also an IEF
cut-off value of 10^{-3} y^{-1}. At both of these extremes, this equates to a risk of

$$2 \times 10^{-3} \text{ Sv} \times 0.05 \text{ Sv}^{-1} \times 10^{-3} \text{ y}^{-1} = 10^{-7} \text{ y}^{-1},$$

where 0.05 Sv^{-1} is the chance of fatality (see Section 5.2.5). This risk is below the risk
BSO of 10^{-6} y^{-1} (Table 2.2) even without accounting for any safety measures being
present or utilisation of a best-estimate consequence to calculate the risk.

In our worked example, the other end of the low consequence region is taken
to be 20 mSv. If we have the same cut-off value for the IEF, this would equate to a
risk 10 times that calculated above, which would be at the BSO. Therefore, a safety
measure (of modest reliability) would be needed to reduce the risk (for this fault) to
below the BSO. It would also be needed to ensure that the overall risk from **all** faults
that could affect the worker would not exceed the BSO.

We can leave it to an exercise for the reader to determine equivalent risk values
for low consequence regions associated with the public.

7.3.2   Beyond design basis

The successful application of DBA will demonstrate that the plant is tolerant to the
design basis events, i.e. that there are adequate levels of defence to prevent (or mitigate)
against the design basis events. For the events that fall outside of the design basis,
explicit lines of protection may not be required on a deterministic basis. If the events
occur, they are BDB. Design basis events may be internally generated faults or faults

Table 7.3: Example ball park initiating event rates for events based upon author engineering judgement (per demand events to be multiplied by number of demands per year). Of the events listed, only random aircraft crash would confidently fall outside of the design basis irrespective of consequence. Guillotine pipework failure may fall outside of the design basis depending on length, noting that there are other failure modes that may need to be assessed.

Hazard	Frequency
Computer-based control system	0.1–0.5
Operator error	$10^{-3} - 10^{-1}$ per task
Valve fails to open	10^{-3} per demand
Guillotine failure of welded stainless steel pipework	$10^{-7} - 10^{-6}$ m^{-1} y^{-1}
Random aircraft impact on a typical sized plant	10^{-7} y^{-1}

initiated by external hazards, e.g. random intrinsic failure of pipework or pipework failing due to a seismic event.

In terms of IEFs, the majority of plant-based internal faults are likely to have a frequency $> 10^{-5}$ y^{-1} and many $> 10^{-3}$ y^{-1}. Table 7.3 provides a list if typical ball park IEFs, either directly or per demand (from which the frequency can be determined from the number of demands per year).[2] Many external hazards (such as seismic events or weather conditions) do not have a discrete frequency and it is not strictly correct to state the IEF of such an external hazard is x y^{-1}. These events have a continuous spectrum of frequency and severity; i.e. the more significant events are more rare. Therefore, one refers to a *magnitude* of such an event at a defined *return frequency*.

It is not an absolute black or white as to whether there are safety measures for BDB events and this will depend upon factors that may include:

1. The risk position;

2. Whether there are cliff-edge effects between being on one side of the design basis and the other side;

3. Whether it is reasonably practicable to provide protection, i.e. the ALARP position of the options.

The term *cliff-edge* is used in safety cases. Having undertaken the design basis assessment and assessed the risk, it is important to ensure that there should not be a disproportionate increase in risk beyond the design basis. We cannot be 'safe' on one side of the line and 'unsafe' just on the other side.

---

[2]See Eq. 8.2 for nuances to the IEF calculation whereby conditions can suppress the frequencies from the raw 'mechanical' failures.

> *Example: Beyond Design Basis—Seismic*
> Design basis qualification to a 10^{-4} y^{-1} event is required by the safety analysis. However, should an event occur just beyond the magnitude associated with 10^{-4} y^{-1}, we would not desire catastrophic structure failure and a step change in consequences, i.e. a cliff-edge effect.
>
> The civil design will ensure that cliff-edge effects do not occur. This can be achieved by ensuring conservatisms in the design to provide margin beyond the design basis and, secondly, by ensuring that failures beyond the design basis are progressive rather than catastrophic.

7.3.3 Probabilistic safety analysis

A deterministic assessment looks at the number of barriers that must fail for an initiating event to progress to a consequence. The PSA is a tool that can determine the likelihood that the barriers fail and hence the frequency at which a particular event occurs. From the knowledge of frequency and consequence, the risk can be determined and this is essentially the purpose of PSA. Frequency and risk targets (probabilistic safety criteria) were defined in Section 2.4 and PSA is the appropriate tool to determine whether the targets are met or not. Overall, we can say that the principal objectives of PSA are to identify the significant factors that contribute to the nuclear risk from a plant and to demonstrate that the probabilistic targets have been achieved.

The degree of PSA required is related to the magnitude of the potential consequences and the complexity of the plant. Typically, the PSA associated with nuclear reactor plant is more complex and involved than that associated with waste processing or storage plants. Nuclear reactor plants, in particular, consider three levels of PSA, i.e.

Level 1 PSA: Analysis of the plant's design and modes of operation to determine the sequences that can lead to core damage and the frequency of core damage. Level 1 PSA provides information on the contribution that operational procedures and safety-related equipment make to prevent core damage.

Level 2 PSA: Involves the sequences identified in the Level 1 PSA to determine how a radioactive release to the environment can occur and determine the frequency of release. The Level 2 PSA can help to determine the contributions made from measures to prevent progression of the fault and measures to mitigate the release.

Level 3 PSA: Involves the sequences analysed in the Levels 1 and 2 PSA to determine the risk to the public (individual and as a society), which requires an understanding of the dispersion of activity and dose.

Clearly core damage frequency is not relevant to non-reactor plant, but it is still necessary to undertake an appropriate level of PSA for such non-reactor plant. For non-reactor plant it is custom to calculate the frequency of a particular consequence and from that determine the risk. This is effectively combining the Level 2 and 3 PSA in one step without the formal and explicit declaration of different levels of PSA. The basis of conducting PSA is the determination of an accident frequency for which the tools used are described in Section 8 together with the determination of dose, as described in Section 5.2.

7.3.4   Severe accident analysis

The DBA, BDB and PSA are the principal tools utilised within the safety analysis to determine the adequacy of the design. The potential for a significant event to occur that leads to a large release of activity and/or a dose to the workers and the public should be very low. Nevertheless, an accident could still happen and this could arise because:

- The fault initiates, but the identified safety measures do not work as intended;

- A fault that was 'written off' or deemed to be beyond the design basis occurs and has insufficient safety measures;

- A significant terrorist or criminal event occurs;

- Something happens that was not thought about.

Severe accident analysis (SAA) takes the position that the accident has occurred, what conditions the plant could be in and seeks to determine what should be done next to bring the plant under control. SAA is part of the last layers of defence as given in Table 2.6. The SAA may also look at the liaison with external services, police, local authorities and government and the arrangements for emergency control and accident management

A paraphrasing of the definition of a SAA from the ONR SAPs [1] is

The fault sequences that could lead either to public consequences >100 mSv (conservatively assessed) or to an unintended relocation of a substantial quantity of radioactive material within the plant which places a demand on the integrity of the remaining physical barriers.

For a nuclear reactor, a severe accident is generally taken to be one associated with a core melt or significant degradation of the fuel. A severe accident could also extend to a loss of water cover to the fuel ponds, as the water is required for both shielding and ensuring that the fuel is cooled. Other non-reactor plants could have severe accidents, such as a loss of containment from highly active liquor tanks, which would lead to a release significant levels of activity to secondary containment.

The aim of SAA is to:

- Identify any further reasonably practicable preventative or mitigating measures beyond those derived from DBA, BDB and PSA;

- Develop accident management strategies and procedures and support the preparation of emergency plans;

- Provide further input into the PSA for the plant's design and operation.

Fundamentally, SAA may be seeking answers on how to restore one or more of the four critical safety functions (see Section 9.2) of reactivity control, temperature control, shielding and containment.

Should equipment be identified as having a role in SAA, safety functions and performance requirements should be identified (see Section 9). In identifying performance requirements, the potentially extreme conditions associated with the event should be accounted for. It must also be recognised that there may have been a CCF that has enabled the accident to develop and that equipment identified in the DBA is likely to not be available. Emergency equipment may need to be shown to be tolerant to the failures associated with the severe accident. The equipment may need to come from defined places off-site.

The SAA needs to consider other factors than just equipment. For instance, are there any services or consumables needed for safety measures, e.g. fuel for generators and for how long? The provision of site self-sufficiency of at least a week is often taken as a minimum requirement. Additionally, what are the staffing levels required and what is their training in the emergency arrangements and what PPE may be needed? What are the command-and-control aspects? Finally, a robust SAA must recognise that it will be down to personnel to implement the actions of any plan. Human factors assessment will be key and this must recognise the following fact:

- By definition, a significant event has occurred and the site may not be in the pre-event condition leading to disorientation and shock;

- Equipment to be relied upon may in fact not be available due to the event;

- Emergency personnel may be injured or unavailable and there may be dead and injured in the area;

- Emergency personnel may be worried about their own safety and that of family members.

7.4 Criticality

The nuclear power process involves the utilisation of uranium or plutonium that undergoes criticality to generate power. Within a reactor, a controlled criticality is a desirable thing. However, outside of a reactor, a criticality is a fault that must always be avoided. Section 4.6 defined what is meant by criticality (a self-sustaining chain reaction) and referred to k, the neutron multiplication factor. As a recap, for a criticality to occur, k must be ≥ 1.

In many respects, an assessment of criticality hazards is no different from the consideration of a release of radioactive material and an inhalation of activity. The initiating events must be identified, the fault progression understood and sufficient lines of defence identified to ensure a tolerable and ALARP level of risk with appropriate utilisation of DBA and PSA.

A criticality assessment does need to demonstrate a detailed understanding of the *conditions* during normal operations which ensure that k does not approach unity. The assessment is required to focus on how the conditions (MAGIC MERV) may change due to the faults and what is required to occur for a criticality to arise.

To achieve criticality safety, there are generally controls on the MAGIC MERV parameters such as the mass of moderator, the accumulation of fissile mass or its concentration and geometry and spacing of the fissile material. As an example, geometry and spacing are important because they determine how neutrons may be lost from the fissile material (via its surfaces) and potentially captured by a neighbouring fissile package. The optimum geometry for fission to occur in a single package is, therefore, a sphere as this has the minimum surface area to volume. Maintaining adequate spacing between individual packages ensures *neutronic isolation* of the packages. This approach leads to fissile package storage areas resembling lattice-type structures or horizontal arrays with free spaces between each package.

For fissile liquor, it may be stored in thin tanks that have large surface areas or in a series of pipes. These will all be physically separated from each other in space. Ideally, the room or cell in which the tanks and pipes are contained will have a stainless steel clad bund. This will provide *secondary containment* and should a leak occur, it will be contained in a horizontal slab. The slab depth from a failure of all of the primary containment should be insufficient to enable a criticality to occur. This is always a key calculation for any criticality assessment of the containment system. It will also need to be confirmed that the *sump* of the bund cannot hold a critical mass.

When fissile material is transported in a plant, it is sometimes undertaken manually. The containers in which the fissile material is contained will be of limited volume to restrict the absolute mass of fissile material that may be located in one container. There may be widespread embargoes of containers above a certain size throughout the entire plant, e.g. no containers with a volume of more than two litres. The material may also be moved around the plant within special trolleys that have a physically defined space for the container. These trolleys may have fixed features to maintain a minimum spacing to prevent close approach between one package in transit and another or with fixed plant.

It is worth noting that some physical systems can also lead to neutron reflection and these may include water, concrete, hydrocarbons (plastics) and heavy metals. Reflection will contribute to the determination of the k value, and water and hydrocarbons may also be good moderators. Human operators are full of water and are very good sources of moderation. Therefore, a safety assessment needs to ensure that the presence of the operator does not give rise to a criticality event when moving between stored fissile material. This is achieved by taking into account optimum moderation and reflection conditions when establishing safe storage conditions.

Double contingency

Criticality assessments may refer to the *double contingency principle* (DCP). When applied, DCP helps to demonstrate that there is defence-in-depth such that there must be more than one change in normal conditions for a criticality to arise. Normal conditions may relate to spacing, moderation, enrichment, concentration and so on.

The DCP can be defined as *a demonstration that unintended criticality cannot occur unless at least two unlikely, independent, concurrent changes in the conditions originally specified as essential to criticality safety have occurred.*[3] Independent means that there can be no CCF between the two changes. Concurrent does not require them to occur at the same time (perhaps to a single event). There could be a latent failure or change in one condition that is not detected.

The use of the DCP can be used in addition to DBA and PSA or it may be used instead of DBA (depending on the licensee's arrangements). Demonstrating compliance with the DCP does not necessarily imply that the risk is negligible nor that there is room for ALARP improvement. The use of DBA may help to ensure that a change to one or more conditions can be prevented by the designation of safety measures.

Example: Double Contingency

Fissile material is held inside containers that are stored within an array within a cell. The array ensures that there is adequate spacing between the containers to enable neutron loss to limit the number of neutrons leaving one container and initiating a fission event in another container. The spacing between the containers in the array is free air, which is not a good moderator of neutrons.

Double contingency should show that:

1. A loss of spacing by itself does not give rise to a criticality, i.e. even if all of the containers were to be erroneously placed together without spacing there would not be a criticality;

2. A flooding of the cell and the accumulation of water (a good moderator) between containers by itself does not give rise to a criticality, e.g. if a water line were to fracture.

Therefore, it would take a minimum of both a loss of spacing **and** a flooding event for a criticality to occur. In these examples, a container could, in principle, be erroneously placed for a number of years before a flooding event occurs.

Moreover, double contingency is required to show that either of these events is *unlikely*. It may be that the likelihood of erroneously placing the containers in the wrong place is very low, which may be due to:

- The physical impossibility of placing containers in the wrong place due to the physical nature of the array and features that prevent interstitial placement;

- The revealed visual nature of the placement operations.

It would also need to be shown that flooding is unlikely, perhaps by reference to the exclusion of water lines in the cell and elimination of flooding routes. Finally and of some importance, it must be shown that the flooding and loss of spacing are truly independent—if the flood can lead to coalescence of the packages the conditions are not independent!

---

[3]Taken from the ONR SAPS [1].

Expanding on the term *unlikely* within the DCP, this could be taken to be that each deviation should be expected to not occur within the plant lifetime. Taking a value of 50 years for a plant's lifetime, this implies a minimum frequency for each deviation of 0.02 y^{-1}. How can we infer an overall frequency of a criticality when we have two frequency values of 0.02 y^{-1} or better for each deviation? The answer is to assume that the second deviation occurs in the 'window' in which the conditions of the first deviation have occurred.

As an example, let us assume that deviation one is revealed and can be corrected or is self-limiting in time, perhaps a flood that will naturally drain away. If there is an argument that the deviation will be corrected or self-terminate within one week, then we can calculate the probability that the deviation is present when the second deviation subsequently occurs. If we establish that deviation 1 has a rate of 0.02 y^{-1} and deviation 2 has a rate of 0.01 y^{-1}, then the frequency can be estimated to be

$$\text{Frequency} = 0.02 \ y^{-1} \ \times \ 0.01 \ y^{-1} \ \times \ \frac{1 \text{ week}}{52 \text{ week } y^{-1}} = 3.8 \ \times \ 10^{-6} \ y^{-1}. \qquad (7.1)$$

The simple calculation mentioned above is above the risk BSO of $10^{-6} \ y^{-1}$ (Table 2.2) assuming a worker dose >1 Gy and further refinement may be required. A word of caution is that if there is a latent condition that is not revealed and corrected or is not self-terminating, then the size of the 'window' will increase, as the deviation will remain. It can be seen from Eq. 7.1 that if the number of weeks that the deviation is present increases, the simple calculation would tend to a frequency of $2 \times 10^{-4} \ y^{-1}$, which is far from being tolerable. Additional lines of defence may be required. This risk calculation is for illustration and shows how criticality risk could be calculated. However, explicit numerical criticality risk is routinely not undertaken in the industry.

7.5   Internal hazards

Internal hazards are those that may exist within a nuclear plant and pose a hazard to the control or containment of nuclear material. For example, a water tank may not contain any radioactive material, but its failure could lead to a flood that may affect nuclear material. Internal hazards may affect a plant 'globally' and the degree of hazard posed will be strongly influenced by the topography of the plant. Internal hazards can only be understood via a 'walkthrough' of the plant. For an existing plant this will be via plant walkdown, but for a plant in design may require examination of the layout model or GAS. In this section we will focus on some of the more common internal hazards:

- Fire;

- Compressed gases;

- Flooding.

7.5.1 Fire

Fire poses a direct threat to life, which is a familiar hazard to all of us be it at home or at work. It is not different within nuclear plants where a fire occurring within the plant should prompt the evacuation of personnel to a safe location. Quite often, a *conventional fire assessment* will consider the direct risk to life from fire and a *nuclear fire assessment* will consider the effects of fire on the nuclear material.

Nuclear sites generally will have their own fire service to respond to fire events: fight the fire and rescue persons who may be trapped or injured. Fire fighters would also play a role in minimising the potential for fires to occur by undertaking inspections, providing training and undertaking exercises. The fire fighters may also be amongst the first to respond to any event that leads to a nuclear accident. Fire fighters must be trained to understand the nuclear hazards that the nuclear plant possesses. Without prior understanding of the hazards in a particular plant and the undertaking of adequate *dynamic risk assessments*, responding to a fire could compound a nuclear hazard.

A fire occurring within a nuclear plant poses a number of nuclear hazards over and above the potential for an immediate risk to life that must be considered and protected against. Examples of these hazards are given in Table 7.4. A fire assessment needs to consider the effects of fire-fighting as well as the direct effects of fire and smoke. This is important for criticality aspects, as water can provide additional moderator and the action of fire hose jets can lead to pushing together of sub-critical masses. A criticality assessment will normally give a positive statement that water can (or cannot) be used for fire-fighting.

Many of the fire hazards can be eliminated from a nuclear perspective by good design and by maintaining of high standards of house-keeping. Table 7.5 lists a number of approaches to ensuring that the nuclear hazard posed by fire is adequately managed.

Example: Waste Plant and Combustible Storage Racks
A nuclear plant contained legacy waste that was held in steel containers. The waste was sensitive to heat and there was a concern that a release from the containers could occur during a fire. For operational reasons, the containers were stored on plastic blocks. Whilst some fire assessment had been undertaken, there was emerging evidence that should a significant fire develop, the containers could be compromised.

An ALARP case had to be made to justify the continuation of the storage arrangement. It was not reasonable to replace the storage system with a non-combustible alternative due to the extensive operational dose that the large-scale movement operation would entail. Practicable means to suppress the risk of fire initiation and/or fire detection and fighting were explored in the ALARP justification for continued operations.

In addition to an existing storage plant, a new storage plant was required. Given that this would be considered to be a *new build*, it was much more challenging to write an ALARP justification to utilise a plastic-based system. Other sites had moved away from plastic, and RGP across the industry was to no longer use plastic. Therefore, the new plant utilised a new design that was overwhelmingly made from non-combustible

---

metal with an insignificant mass of plastic to preserve the minimum operational requirement. The fire hazard, to the extent that a release could occur, was eliminated.

Operationally, the new design was acceptable, but it is noted that the overall cost of the new system was more expensive than the original plastic system. There were also project delays in implementing the new system.

Example: Vulnerability of Services
A new nuclear plant required services to run to ensure its safety. During the plant's early design stages, the external systems providing services were presented to the main project team. It was immediately apparent that there had been no safety input into this aspect of the design. There was no segregation between duty and back-up supplies of electricity, water or compressed air. These were routed together into the plant and were perceived to be vulnerable to one event taking out all of the systems. A local fire or explosion was a concern due to the mass of combustible cabling and the hazards from nearby roads and railway lines.

Costly last-minute design changes had to be made. A more preferable solution was to have entirely segregated routes for duty and back-up supplies that would come into the plant from opposite sides.

7.5.2   Compressed gases

Many nuclear plants utilise compressed gases for process operations, which may range from compressed air to specialist gases such as methane or helium. Gases into a plant may be sourced from:

- A site ring main;

- Local bottle supply;

- Air compressors and accumulator buffer vessels;

- Cryogenic containers containing liquid nitrogen, for example.

It is often preferable and more economical for some gases to be sourced from a central supply that is distributed around the site via a ring main, such as compressed air. However, even if this is undertaken, a local emergency supply may be required if there is a safety or operational requirement for plant self-sufficiency. The use of bottles, compressors, buffer vessels and cryogenic vessels introduces items that have stored or potential energy due to pressurisation. Energetic rupture can relieve the pressure and this can cause significant damage to adjacent plant. Pressurised systems, therefore, can pose a hazard to nuclear plants: direct loss of life and injury and also damage to primary containment. Failure of the systems can also compromise control and protection systems in a similar manner to the hazards posed by fire.

Table 7.4: Example nuclear concerns due to the effects of fire and fire-fighting.

Fire effect	Example nuclear concern
Direct combustion of radioactive material	Release of activity and inhalation doses to workers and the public Contamination of the plant and environment
Structural failure	Building collapse Loss of shielding Loss of containment layers (primary and secondary, etc.) Loss of safe criticality spacing Impact damage
Fire and smoke damage	Control and protection circuits compromised due to short circuits leading to spurious operation
Pressurisation (thermal expansion, boiling, chemical reactions, etc.)	Package failure and release of activity Loss of safe criticality geometry (such as from a slab tank)
Fire-fighting	Water acting as moderator giving rise to criticality Jets of water coalescing segregated items leading to a loss of safe criticality spacing Water reacts with chemicals and releases activity

Table 7.5: Example fire mitigation strategies.

Fire mitigation	Function
Non-combustible materials	Prevents large-scale fires from occurring by ensuring that there is minimal fuel. Plants are built from steel and concrete and not wood and plastic
Management of transient combustibles	Most plants will require some combustible materials to enter into the plant, e.g. paper, oils, and packaging. These should not accumulate or be stored near nuclear inventory, as far as reasonably practicable. Minimising the accumulation of such transients is good practice to reduce the volume of potentially contaminated material requiring monitoring and disposal as LLW
Nuclear fire compartments	To ensure that if a fire does initiate it cannot propagate throughout the plant. The boundary of the fire compartment should be able to withstand 100% combustion of all combustible material within it. Typically, fire compartments may have 30, 60, 120 min of fire resistance
Intumescent and ablative paints	Structural steel loses approximately 50% of its structural strength when heated in a fire to 500 °C. Intumescent substances expand on heating and provide a protecting insulating layer, whilst ablative substances decompose on heating to release water that provides a cooling effect. These substances can be used to coat structural steel to prevent its failure in fire
Segregation of safety functions	Ensuring that safety systems are segregated, potentially in separate fire compartments, to ensure that the fire does not disable multiple systems

Table 7.5: Continued

Fire-resisting and armoured cabling	Important safety cabling can be protected against fire, application of water and impact damage to ensure it continues to function even if the insulating layers are damaged in a fire or during the application of fire-fighting water
Fire detection and fire-fighting equipment	As well as life safety, a fire alarm will alert emergency services to a fire and mitigate any nuclear incident. Fire-fighting equipment may be available for operators, which could include sand boxes or fire blankets within working areas where there may be a risk of equipment over-heating or fires occurring (e.g. pyrophoric materials)

Compressed gas bottles should be able to be used safely. After all, they are used throughout industry, hospitals, retirement homes and so on. They do pose a hazard if not handled properly, notably if the valve stem is damaged, which can lead to them acting as a missile. They can rupture if heated in fire. Safe handling of such bottles should be embedded in standard site practices. Safe handling processes include: the use of valve covers when being transported, the use of bottle trolleys for movement and chaining the bottles in position to a wall. Ideally, such bottles are held outside of the building away from vulnerable nuclear plants with a piped supply into the building.

Example: Compressed Gas Bottles
During a safety case review of a plant, it was noted that there were a number of compressed gas bottles on the plant. These contained helium for leak testing and a methane/argon mixture for the installed contamination monitors. The argon/methane bottles were stored relatively close to gloveboxes used for uranium handling where they would be vulnerable to bottle failure. It was acknowledged that the potential for mishandling the bottles was low and the numerical risk was also found to be low.

An ALARP recommendation was made to reduce the risk. The ALARP proposal was to either utilise alternative gasless technology for the monitors or relocate the bottles. Utilisation of alternative technology was deemed to be not reasonable, as this would necessitate complete change to site practice and equipment. However, relocation of the monitors and their bottles was selected as it was a reasonably practicable solution to implement.

An air compressor will be used to generate compressed air for a plant, which may be for operational or safety benefit including the generation of *breathing air* for pressurised suit use. The compressors will not feed directly into a piped distribution network on a plant, but they will be fed in via an *air accumulator* or *buffer vessel*. The accumulator will help to smooth out the supply of the compressed air to the network and it will also provide a reserve volume of air should the compressor fail. This is important for breathing air use, where the reserve volume will give the operators time to safely withdraw before the piped air supplies are exhausted.

Air accumulators are vessels and pose an explosion hazard due to the large pressure and volume of air held inside. The design and operation of such vessels is well understood in the industry and safety measures will include pressure interlocks, bursting discs and so on, to ensure controlled pressure relief if necessary. Consequently, the frequency of catastrophic failure is very low.

Finally, we should note that the use of gases within a plant may pose asphyxiation hazards. The oxygen content in the Earth's atmosphere is 21% and a release of gases in an enclosed space can decrease the relative concentration of oxygen. An impairment to operator action can occur when the oxygen concentration reduces to 19%. This is not strictly a nuclear hazard. However, the impairment may initiate operator-based faults and it may compromise operator-based safety measures on the plant. There must always be consideration of such *confined space hazards*.

Liquid nitrogen is an obvious example of a substance that poses a confined space hazard. Over time, the nitrogen will evaporate from a Dewar or cryogenic vessel and it may fill the enclosed room it resides in. The room should be large enough to ensure that the reduction in oxygen concentration is not dangerous even if all of the nitrogen were to be released. Ventilation systems can help to remove released gases, but it must be recognised that the released gases may be cold and dense and accumulate in low and poorly ventilated parts of the plant.

7.5.3 Flooding

Flooding in a plant can arise from a number of sources that may originate either within the plant or external to it. In this sub-section, we focus on internal mechanisms and sources. The most obvious source for flooding is the presence of pipes and vessels. These may not necessarily be water as liquid chemicals (such as acids) may be transferred or stored. Nitric acid is used in the nuclear reprocessing industry and plants may contain bulk quantities of the acid.

Water is the most likely liquid capable of giving rise to a significant flood in any plant. Water is used as a process fluid, for cooling, welfare use and for fire-fighting. Therefore, there is an expectation that most plants will have some pipework containing water and potentially buffer vessels. Due to connection to site main supplies,[4] there is also the potential for an unlimited supply of water that could pose a considerable concern during silent hours when a flood may not be visually detected.

A failure of pipework or a vessel may have a direct safety concern due the impact on the process with the obvious example being the loss of cooling water to ensure safe conditions. This hazard should be addressed directly, but what is of concern here for a flood is the *presence* of bulk liquid where it should not be, i.e. outside of primary containment.

On release, liquids can find themselves in many places and give rise to a wide range of operational and safety issues. The safety issues may be of concern even if the actual loss of supply of the liquid does not pose a hazard. An obvious example is the failure of pipework supplying fire-fighting water, as this would not be used in the nuclear process.

Understanding whether flood events pose a credible hazard to a plant must be ascertained by walking the plant. A HAZOP of a drawing will determine that there are liquid systems capable of flooding. However, it will require a walkdown of the plant to determine whether the loss of containment from pipes and vessels could affect nuclear aspects, either directly on nuclear material or other safety systems that help ensure nuclear safety.

It is unlikely that the potential for flooding can be eliminated within a plant as a whole, as fire-fighting water is likely to be always required (though the water supply may be via dry risers). However, the impact on nuclear safety can be significantly

---

[4]Should a pipe undergo guillotine failure, there will be two open ends and each of these will be a source of the flood. If the pipework is on a ring main then the flow will not be exhausted and the rate of flow will be double that associated with a release from a single open pipe.

Table 7.6: Example hazard management options against flooding. In all cases, there should be the preference to site sources of flooding away from parts of the plant that may be vulnerable and if this cannot be achieved, secondary containment may be a viable alternative to contain or direct spills away from nuclear plant. Where this is not practicable or additional lines of defence are required, the above examples show how safety may be delivered.

Concern	Example hazard management
Washing of loose contamination and discharge via non-authorised routes	Ensure contamination is removed or is sealed Isolate drains
Damage to electrical systems, notably those providing control and protection (a source of CCF)	Segregation of control and protection Placement of electrical systems above the maximum flood height Water ingress protection rating on cabinets
Introduction of criticality moderator	Account for optimum moderation (flood) in the normal conditions Placement of fissile material above the maximum flood height
Floating of vessels in a sealed cell and disconnection of process lines	Securely anchored vessels capable of withstanding buoyant forces

reduced if the location of pipes and vessels is carefully chosen. Table 7.6 shows some typical hazards associated with flooding and means of their control.

7.6 External hazards

External hazards are hazards that are imposed upon a nuclear plant that are beyond the control of the nuclear site and are due to external influences. There are two broad type of hazards: *natural external hazards* and *man-made external hazards*. Table 7.7 lists a number of external hazards that safety cases may be required to consider. Not all are relevant and this will depend upon the specifics of the site. Following the listing, we will describe three external hazards that need to be considered for all nuclear plants.

7.6.1 Seismic events

The behaviour and response of a nuclear plant in a seismic event will be dependent upon many factors: the event magnitude, underlying ground conditions, mode of construction, size and whether it is above or below the ground. Understanding how the plant responds is, therefore, complex and is an area of detailed specialism that is

Table 7.7: Example of external hazards. Rotating machinery (such as power turbines) could fail catastrophically leading to the release of rapidly moving debris. Vehicle impact normally refers to cars or lorries, but can include ships (for a dockyard nuclear plant). External road vehicles are not normally a hazard for nuclear plants due to the presence of security fences and crash barriers etc. Road vehicles are of concern for transport safety cases when radiological packages are moved on the road network.

Natural	Man-made
Seismic	Aircraft crash
Extreme wind	Off-site vehicle impact
Extreme temperature	Off-site failure of rotating equipment
Snow/ice loading	Electromagnetic interference
Extreme rainfall and flooding	Off-site explosion
Humidity	Off-site chemical or gas leak
Lightning	
Tsunami	
Animal infestation	

far beyond the scope of this book. Only a brief introduction will be given here and specialist literature should be consulted for more detailed information.

The seismic event will give rise to *ground acceleration* that will have both horizontal and vertical components for which there is a relationship between the two components. The magnitude of the acceleration will be dependent upon the local geology. The ground acceleration is given in terms of a fraction of one Earth gravity, g, which has a value of 9.8 m s^{-2}. The ground acceleration is given in terms of the horizontal component, e.g. 0.3 g.

It is usual for a *design basis earthquake* (DBE) to be determined for a given nuclear site location that can be defined for a range of *return periods*, e.g. 10^{-2}, 10^{-3} or 10^{-4} y^{-1}. There should be no cliff edge effects beyond the given DBE to ensure that a small increase in the magnitude of the event from the DBE does not give rise to a step change in consequences. Even for the most hazardous plant, the most onerous design basis event is normally taken to be 10^{-4} y^{-1}, i.e. the event to which the plant must have specific design provision to ensure nuclear safety. However, even beyond the design basis, it is still necessary to consider the risk posed by the plant during a seismic event.

Seismic hazard assessment is undertaken by initially assuming the failure of structures and control and protection systems, determining the consequences and ascertaining which structures and systems are required to be *seismically qualified*. For instance, should a loss of primary and secondary containment occur, there could be a direct release of activity to the environment and also a loss of criticality-safe geometry. Thus, the primary and secondary containment may be required to withstand the event, i.e. to maintain structural integrity. This will then cascade to require the cell structure and potentially the building structure to be seismically qualified. Therefore, for a complex plant, the approach must be undertaken systematically.

A control system may spuriously operate in a seismic event and it may be necessary to require protection systems to be seismically qualified. For plants that require services to maintain safety, e.g. to remove decay heat, this can make seismic tolerance an engineering challenge. The provision of services is likely to include an independent source of electrical power together with cooling systems and potentially hydrogen removal systems. Services are discussed in more detail in Section 12.

It is important to note that just because a plant requires aspects of it to be seismically qualified does not mean all of the plant has to be. It would be acceptable for some systems to fail including some structures, provided that it is shown that their failure does not compromise the delivery of important seismic safety functions. This will require a systematic approach in considering what is and what is not required to be seismically qualified.

Example: Seismic Qualification

A plant store contains packages that contain fissile material. The packages are held on shelves and it has been determined that should the shelves fail in a seismic event, it is not possible to satisfactorily conclude that a criticality event would not occur. It might be found that there would need to be other failures for criticality to occur, e.g. that the packages are out of specification (in terms of too many moderators), but nevertheless, the safety assessment requires the shelves to be seismically qualified.

Given the magnitude of the consequences (>1 Sv), this requires seismic qualification of the shelves to the 10^{-4} y^{-1} DBE no cliff edge. Of course, the shelves are within a building and this also requires the building to achieve the same level of qualification as the shelves to prevent the building's collapse onto the shelves and domino failure of the shelves. It would be acceptable for separate parts of the building, remote and not able to affect the store, failing. However it would reasonably be expected that post-seismic access to the shelving system would be required to facilitate post-event monitoring or inspection and potentially retrieval at some future stage.

There will also be a defined *operating basis earthquake* (OBE), which corresponds to a much lower magnitude event. During such an OBE, SSCs important to safety should not fail following the repeated occurrence of ground motions at the OBE level. If the requirement of the plant on an OBE occurring is to cease operations, the operations should not be restated until an inspection confirms that it is safe to restart. The rationale for the OBE is that the event has a reasonable chance of occurring during the plant's lifetime.

7.6.2   Extreme weather

There are a range of weather conditions that need to be considered, as shown in Table 7.7. Low temperatures can cause embrittlement or freezing of water lines. Rainfall can give rise to flooding, which may lead to the spread of contamination, damage to safety-related equipment or even introduce additional moderators into criticality storage areas as discussed in Section 7.5.3. Wind and snow loads can give rise to collapse of structures and for the former, the generation of wind-borne debris. Lightning can cause structural damage, start fires or damage control and safety systems. However, lightning would normally be expected to be an additional low-frequency contributor to those already identified that can give rise to a loss of control or fire.

If there are credible hazards to the storage or control of nuclear material, then consequences to the public and workers should be assessed. Weather events, notably of the more extreme variety, can be forecast with good accuracy. Standard site procedures may involve the removal of non-essential personnel, which may see some plants devoid of workers and shut down. Outdoor operations, such as lifts by cranes, would be stopped if extreme weather were to be forecast and the safety case may impose restrictions if these are not mandated at the site level. Therefore, it may be possible to argue in the safety case that there would be no credible hazards from such events.

Many aspects of design against weather events will solely be via reference to codes, e.g. lightning, humidity and water ingress protection irrespective of any return frequency. There are, however, natural hazards where there is a distribution of severity with return frequency, notably, wind, snow loads, rainfall and temperatures. The design basis could be to withstand up to the 10^{-4} y^{-1} event, but a less demanding value could be used for a lower-hazard plant.

Plants that give rise to low consequences would not need any specific withstand over and above normal building codes and standards. For more demanding withstand requirements, there are also relevant codes and standards that address the loads associated with the larger wind speeds, snow loads and so on. Given the specified return frequency demanded by the safety case, civil engineers should be able to design a new building or structure to withstand the event at a specified frequency. For an existing building or structure, it must be recognised that codes and standards change with time and they may have been built to an earlier, less demanding, requirement. This may give rise to shortfalls in the engineering when compared against modern standards that will need to be addressed through the ALARP process.

7.6.3   Aircraft crash

The crash of an aircraft onto a nuclear plant can have significant consequences. This is due to the kinetic energy of the aircraft and the subsequent burning of the fuel carried on board. There can then be direct damage to both primary and secondary containment structures giving rise to a significant release of activity. This can be readily injected into the atmosphere due to the uplift of air generated by the fire that will entrain activity into it. Additionally, safety systems and/or the provision of safety-related services can be compromised even if there has been no direct release of activity. There are normally low-level flight restrictions over nuclear plants to minimise the potential for accidental crashes occurring.

Within a safety case, an aircraft crash is generally taken to be as a result of an accident. Regrettably, the potential for terrorist attack now has to be considered as a nuclear plant may be directly targeted. The potential for a *malicious aircraft crash*

Table 7.8: UK background crash rates. Data taken from [20].

Aircraft	Crash rate 10^{-5} y^{-1} km^{-2}
Light aircraft	1.85
Helicopters	1.03
Small transport	0.22
Large transport	0.07
Military combat	0.67
Total	**3.84**

(MAC) is primarily an issue for the security of the site and will not be considered in this book.

A non-malicious aircraft crash onto a nuclear plant will occur through a chance impact and the rate of aircraft crash can be determined for any given location in a country based upon accident statistics. The background rates of aircraft crash are given in units of 10^{-5} y^{-1} km^{-2} for broad types of plane as illustrated in Table 7.8. The background crash rates may be supplemented by consideration of the nuclear plant's proximity to airports and their flight paths including the position and orientation of an airport runway.

The frequency of aircraft impact is simply the product of the background crash rate (or a more refined crash rate if site specific factors are required to be considered) and the *target area* of the plant. The target area of a plant can become a complicated function to calculate. Should an aircraft solely fall vertically from the sky, the target area is simply the surface area taken by the plant as projected downwards onto the ground. However, planes may approach the plant from a range of different flight (or crash) angles. Therefore, they will 'see' the sides of the plant and this will lead to a projected area whereby, to reach that area of the ground, the plane will have had to pass through the side of the building. This is sometimes known as a *shadow effect* and is illustrated in Fig. 7.3.

For a building of width w, length l and height h, Byrne [21] gives the target area for isotrophic approach directions as

$$\text{Target area} = wl + \frac{2h}{\pi}(w + l)\sum_{i=1}^{i=n} f_i \cot \theta_i, \tag{7.2}$$

where θ_i is the assumed crash angle and f_i is the distribution of crashes per angle. The impact angle may be a function of aircraft type and height. For example, fast military jets flying at low levels may have a shallow angle of decent whilst high-altitude planes may approach at a steeper angle. Equations are available to derive the target area for the different classes of aircraft [21]. For general planes, including military above 2000 ft, the target area is given by

$$\text{Target area} = wl + 0.8h(w + l), \tag{7.3}$$

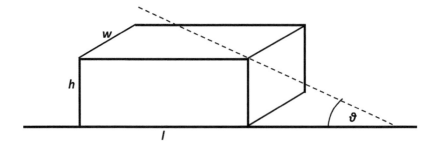

Figure 7.3: Shadow effect where the aircraft crash angle is θ and the usual cuboid dimensions of the building are given by l, w and h.

for military aircraft below 2000 ft

$$\text{Target area} = wl + 3.6h(w + l), \tag{7.4}$$

and for helicopters

$$\text{Target area} = wl + 0.62h(w + l). \tag{7.5}$$

Extensive open and flat areas around the plant can enable an aircraft to skid into the plant, which has the effect of increasing the target area. Conversely, a nuclear plant may be shielded or protected by adjacent non-nuclear plants or structures which can prevent direct impact from that direction. These facts can lead to complexities in the target area analysis which is beyond the scope of this book and the literature should be consulted if required.

For the majority of nuclear plants, it is possible to demonstrate that the chance of aircraft crash is beyond the design basis, i.e. has an IEF of $< 10^{-5}$ y^{-1}. This is achieved by simply finding the product of the aircraft crash rate and the target area of the plant. Should it be demonstrated that the plant is below the design basis, then there will be no formal requirement to provide protection against the hazard. It may then be possible to make an ALARP justification that there are no reasonably practicable improvements that can be made to protect against the hazard. In contrast, it may be found that the hazard is a relatively high contributor to off-site risk particularly if the plant is 'large' (typical accidental rates of crash onto nuclear plants have a frequency of the order of 10^{-7} y^{-1} and there may be significant best-estimate off-site consequences). Thus, there should be robust ALARP demonstration that there is nothing that can be done to reasonably protect against the hazard, unless of course it actually is reasonably practicable to protect against the hazard.

7.6.4   Miscellaneous external hazards

Many of the remaining external hazards listed in Table 7.7 will be very site specific. Off-site vehicle impact is not normally a concern for a plant due to the security barriers around the site, but it is of concern for road or rail transport of nuclear material.

Marine vessel impacts can be of concern for dry-docking facilities where nuclear submarines undergo maintenance. A line of protection may be to ensure that the dock structure is robust to the vessels that may credibly impact it.

Tsunami (or tidal wave) may envelope a coastal site after a seismic event. Protection of the plant should be demonstrated for the predicted design basis wave height, either through the natural height of the site above the sea level or through the provision of barriers. It is preferable that a site does not rely on artificial barriers to ensure safety. It was the failure of the barriers that led to the Fukushima Daiichi nuclear disaster in 2011 with the sea wall being overwhelmed. The inflow of water and flooding of the plant led to a loss of the heat removal systems. Note that there was evidence before the Tsunami that the barriers were not adequate, but improvements had not been made.

7.7   Package transport

Individual nuclear sites are not all encompassing of the nuclear life-cycle, and it is necessary for nuclear material to be moved within a country and also across the world. For instance, uranium ore must be mined (e.g. in Australia) and uranium processing, enrichment and fuel production plants do not exist in all of the countries that have nuclear reactors. Nuclear waste processing and storage sites are also often located separately to the nuclear reactor sites. Not only is nuclear material moved by road and rail, but also by ship and plane. In the extreme, nuclear material is also launched into space on rockets as nuclear sources are used to provide power for deep space probe missions (radioisotope thermoelectric generators). However, nuclear fission powered space rockets are still science fiction.[5]

There is a spectrum of hazards associated with nuclear material, and a proportionate approach must be taken to ensure that it is transported safely. For instance, irradiated nuclear fuel removed from a reactor will be heat generating due to the fission products and it will be significantly more hazardous than LLW that may have been generated in a laboratory. There are international conventions for the packaging and the manner of the transport of nuclear material. The IAEA take a lead on the issue, but it is up to individual countries to determine the specific regulations applicable in their country. For instance, within the UK, the ONR is responsible for regulating activities of nuclear material transport.

Essentially, the transport of nuclear material is often justified by reference to regulation and the requirements placed upon the type of package used. Detailed consideration of transport regulations is beyond the scope of this book and only a brief introduction is given. There will always be additional security aspects to be considered when nuclear material is transported as the material maybe more vulnerable to terrorist assault or criminal activity when it is beyond the security barriers of a nuclear

---

[5] Operation Orion in the US was a research project to use a sequence of nuclear bombs to be detonated underneath a pusher plate to propel an attached spaceship into orbit and beyond. Both the US and the then Soviet Union have utilised fission reactors to power satellites in Earth's orbit.

site. For a more detailed understanding of the regulations, it is recommended that the IAEA [22] be consulted.

A number of package types are defined for transport, such Type A or Type B(U) and the package used for transport will depend on a number of factors including the inventory, its physical and chemical forms and the degree of protection that is required to be provided to it. The regulations define many aspects associated with the packages such as external surface radiation levels, external contamination and even package labelling.

It is essential that the means of ensuring the safe transport of nuclear material is proportionate to the harm potential of the material. Therefore, proportionate consideration of the following is required:

- The protection of the public and those transporting the nuclear material during the normal transport process, i.e. adequate containment of activity, shielding of external radiation and if relevant, maintenance of a sub-critical arrangement;

- The impact, fire and water immersion withstand capability to prevent a release of activity, loss of shielding or loss of sub-critical arrangement in the unlikely event of an accident.

There are a number of standard accident tests specified in [22] that different package types must be able to withstand. For the most robust of packages, these include:

- A 9 m drop test onto a flat horizontal surface;

- Drop onto a puncture target;

- Exposure to a 800 °C fire for 30 min.

Compliance with specific regulations for transport will normally be sufficient to justify the movement of the nuclear material both within a country and across international borders. However, to demonstrate ALARP it may be necessary to show that all reasonably practicable steps have been undertaken to prevent the requirement to move the material in the first instance. As an example, rather than a central national radioactive waste disposal plant, there may be a national requirement to dispose of waste at the site where it is generated. Adopting such a policy would remove the requirement to transport nuclear material on the road or rail network, but it would require more waste disposal plants. There are 'swings and roundabouts' in any ALARP consideration.

7.8   Fault schedule

A safety case can include the analysis of a handful of FSGs to potentially hundreds for the largest and most complex plants. Plant operators, managers, safety assessors and so on have the need for a concise 'go-to' consolidation of the key aspects of each FSG. The *fault schedule* is a vehicle for providing this information, which is provided in a systematic and tabular presentation.

Table 7.9 provides an outline of the minimum of information that is generally included in a fault schedule. At a glance, on an FSG-by-FSG basis, it is possible to ascertain the fault, the unmitigated consequences and the key protection. The fault schedule should include the detection, logic and termination aspects of a particular safety measure, e.g. the alarm and the operator action required or an automatic trip system.

The fault schedule avoids the requirement to read through all of the safety analysis to ascertain what is important. Therefore, the fault schedule is a useful tool for training of operators. It is not uncommon (especially in older safety cases) for fault schedules to contain a 'dump' of everything that is deemed to provide protection, but this should be avoided. An operator needs to know what is required to remain in the SOE and this should be clearly laid out in the fault schedule. What really matters to safety should be clear and not lost in lots of detail or trivial aspects.

Table 7.9: Example presentation layout of a fault schedule with descriptions for column entries.

Fault group—initiating event and fault description	IEF y^{-1}	HAZID refs.	Unmitigated consequences	Design basis	Safety measures
Fault group ref. number	The IEF being the sum of all identified initiators (with conditions)	The HAZID refs., such as the HAZOP deviation refs.	Description of the unmitigated consequences to the public and workers	Whether the fault is within the design basis or not	The safety measures claimed to satisfy design basis requirements
Description of the initiating event as identified in, for example, the HAZOPS			Doses can be presented in terms of dose bands, e.g. public 10–100 mSv	How many design basis safety measures are required	Safety measures that provide defence-in-depth
Brief description of the fault, e.g. control system valve fails to close leading to overfilling of vessel and potential overflow					Separate rows may be required because the safety measures for the public and workers may differ

Chapter 8

Frequency Assessment

This chapter provides an introduction to *frequency assessment*, which is an essential component of a safety case. DBA requires the determination of the IEF and there are a set of frequency and risk targets that require the determination of the *top event frequency*.

This chapter will provide further definition of the initiating event and how it is determined. The distinction between the fault *initiator* and any associated *condition* is given. The chapter will then describe how accounting for the action of safety measures will determine the top event frequency. It is also necessary to discuss the action of the safety measures that will prevent the initiating event from progressing to the undesirable end state. Therefore, this chapter will discuss *reliability assessment* and the determination of the top event frequency with a reference to fault tree analysis. The failure of safety measures may be *revealed* or *unrevealed*, and these terms are defined with a basic introduction into the manner of determining the *unavailability* of safety measures.

Any frequency assessment is only as good as the data used and the associated model to simulate how the fault transient develops. The model may consider how the events happen or how equipment may fail to operate as intended. The approach utilised to obtain relevant reliability data is discussed in this chapter. The development of reliability data and its use in frequency calculation can quickly develop into a detailed and specialist area. Statistical analysis can be used to underpin the selection of reliability data. There is no intent to delve into statistical techniques in this book as it is far beyond the scope of principles and applications. However, it is worth a brief introduction to Poisson statistics and the use of the *half-rule* as these can be used to describe how frequently events or failures may occur with time on a plant.

8.1 Initiating event frequency

There are various techniques to identify the initiating events that underpin the fault assessments and these may include HAZOP (see Section 7.1), reviews of plant records

of incidents or through generic knowledge of how systems work and the faults that
are typically associated with them.

A closer examination of the identified faults may show that the first true failure in
the fault sequence has not actually been identified. For example, the HAZOP may have
correctly identified an erroneously closed valve, but not necessarily recorded that it is
due to a software failure in the control system, a maintenance error, or a failure of the
valve actuator or spring.

In determining the IEF, the safety assessor must have a good understanding of the
fault, how it initiates and importantly, the ability to tease out the difference between
the actual initiator and the action of any safety measures. Normally, the safety measure
is easy to spot, but sometimes it may be hidden in what is first thought to be the
initiating event.

First of all, let us remember that for our safety case, an initiating event is defined
as an undesirable occurrence that is not within the envelope of normal operations;
i.e. it is a fault. This fault, if unchecked by the action of safety measures, may lead
to an unacceptable consequence. The safety case is primarily concerned with radiological consequences and generally of the more significant variety. It is expected that
a HAZOP will identify a whole host of faults that on inspection do not lead to radiological consequences if unchecked. These faults may lead to operational difficulties,
process faults, environmental hazards and so on, that may themselves warrant non-
radiological safety measures.

The IEF is defined as the frequency with which the initiating event occurs. This
is expressed in units of time^{-1}, normally per hour (h^{-1}) or per year (y^{-1}). Therefore,
the IEF is a rate of occurrence. The determination of failure rates can be undertaken
by reference to plant data or reference data books. This works well for equipment that
is in continuous use. For example, the failure of a pipe is quoted at a rate per metre
per year and may even be broken down into failure modes such as guillotine failure
or pinhole failure.

However, there are many instances when it is more appropriate to derive the IEF
by assigning the probability of failure of a task P_f to the number of tasks taken per
year n. This is an approach used where the initial fault is due to human error where a
human error probability (HEP) is used. Mathematically, the IEF is then given as

$$\text{IEF} = nP_f. \tag{8.1}$$

Frequencies can be determined on a best-estimate basis. This allows us to further
refine the definition of the initiating event. Should a fault occur it is not always certain
that unacceptable radiological consequences may arise—it may also require a degree
of random bad luck for this to occur.

Therefore, we can then distinguish between the actual initiator i as the initial fault
and one or more conditions C_1, C_2, C_3, and so on being the state that must be present
in which the defined unacceptable radiological consequences arise. The initiator, being the fault, has the units of time^{-1} and the condition is a probability between 0 and
1 and has no units. If there is more than one condition, the product is taken. Mathematically, the IEF is refined to be

$$\text{IEF} = iC_1C_2C_3 \dots. \tag{8.2}$$

It must be emphasised that the condition cannot be a fault itself. It can only be the probability that the initiator occurs at the time that the plant is in the particular normal condition that must be present for the unacceptable consequence to arise. If the condition were a fault, we would end up with units of time^{-1} × time^{-1}, which does not make sense.

A condition is also not the failure of a safety measure. It is simply the unfortunate (unlucky) state of normal operations or co-incidence that must be present for the initiator to progress to the unacceptable radiological consequence. Without the condition, the initiator may occur, but there would be no radiological consequence. If more than one condition is applied, care must be taken to ensure that they are truly independent of each other, otherwise the multiplication in Eq. 8.2 may make for an erroneously low frequency. In practice, there are often no conditions to apply or, at most, one or two. There may be a number of initiators $(i_1, i_2, i_3 \ldots i_n)$ that require the same safety measures. We can define these as giving rise to a *common demand event*. Mathematically, we can then sum the individual initiators and their conditions for this common demand event, i.e.

$$\text{IEF} = \sum_{a=1}^{n} i_a C_a. \tag{8.3}$$

It is important to emphasise that the summation of individual initiators will only be valid in subsequent frequency and risk calculations where we will place demand for the same safety measures; i.e. the faults develop in the same manner. This approach simplifies fault assessments by enabling the grouping of faults to occur and eliminates extensive assessment of every single identified fault.

LFE: *A Note of Warning*
We have deliberately considered the IEF to be in terms of unacceptable radiological consequences, which is necessary to undertake DBA, frequency and radiological risk calculations to demonstrate nuclear safety.

Even if the safety case for the plant were to argue that there was negligible radiological risk, the overall safety of the plant is reliant on adequate industrial and environmental safety being maintained. The nuances of conditions outlined above are not necessarily relevant in terms of conventional safety; a dropped load from a crane needs to be avoided even if the radiological risk from the same crane is negligible.

Regulators do prosecute licensees for these sorts of failures even if there is no resulting radiological dose or even no potential for a radiological dose. An example will be a dropped load from a crane that does not involve a nuclear package or nuclear material.

Example: Tank Fill Mechanism

A tank fill mechanism may rely on a level instrument to determine the liquor level. The level instrument feeds a signal to a computer control system which commences the transfer of liquor to fill the tank by running a steam ejector. The computer will stop the transfer when the operational high level, as determined by the level instrument, is reached. In this example, a failure of the:

- level instrument, or

- control system, or

- isolation of the steam ejector

will lead to continued transfer, which if unchecked by any further protection system will lead to a potential overflow of the tank. The overflow of the tank is not within the bounds of normal operations and we determine it to be an unacceptable consequence. It is thus a fault.

In this example, we have three initiators, but they all lead to a common event – the overflow. Looking at the above bullet points, we have said 'or' between each of the three potential initiating events. So, assuming we have established individual IEFs of 10^{-2} y^{-1} (level measurement), 10^{-1} y^{-1} (computer control system) and ejector isolation (8×10^{-2} y^{-1}), the common demand event IEF is 0.19 y^{-1}, for which 0.2 y^{-1} is normally sufficient approximation.

Example: Can Drop

A store may contain overpacked cans of radiological material and it may be necessary to manually move 100 cans per year. Clearly, a mishandling of the can leading to a drop can be seen is a fault because it is not a normal operation. We determine a HEP of dropping the package to be 10^{-3} per movement. The IEF would be 10^{-1} y^{-1}.

Let us assume that the radiological dose from a dropped can is actually insignificant. However, some of these cans may contain radiolytically generated hydrogen in their ullage for which the evidence is 3% of the cans contain hydrogen. On the assumption that the energies involved in a can drop can ignite the hydrogen, we may have a significantly greater release of activity and potentially significant radiological dose. What was an insignificant dose for 97% of the packages is now very significant for the 3%.

Therefore, we can apply the 3% as a condition to give an IEF of

$$\text{IEF} = 10^{-1}\,y^{-1} \times 0.03 = 3 \times 10^{-3}\,y^{-1}. \tag{8.4}$$

One could argue that the presence of hydrogen in the cans is a fault condition. It may well have been a historic fault that enabled hydrogen to be produced (e.g. a failure to dry material before packaging leading to moisture and radiolysis[a]). However, given where we are now many years later, the normal condition of store handling includes all of the cans of which 3% contain hydrogen.

Example: Crane Failure

A crane may be used to lift a flask from one part of the plant to another. Most flasks may be robust flasks used for external transport that are tolerant to credible drops within the plant. However, occasionally, an internal flask is used that may not be tolerant to the potential drop scenarios. There are a large number of potential initiators for the drop from a crane, but for this example we solely focus on one simple initiator, the breaking of the crane rope. Should the rope fail, the lifted load will free fall to the ground, resulting in potential damage to the flask and release of activity.

Catastrophic rope failure in this manner is unlikely and let us assume we establish a failure rate of 10^{-5} y^{-1}. Only 10% of flask moves are of the internal flask type and it may actually be found that the internal flasks are robust to the potential drop heights within the plant, but they are not tolerant to impact upon a section of the floorplan that has metal structures that can puncture the flask. In contrast, external flasks are found to be tolerant to these puncture targets. We then can apply two conditions, whether the flask is internal (C_1) and whether the drop occurs over the puncture target (C_2). The puncture targets may represent only 5% of the operating envelope of the crane. Thus, the IEF is given by

$$IEF = 10^{-5} \ y^{-1} \times 0.1 \times 0.05 = 5 \times 10^{-8} \ y^{-1}. \tag{8.5}$$

This is an area where care must be taken. A crane may be controlled with a series of zones that prevent x-y travel into areas of the plant. This zoning system will utilise position sensors on the crane rails that tell the crane's control system where it is. This zoning system may actually have been set up to prevent travel over the puncture targets (or at least the majority of them), which is how we initially and naively arrived at our condition of 5%. Without the zoning system being present, over 50% of the crane's operating envelope may contain puncture targets. Thus, the zoning system provides protection and is a safety measure (albeit not a particularly robust one due to the residual 5%); we should have applied a condition of 50% in the initiating event.

---

[a]Radiolysis is the process by which water is decomposed into oxygen and hydrogen through the interaction with alpha, beta or gamma radiation. It is subsequently possible for the hydrogen that is released to accumulate as a gas and give rise to flammable or explosive mixtures. It is a big concern to many safety cases.

8.2 Top event frequency

We have defined the IEF in terms of the initiator and applicable conditions. If there are no safety measures available, the defined unacceptable radiological consequences will be realised at this IEF. The safety measures should prevent an initiating event from progressing to such a consequence, or they may mitigate the consequence. Safety measures act as one or more barriers in the fault progression. We expect each safety measure to have a reasonably high chance of success in preventing or adequately mitigating the dose that may arise from the unchecked initiating event.

Therefore, we need to consider the different types of safety measures that may be present and the role they have in preventing or reducing the dose that is realised. In simple terms, the top event frequency is the product of the IEF and the probability of failure of each of the subsequent safety measures with due account for CCF.

8.2.1 Unrevealed and revealed failures

Many safety measures operate in the background and only act to terminate the fault when a demand is placed upon them. The safety measures will only positively act when either:

- The initiating event occurs; or

- They are proof tested to confirm that they are working.

It would be hoped that a good plant design will ensure that they are rarely, if ever, required to act in response to an actual initiating event. Good safety culture should ensure that a functional proof test is undertaken on the safety measures at least annually, i.e. a *proof test interval* (PTI) of $1\,\mathrm{y}^{-1}$. A proof test should simulate the fault conditions and test the detection, logic and termination components of the safety measure, as far as reasonably practicable.

Examples of safety measures that operate in the background include:

- Vessel high-level liquor trips to prevent overfilling (e.g. a level detector acting upon a safety valve);

- A gamma interlock on a shield door (to lock the shield door in position and prevent inadvertent access should erroneous entry be attempted);

- A high-level acidity alarm in a vessel (to alert the operator to out of specification conditions);

- An activity-in-air alarm (to alert operators to a release of activity).

It is possible that any such safety measure has a failure somewhere in the link between the detector and terminator. Ideally, good design will ensure that the failure is revealed to the operator so that corrective action can be made, e.g. repairs made or contingency arrangements put into action. Contingency arrangements could include stopping work or using a standby safety measure.

It is also good design that the safety measure *fails to safety* or *fails-safe*. For example, the vessel high-level trip should work by powering open the safety measure isolation valve. Therefore, should there be an interruption to the power supply, the valve will return to a closed position and fail-safe. This will, by default, prevent the potential for continued liquor transfer and overflow of the vessel. However, there will always be some failure modes of the safety measure that cannot fail-safe or be revealed, for example:

- Fail closed valve could stick in the open position; or

- Annunciator on an alarm system could be faulty.

Thus, the safety measure may be in a state of *unrevealed failure* at the time of demand. The above examples are also of *dangerous failure modes* and it is of these that we are concerned about; they will inhibit the ability of the safety measure to function and will not be revealed preventing action on outage to be undertaken.

To undertake frequency analysis, we therefore need to know the probability that the safety measure is failed at the time of demand, i.e. its unavailability. How we do this differs depending on whether the failure is revealed or unrevealed, which we will explore in the sections below.

8.2.2   Constant failure rate

We know from our own experience that, from time-to-time, equipment breaks and fails to do as it is meant to do. This can occur at random times and the reason for the failure may never be known. Quite often, however, equipment will break towards the end of its life as the effects of wear and tear lead to irreparable damage. We only need to think of a motor car to know what age does to its ability to function without spending a lot of money on maintenance.

It is also found that equipment can fail when it is first utilised. Despite being fresh from the manufacturer, the equipment may have some latent defect that causes it to fail on first or early use. We keep our receipts of purchases in case the equipment fails in the first 12 months.

Safety-related equipment in a nuclear plant, in principle, is no different from what we experience at home. There may be a propensity for failures early in the life of the equipment and perhaps more so towards the end of the lifetime of the equipment. During the mid-period of its life, there may be a chance of failure, but we hope that this is low. Indeed, this is borne out by an analysis of equipment failures and when they occur. This analysis gives rise to what is known as the *bathtub curve* of failure rate against equipment age. A schematic bath tub curve is shown in Fig. 8.1.

Once equipment is installed on a plant, it is the role of commissioning and the associated commissioning tests to weed out early failures. Preventative maintenance should occur before the predicted end-of-life conditions are reached and this should weed out late failures. Therefore, the commissioning and maintenance regimes on the plant should ensure that the equipment operates in the mid of the bath tub where the failure rate is more or less constant and is random with time.

If we assume, therefore, that we are operating in the flat of the bath tub region, then the constant failure rate model can be used to determine unavailability. This is an exponential model that gives the probability P_t that a piece of equipment will fail by time t to be

$$P_t = 1 - e^{-\lambda t}, \tag{8.6}$$

where λ is the equipment failure rate that is assumed to be constant. For small failure rates, such that $\lambda \ll t$, Eq. 8.6 approximates via the Taylor series expansion[1] to λt. The mean time to failure (*MTTF*) is given by

$$MTTF = \frac{1}{\lambda}. \tag{8.7}$$

---

[1] The Taylor series expansion is an infinite series that can approximate a function and for e^{-x} is written as $1 - x + \frac{x^2}{2!} - \frac{x^3}{3!} \ldots \approx 1 - x$ when x is small.

Unrevealed failure

As noted, safety equipment often acts in the background and it may be in an unrevealed failed state. We need to know what its failure probability is, i.e. the likelihood
it will not operate when required. With equipment failures being random and if we
have a constant failure rate, the mean probability of the equipment being failed at any
time is given by

$$\text{Mean failure probability at any time} = \frac{\lambda_u T}{2}, \tag{8.8}$$

where T is the proof test interval (EMIT) and λ_u refers to the unrevealed failure rate.
Equation 8.8 is sometimes known as the *probability of failure on demand* (pfd). The
important aspect of Eq. 8.8 is that the more frequently we proof test the item and
reduce T, the more reliable it is likely to be. Simply put, by increasing the rate of
proof testing, we increase the chance that we detect the unrevealed failure and repair
it before the actual fault occurs to place a real demand upon it. As with any test in life,
we are most confident that something works just after we have successfully tested it.
Conversely, we are least confident that it will work just before its functional test.

So, to improve reliability as safety assessors, we could insist that a safety measure
is tested every month or even every week to ensure a very reliable system and confirm
it is not in an unrevealed failure state. However, we would get no thanks for this approach from those responsible for running the plant. Proof testing at this frequency
would pose an enormous and disproportionate burden on plant maintenance personnel and may expose them to unnecessary risk and dose from the background radiation
levels on the plant. An annual proof test is normally sufficient to ensure adequate reliability. Six-monthly or even three-monthly proof tests may be justified in only the
most exceptional circumstances. If a plant needs to proof test more frequently than
this to meet risk targets, it may suggest either excess pessimism in the calculations or
a need to make improvements to the plant through the inclusion of additional diverse
lines of protection.

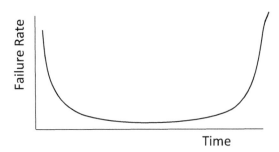

Figure 8.1: Schematic drawing of the failure rate with time as utilised in the constant failure rate
model. The shape broadly matches that of a bath hence it is sometimes referred to the *bathtub
curve*.

Revealed failure

As noted above, should the failure of a safety measure be revealed, contingency arrangements will normally be quickly put in place. This involves cessation of the relevant normal operations of the plant. For example, if a gamma monitor is revealed to be faulty and this monitor forms part of a shield door interlock, cell entries would not be allowed until the monitor is repaired. The unrevealed failure mode will normally solely be used in reliability analysis. To be exact, we could also use the revealed failure rate combined with the probability of failing to implement the outage. This approach, whilst being more rigorous, is also more complex. With good managerial control around important safety measures, the likelihood of failing to implement *action-on-failure* is small in comparison to the unrevealed failure rate. Therefore, revealed failures do not normally feature in the reliability analysis.

There are, however, circumstances when a plant may be required to continue operating when one of the safety measures is unavailable due to a revealed failure or even during EMIT. In these situations, we do need to explicitly consider the unavailability. Unavailability is also used when considering the reliability of ventilation systems to minimise the migration of activity across plant containment barriers, or filtration systems in the extract ductwork. These systems operate continuously and it is not appropriate to consider a pfd associated with them should there suddenly be an acute release of activity beyond that associated with normal operations. The systems will not suddenly act differently to mitigate or prevent a release, but they will continue to undertake the same role as they do in normal operations. In the frequency analysis we want to know if there is a release of activity due to an initiating fault, what is the chance that this is co-incident with the ventilation system or filtration system being unavailable.

The unavailability, U, of a safety system is defined by

$$U = 1 - \text{availability} = \frac{\text{downtime}}{\text{total time}}, \tag{8.9}$$

which by itself is not very helpful. If we consider an equipment 'cycle' there will be the downtime, i.e. the mean time to repair ($MTTR$) after failure and the total time, i.e. $MTTF + MTTR$, where $MTTF$ is the mean time to failure. The total time approximates $MTTF$ when $MTTR \ll MTTF$. Therefore, combining Eqs. 8.7 and 8.9, we get

$$U \approx \frac{MTTR}{MTTF} \approx MTTR\,\lambda. \tag{8.10}$$

There may also be situations where a system is taken out of service for EMIT. Ideally, the radiological hazard would be removed, but this may not always be practicable and there will be a window or *outage time* in which the particular safety system is not available.

The unavailability of the system due to EMIT is simply the fraction of the year that the system is unavailable, which is ideally a very small number (e.g. a few hours in 8760 hours in a year). We can take the total unavailability as that due to EMIT and that due to revealed failure. As we have identified, crucial in determining the unavailability is the repair time (or outage time). It is essential that plant managers are aware of the assumed outage time for EMIT, as working in excess of the outage time will invalidate the frequency analysis and potentially the declared risk posed by the plant. This outage time should feed into the *plant maintenance schedule* (PMS) via the *engineering schedule* (see Section 10.3) and be clearly spelt out.

Example: Ventilation Fan

The ventilation system of a plant utilises a duty centrifugal fan system. There is also a standby fan available, which should auto-start should the duty fan cease operation during running. The standby fan will undergo EMIT whilst it is in standby mode, but during EMIT there is a chance that a demand will be placed upon it due to duty fan failure.

We establish from our reliability data that the failure rate of a centrifugal fan system is 3×10^{-6} h^{-1}. We also know that every year (8760 h) plant maintenance will spend an average of eight hours undertaking EMIT for which the fan is out of action. Therefore, the unavailability of the standby fan due to EMIT is $\frac{8}{8760} = 9 \times 10^{-4}$.

Now let's compare this unavailability to that of the duty fan being unavailable due to mechanical failure. We bound the time to repair the fan from any failure by three days (72 h), which we take to be *MTTR*. Hence, the unavailability due to mechanical failure is 3×10^{-6} h^{-1} $\times$ 72 h $= 2 \times 10^{-4}$. The total system unavailability is 1.1×10^{-3}.

In this example, we should make it clear in the safety case that unavailability of the standby fan is limited to eight hours and that we would expect all repairs to the fan to be fixed within three days. If a longer time were to be needed contingency arrangements would need to be in place, perhaps cessation of plant operations.

A complete reliability assessment would also factor in the potential for the auto-changeover system to be in an unrevealed failure mode and not instigate operation of the standby fan. There should also be consideration of the standby fan (now the duty fan) ceasing operation during the repair window of the former duty fan, though this probability may be expected to be small and be able to be neglected unless the repair time is long.

8.2.3 Low and high demand rates of safety measures

We do not expect safety measures to act all of the time. They may be there in the background checking that the plant is operating within the correct limits, but they are not actively preventing the exposure of personnel or release of activity. There are normally other failures that must occur before an exposure or activity release occurs. We normally expect safety measures to operate in a *low-demand mode*.

However, there may be circumstances that we find ourselves in with safety measures operating in *high-demand mode*; i.e. they are operating frequently or almost continuously. Consider the brakes on a car; are they part of the control system for driving the car or are they a safety measure? We use them to slow down the car when approaching a bend, but we will frequently use them to correct for other peoples' driving and prevent an accident. This will occur numerous times on even the shortest of journeys. In reality, the car brakes are a mixture of the normal control system and a safety measure.

It would not be appropriate to utilise a pfd value for the car brakes, as they are used thousands of times between each annual service test. A very reliable safety measure could have a pfd as high as 0.001. Thus, if we were to consider 100 uses of the brake on a modest journey, we might expect a crash rate of 0.1 per journey. This does not match experience.

The car brakes are an example of a safety measure acting in high-demand mode. Specifically, if the demand for the safety measure (normally the IEF) is greater than T, we should consider that we are operating be in high-demand mode, i.e.

$$\text{IEF } T > 1. \tag{8.11}$$

When in high-demand mode we are effectively saying that it is more likely that the initiating event will occur before we undertake a functional proof test of the safety measure to find (and correct) its unrevealed failure. The top event frequency then tends to the failure rate of the safety measure. In our example, the failure rate of a car's braking system is a very small number. Hence, we rarely crash cars due to brake failure, but we do crash cars more frequently due to operator error. In contrast, we would expect safety measures on a plant to have a minimum PTI of one year, which should be more frequent than the rate of demand on the safety measure to prevent the fault progression.

Example: Cell Entry

An operator may be required to enter a cell that frequently contains radiation sources. The operators should ensure that the radiation sources are removed prior to entry. There is a gamma interlock system on the access door to prevent entry if high radiation levels are detected. There should be an independent check that the cell is free of radiation sources before authorisation is given to the operator to make the entry. Entry to the cell is undertaken a dozen or so times per year.

There is an obvious fault here, i.e. entry to the cell whilst a radiation source is present. There is also an obvious safety measure. The gamma interlock system feels like it is the safety measure, but does it operate in high or low demand? Indeed, is it actually the control system for door opening? Let us examine.

Let us assume the interlock system is a high-demand safety measure. This is on the basis that we are making cell entry every month and the system prevents the operator from being exposed at this rate. Additionally, functional proof testing is undertaken annually. The plant cannot commit to more frequent testing. It certainly cannot commit to testing every month, which would need to be undertaken to ensure that we operate in low-demand mode, i.e. IEF $T < 1$.

We must take the failure rate of the safety measure to be the frequency of being exposed to the cell contents. If we have determined that the potential dose from exposure to cell contents was significant (300 mSv), the BSO for this frequency is 10^{-5} y^{-1}. Thus, we require the gamma interlock safety measure to have a failure frequency of 10^{-5} y^{-1} to reach the BSO for this one fault. This is a big ask for engineering and is likely to be difficult, impracticable and costly to engineer. Therefore, we conclude that assuming a high-demand mode is leading to difficultly in meeting our frequency requirements, let alone DBA that will require independence between initiators and protection.

Let's look carefully at the first paragraph: 'The operators should ensure that the radiation sources are removed prior to entry'. Hopefully, this involves a visual check through a shield window. The potential radiation sources are large and easily visible.

We now need to more carefully define the initiating event. It is not failure of the gamma interlock system—it is the operator failing to ensure that the cell is clear of sources before attempting entry. This is how the plant is normally controlled; failure of the normal control system (operator error) leads to a demand on the safety measures. In this example, the gamma interlock system is at least one of the safety measures.

Putting some numbers together, in conjunction with human factors assessors, we may be able to justify a HEP of failure to ensure that the cell is free of the radiation source of 0.01. Using Eq. 8.1 we can combine the HEP with 12 entries per year to give an IEF of 1.2×10^{-1} y^{-1}. We may also be able to justify a HEP for an independent check by a supervisor of 0.1. This will give a rate of demand on the gamma interlock of 1.2 $\times 10^{-2}$ y^{-1}. With an annual proof test, IEF $T < 1$ and we can conclude the safety measure is in low-demand mode. It is appropriate then to use a pfd based upon the approximation $\frac{\lambda T}{2}$.

8.3   Designing for reliability

We have established that the top event frequency is determined by the product of the IEF and the probability that the safety measures fail to operate on demand or are unavailable. Strictly, this approach assumes that the initiating event and the safety measures are fully independent, but in reality, there will also be some dependency between these aspects of the fault progression. In simple terms, if one safety measure fails, then there will be a probability that a second safety measure also fails for the same reason; i.e. there is a CCF. This is not random bad luck, but is due to an aspect that affects both simultaneously. The random bad luck is accounted for by utilising the pfd or the unavailability, whilst the CCF is accounted for by explicit consideration. It can also be necessary to account for CCF between the initiating event and the safety measures.

The most obvious reason for CCF is a maintenance error, particularly if the same maintainers go from one system to another and have an equally 'bad day' at each.

This can be protected against by having different maintenance teams and staggered maintenance. Therefore, all of the maintenance is not all done at once and there is an opportunity to identify and correct maintenance deficiencies.

There are, however, a whole range of other mechanisms that give rise to CCF and examples of CCF include:

- Loss of electrical power;

- Flood;

- Fire;

- Calibration errors;

- Vibration;

- Moisture ingress;

- Contaminated fuel and so on.

Where practicable, the CCF is accounted for explicitly in fault analysis and frequency calculations, particularly loss of electrical power. However, it is not always practicable to account for all aspects of CCF. There will always be mechanisms for CCF that cannot be thought of. Therefore, CCF is accounted for by a modification factor in the frequency calculation. There are a number of standard safety engineering techniques to minimise the potential for CCF and these are now briefly discussed.

Redundancy

Redundant systems utilise two or more components where only one is required to deliver the safety function. The system may be fully redundant such that there are separate detectors, logic circuits and terminators or there may be, for instance, two detectors that feed into a common logic circuit and terminator. Redundant systems are connected in parallel ensuring that a sole failure of one redundant component does not compromise the delivery of the overall safety function. Redundant systems offer improved reliability due to random failure, but offer limited protection against CCF.

Examples of redundant systems include duty/standby ventilation fans, primary/secondary filters and even gamma interlock systems with two or more gamma detectors. It is likely that should CCF occur, redundant systems will fail in the same manner, which is known as *common mode failure* (CMF). Note that the terms CCF and CMF are sometimes used interchangeably, but strictly, CCF refers to the common reason for failure and CMF refers to the common manner in which they fail—there is a difference.

Example: Redundant Filters
Primary and secondary filters are located in an extract system. They are placed *in series* as the secondary filters are required to filter the 'cleaner' air initially filtered by the primary filters. It is not possible to have parallel primary and secondary filters.

Should there be a large release of moisture to the extract system, it is possible that the filters could fail due to deterioration of the filter medium (unless they are made from moisture-resisting materials, which should be the case if such a moisture release is a credible hazard).

A release of moisture in this manner is a CCF that can lead to failure of all of the filtration systems. The filters would all fail in the same manner; i.e. there would also be a CMF.

Diversity

Diverse systems may deliver the same safety function, but utilise different types of systems to deliver the function. Diversity can be as simple as using different types of components to do the same thing (e.g. from different manufacturers) or to use different technology altogether. The greater the diversity in the components or the system, the less likely they will suffer from CCF and they may fail in different manners, reducing the potential for CMF.

Having diverse systems can increase the complexity of a plant, with an increase in maintenance costs and potentially a reduction in flexibility. For instance, instead of having one generic type of pump from one manufacturer, there may be different pump types from different sources, reducing the availability of spares and so on. During the plant design stages and specification of equipment, providing for diversity sometimes needs the 'buy-in' of the plant operators and maintainers due to the potential impact on operational efficiency.

Example: Diverse Level Measurement
A plant is required to measure liquor level and diverse systems are to be utilised. One system utilises a pneumercator and a separate system utilises radar. In this example, the technology for level detection is clearly diverse, but the information could be relayed to a common annunciator panel so that only some aspects of the overall system are diverse.

To achieve a greater degree of diversity, it may be necessary to:

1. Have one system relayed through a computer system and one through a diverse relay logic system with an analogue display;

2. Utilise different maintenance teams to undertake proof testing, calibration and so on.

In our simple example, the level measurement is relayed to an operator, which is clearly a common link between the two systems. This defeats the point of having diverse level measurement. To achieve true diversity, there should be mechanisms to automatically isolate the incoming liquor feed if that is what is required overall.

Segregation

Segregated systems are located or routed so that components are physically separated and ideally segregated in different plant areas. There can be physical constraints to achieving segregation. For instance, detection and termination aspects of a safety system may need to act on the same process aspects of the plant. However, the placement of separate logic circuits for different safety circuits in separate parts of the plant will help to achieve some aspects of segregation. Segregation can be an effective means to protect against fire, explosion and flood, as the placement of safety systems within separate compartments can reduce CCF.

8.3.1   Accounting for common cause failure

One model that is widely utilised is known as the *beta* (β) factor model. The model is a simplification to account for the CCF events that cannot be explicitly accounted for, such as loss of incoming electrical supply or fire.

Let us consider redundant components that each have an identical failure rate λ. The β-model assumes that a fraction of the failures are independent, which we denote as λ_i. The remaining fraction of failures are common with other systems λ_c, i.e. due to CCF. Therefore, the total failure rate is

$$\lambda = \lambda_i + \lambda_c. \tag{8.12}$$

The β-factor can be defined as

$$\beta = \frac{\lambda_c}{\lambda}, \tag{8.13}$$

consequently

$$\lambda_i = (1 - \beta)\lambda. \tag{8.14}$$

There are techniques for determining values of β, which can be quite involved and far beyond the scope of this introduction. The simplest technique may be to analyse failure data to determine what fraction of the failures could be attributed to CCF and this would feed into the reliability for use, though there may not be sufficient reliable data to do this. Other techniques are available that utilise question sets to determine β values with the questions being related to the issues of diversity, segregation, safety culture and so on. A licensee will adopt an approach on how to account for CCF. The effect of accounting for CCF is to restrict the overall reliability claim of safety measures.

8.4   Calculating frequencies

We have established some basic reliability terms, and we know that we have frequency and risk BSOs/BSLs to compare against (Section 2.4), but how do we do this? Historically, safety assessors went straight to the production of fault trees to calculate frequencies. Fault trees provide a diagrammatic and logical representation of the fault showing the combination of *base* or *basic events* that must occur for the top event to occur. By assigning frequencies and probabilities to these base events, it is possible to calculate top event frequency with an impressive degree of precision (but arguably not necessarily accuracy).

Fault trees have their use and for many nuclear systems they are required to model the complexity of the system and the number of faults. Analysis of reactors is one area where fault trees have been extensively used. Fault trees are also utilised to model complex non-reactor systems where there may be a number of safety measures or safety measures that have many components where CCF needs to be taken into account.

8.4.1   Semi-quantitative techniques

Certainly, within the decommissioning and waste management arena of nuclear safety, it is possible to utilise semi-quantitative techniques to demonstrate that the frequency of a fault is small in comparison to the relevant BSL/BSO. Reaching for fault tree software is unnecessary. Persuasive arguments backed up with the use of numbers are a powerful tool. Setting out the arguments as a series of bullet points is a clear and concise way of presenting the argument.

Example: Dropped Package
Let us consider the manual transfer of a package or waste material. There is obviously the drop of the package to consider as a potential fault. Should this occur, there will be a suspension of material within the package leading to a puff release of activity to the local environment should the package be breached.

For the sake of argument, we establish that the unmitigated best-estimate consequence is 6 mSv. From Table 2.4, this is in the 2–20 mSv dose band with a BSL and BSO of 10^{-1} y^{-1} and 10^{-3} y^{-1}, respectively. The partially and fully mitigated consequences are < 2 mSv, for which there are no BSL and BSO values to compare against.

The operator should wear a respirator to move these packages, which can be justified to provide a DF of 100. The operator is also trained to evacuate from the area in response to a drop and to not recover the package. These requirements are reinforced by the core training necessitating personnel to withdraw from areas where activity-in-air alarms may be sounding or on the obvious sight of a fault. The clean-up of a spill should be undertaken as a recovery action under the supervision of health physics and so on.

In our earlier example, we utilised a justified probability of a package drop of 10^{-3} per sensitive package movement and in our example there are 10 package moves per year. The rate of dropped package is therefore 10^{-2} y^{-1}. In conjunction with human factors assessors, we can justify a probability of the operator both not evacuating and not wearing a respirator as 10^{-2}. Therefore, the frequency of receiving a dose in the 2–20 mSv dose band is simply 10^{-4} y^{-1}, which is 10% of the BSO.

8.4.2 Fault trees

Fault trees can be an important tool in determining frequencies, especially for complex systems. The fault trees provide a logical description of the failure paths or the fault progression and they enable a detailed interrogation of the fault sequence to be undertaken. The fault tree enables a specified event (the top event) to be determined, and analysis of the fault tree enables the combination of events that lead to the top event to be demonstrated.

The input failures incorporated in a fault tree are known as *base events* or *basic events* and these are combined together through a set of *logic gates*. Attached to each basic event is reliability information (failure frequency or pfd /unavailability). It is the combination of basic events and logic gates that determine the combination of failures required to reach the top event or any intermediate event. The reliability information determines the relative contribution of each combination to the top event.

The principal logic gates used within fault trees are 'AND' and 'OR' gates.

AND—The output of an AND gate is 1 if all of the inputs are 1. The equivalent mathematical operation with an and gate is multiplication (.).

The symbol for an AND gate is given below.

OR—The output of an OR gate is 1 if any of the inputs is 1. The equivalent mathematical operation with an OR gate is addition (+).

The symbol for an OR gate is given below.

An illustrative fault tree showing a combination of 'AND' and 'OR' gates is shown in Fig. 8.2. The fault tree consists of five basic events that must be combined in a particular order to enable the top event to occur.

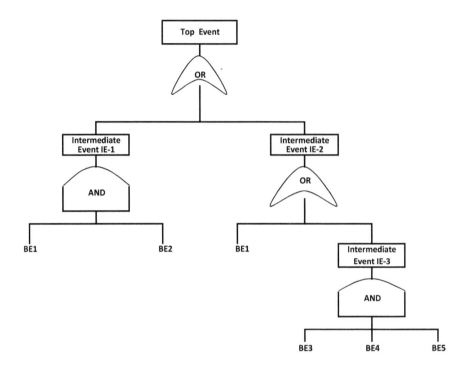

Figure 8.2: Schematic fault tree with five basic events BE1 to BE5. For simplicity, the schematic is shown without reliability data attached to the basic events. (Based on [23].)

When the basic events are combined, each combination that gives rise to the top event is known as a *cutset*. The *minimal cutsets* are generated by the minimum combination of basic events that give rise to the top event. Understanding the minimal cutsets is an important aspect of understanding how the top event may arise. Moreover, with the inclusion of reliability values, the cutsets will reveal which combination of basic events contributes the most to the overall top event frequency and a potential focus for improvement.

Example: Minimal Cutsets

Consider a simple compressed air system which utilises a duty compressor A and a backup compressor B. Both compressors utilise a common electrical supply C. There will be a loss of compressed air if any of the following combinations occur:

$$C \quad AC \quad BC \quad ABC \quad AB.$$

C is a minimal cutset because it is a single event that will disable both compressors and lose compressed air. AB is also a minimal cutset because a failure of both compressors gives rise to a loss of compressed air. However, AC, BC and ABC are not minimal cutsets because a failure of A and/or B is not required to give rise to a loss of compressed air if C also fails.

C is a first-order cutset because it has one basic event, AB is a second-order cutset and ABC is a third-order cutset.

Boolean algebra

The mathematics within faults trees includes *Boolean algebra* for which the principal rules are given in Table 8.1. We will not dwell on the algebra, but will briefly place the algebra into context. The use of the Boolean rules enables the determination of the minimal cutsets as described above to be made. Systematic use of the algebra enables the top event to be determined in its simplest form.

As a demonstration, Table 8.2 shows how the cutsets that are generated from working through the fault tree in Fig. 8.2 are arrived at. The table then shows how the application of Boolean algebra can be used to identify the minimal cutsets, which in this example are BE1 and BE3, BE4, BE5. Either of the two minimal cut sets will give rise to the top event. Therefore, in the world of fault assessment, BE1 must be an initiating event because it is the sole failure in the cutset and there is no protection against that initiating event. Similarly, there would need to be a different initiating event in the second cutset (as there is no BE1) which would be either BE3, BE4 or BE5 with the other two basic events being a necessary failure in conjunction with the initiating event. When determining a top event frequency, each initiating event must have a frequency assigned to it with the other failures in the cutset requiring a probability.

8.5   Reliability data sources

In order to undertake frequency calculations, it is necessary to obtain relevant input data, which is known as *reliability data*. The quality or accuracy of any frequency calculation is dependent upon the quality or accuracy of this information. It is not hard to see that frequencies (and hence risks) can be manipulated by which data sources we choose to use. This is one of the drawbacks of numerical risk assessment and it re-enforces the view that robust good quality argument using sound engineering reasoning backed by evidence should take the primary role in making a safety case. The

Table 8.1: Basic Boolean algebra functions.

Rule	Explanation
$A + A = A$	A is not double counted so A is failed everywhere it appears.
$AA = A$	A is not double counted as A cannot be failed again.
$AB + A = A$	B makes no difference as A is a failure and $A + A = A$.

Table 8.2: Demonstration of how Boolean algebra will reduce the cutsets to the minimal cutsets from Fig. 8.2. Step 1: the two intermediate steps for which either will lead to the top event, i.e. IE-1 OR IE-2 with OR represented by a +. Step 2: expansion of the intermediate events. Step 3: expansion of IE-3. Step 4: BE1 BE2 + BE1 rewritten as BE1 + BE1 BE2. Step 5: BE1 + BE1 BE2 becomes BE1. (Based on [23].)

Step	Expression
1	IE-1 + IE-2
2	(BE1 BE2) + (BE1 + IE-3)
3	BE1 BE2 + BE1 + (BE3 BE4 BE5)
4	BE1 + BE1 BE2 + (BE3 BE4 BE5)
5	BE1 + BE3 BE4 BE5

probabilistic aspects should support these arguments and with good arguments and evidence, the frequencies and risk should largely then take care of themselves.

It is true to say that obtaining good quality data is not straightforward. Ideally, a site will keep its own source of reliability data from maintenance records and observations of plant failures and near misses. Site data should reflect the particular working environment and is therefore preferable to manufacturer's data for component reliability. The actual failure rate of equipment on a site will be a function of many things. Obviously, there is the inherent quality of the item's build, but this will then be influenced by many factors including the:

- Site's environmental conditions such as coastal, humidity, temperature, etc.;

- Age of the component;

- Radiation environment in which the component operates;

- Process conditions in which it operates and the demand rate on the system;

- Quality and frequency of the commissioning and maintenance, including the competence of the maintainers and operators;

- Overall safety culture on the site.

Maintenance data would ideally record the data on individual components, their type and manufacturer. Details of the failure mode and whether it was a revealed failure prompting the maintenance or an unrevealed failure being only identified on inspection or proof testing. From this information it is possible to determine the fraction of the component's failure modes that fail to danger, as this is of primary interest in the frequency assessment. In collating site information, component runtimes should be obtained to enable the failure rate to be determined.

Event data includes other incidents that may happen on a site that are different to maintenance findings. The event data may include the times whereby incoming power supplies to the site have been lost or the times that an operator has failed to adhere to a procedure. The events may also include accidents such as the drop of a radioactive package or a vehicle crash on the site. The event data is likely to be more prone to some uncertainty as to its completeness. Why is this?

Firstly, the event data is only as good as the reporting and this is a function of the safety culture on the site and the openness associated with reporting of incidents. It is inevitable that a number of events that should be reported are not reported as individuals do not want to admit to mistakes.

Secondly, incident data may not record the near misses. Sites do encourage the reporting of near misses, but quite often as nothing actually happened (well the end incident did not occur) it may be felt to be not worthy of reporting. We must remember that given enough near misses, one will eventually manifest itself into an accident so there should really be a focus on a reporting culture of near misses so that corrective action can be taken before it is too late.

If a site does not have data, then there are data sources available to be used in the public domain for electrical and mechanical failures. These may not be complete data sets for the events that need to be modelled and care must be taken in their use to ensure their relevance. Data must always be justified in any assessment.

8.5.1 Poisson statistics

As we have just described above, we may obtain data from the plants and this raw data will be useful for our frequency calculations. This data will be associated with events and failures of equipment and these may occur at random intervals during the plant's operation. It is found that these events often obey something known as a *Poisson distribution*, such that there is an underlying statistical pattern regarding the number of failures that we may expect to occur. As we have stated above, there is no great desire to devote much of this book to statistics, but a little knowledge of Poisson statistics is of great help in safety analysis. Barlow [24] provides a comprehensive and useful introduction to the use of statistics in the realm of physical sciences and is recommended to be consulted for more detail on a wide range of statistical analysis.

A Poisson distribution occurs when there are discrete random and independent events happening in a continuum. Flashes of lightning in a storm is an example as too is radioactive decay. For the former, the flashes are events in a continuum of a storm and for the latter, a radiation detector will either detect a particle (event) or it will not (continuum). Similarly, events on a plant will often follow a Poisson distribution and this can be helpful in predicting mean failure rates or mean event rates. The events may range from the breakdown of equipment to lost time accidents or even to releases of activity.

For a Poisson distribution, the probability of obtaining n events if the mean expected number is λ is given by

$$P(n; \lambda) = \frac{e^{-\lambda} \lambda^n}{n!}. \tag{8.15}$$

Famously, the validity and usefulness of Poisson statistics were born out by matching the calculated number of Prussian soldiers killed by being kicked by horses over a 20-

year period to the actual number killed (see [24]). The match between the two was close.

For our purposes, we will have data indicating a number of events or failures over a particular time period. What value should we then use? As an example, say that three failures of a piece of equipment occurred over 10 years. We may have been lucky and experienced fewer failures than the mean or have been unlucky and experienced more than the mean. It is the mean that we really want to use in our frequency calculation because it is the best-estimate value for the number of failures. We could calculate the mean directly from our limited data set, but how confident are we that we have the *true* mean? Moreover, what if we have no failures observed? Can we really be confident that the chance of the postulated event occurring is zero simply because we have not observed it yet? Of course not.

The more we move away from the true mean value, the less likely we would expect a value to be observed. If the true mean of our distribution is 10 events, we may expect to reasonably find event values between 8 and 12, but find it less likely to observe 2, 15, 30, 100, and so on. To overcome these difficulties, we utilise what is known as the *confidence interval*. The confidence interval is bounded by upper and lower *confidence limits* associated with the value of the confidence value we have chosen.

If we observe n values, then within what range would the mean have to lie to make our observation of n to be *unlikely*. We may define *unlikely* as any number we like, but typical values taken are 1%, 5%, 10% or even down to 40%. The converse of this is that we are defining a confidence of the range where the mean may lie; i.e. with our chosen values this equates to 99%, 95%, 90% or 60%. This is the purpose of the confidence interval. We note that the greater the confidence interval used, then the greater the spread of potential mean values. In simple terms, as the confidence interval increases the size of the net increases to capture more potential values.

It is possible to calculate iteratively and then tabulate values for the upper and lower confidence limits of the mean (N_+ and N_-) and these are shown in Table 8.3. Interestingly and of importance in safety assessment is that it is possible to calculate an upper mean value from zero observed failures. This answers the question we raised above.

In utilising Table 8.3, if we have n observed failures of equipment or events, we would select the appropriate upper confidence limit to determine the mean value N_+ to utilise based upon our data set. We must be clear that the value of N_+ is the upper limit of the range where we are x % confident that the mean lies, it does not mean we are x % confident that the mean is this number. Therefore, using the upper confidence limit with a high confidence interval may arguably be a little too conservative for frequency calculation and a best-estimate value for N_+ at 60% may be more appropriate.

Component failure data is presented in the form of the total number of component failures n in the total runtime T of all of the components. We would determine the N_+ value we wish to use corresponding to our chosen confidence interval. The frequency of component failure λ_c is then simply given by

$$\lambda_c = \frac{N_+}{T}.$$ (8.16)

Table 8.3: Upper and lower Poisson confidence limits. Data adapted from [24]. The confidence limits are for the unknown mean for n observed events, noting that if there are no observed events ($n = 0$), there can still be an upper value for the mean but no lower value (it can't be lower than zero). It is straightforward to calculate other upper confidence limits for $n = 0$ from Eq. 8.15. For example, for a confidence of 60%, the upper limit is 0.92.

	Upper N_+			Lower N_-		
	90%	95%	99%	90%	95%	99%
$n = 0$	2.30	3.00	4.61	-	-	-
$n = 1$	3.89	4.74	6.64	0.11	0.05	0.01
$n = 2$	5.32	6.30	8.41	0.53	0.36	0.15
$n = 3$	6.68	7.75	10.05	01.10	0.82	0.44

Example: Pump Failure Data
Imagine we have 15 pumps running on a plant and these have been running for the last five years. We have 75 years' operational data and, in this time, three have been observed to fail in service; i.e. $n = 3$.

We choose to use a 90% confidence level to determine the mean failure rate going forward, which from Table 8.3 is 6.68. Therefore, the rate of pump failure is, from Eq. 8.16, $\frac{6.68}{75}$ y^{-1} = 0.09 y^{-1}.

Example: Lost Time Accidents
Given that events occurring on a plant may follow Poisson statistics, we must be mindful of the rate of lost time accidents or fatalities. Hopefully on any given plant, they will number zero. This low rate should reflect the safety culture, the nature of the tasks, the training, the safety equipment available and so on. However, statistically, it would not be unreasonable for a serious accident to still occur with all things being equal without any underlying denigration of the safety culture and so on.

It may be found that the previous low rate of zero was fortuitous and an investigation should identify the failures responsible for a particular accident. There are, after all, statistics and real-life events and their impact on individuals.

8.5.2   Half-rule

Another approach adopted in safety case documents is to use the *half-rule*, which is based upon Bayesian techniques [25]. This is used when there have been no observed failures over a period of time and a failure rate is required to be estimated. The half-rule simply assumes one failure occurs tomorrow and the failure rate λ is given by

$$\lambda = \frac{1}{2T},$$ (8.17)

where T is the time period over which no failures have been found. Looking at Table 8.3, assuming one failure is broadly consistent with taking one failure at 60% confidence.

Example: Pipework Failure

Nuclear submarines undergo routine maintenance operations and the operations pose a risk to important pipework associated with the reactors. During the history of the submarine fleet, there have been no occurrences of maintenance lifting operations damaging the pipework such that there is a loss of coolant. With 200 years of maintenance history across the fleet (T), the half-rule gives a failure rate of $\frac{1}{400} = 2.5 \times 10^{-3} \, \text{y}^{-1}$.

Chapter 9

Safety Functions

The establishment of the *safety functions* that must be delivered by a plant is an important part in the development of the plant's design and determination of its mode of operation. The safety functions are key to ensuring a safe plant that will ultimately reduce risk to the public and workers to ALARP. In simple terms, safety functions are the safety-related roles that the equipment and operational procedures must provide.

In addition to engineering, the operators will be required to undertake certain tasks. These tasks themselves may be safety-related with the tasks having safety functions assigned to them. It is quite usual for an operator's task to require the use of a piece of engineering, either to receive information and/or to complete an action, each with its own specific safety function.

In the design of a plant, there is a natural life-cycle for the development of the safety functions. At the beginning of the design, at the concept design stage, detailed engineering may be unknown. There may simply be aspirations of what the engineering will be required to deliver. As the design matures, more detail is available and specific engineering and specific and named safety-related equipment comes into focus and is included in the design.

For the design process we can define different levels of safety functions corresponding to the different design stages for which we can refer to SFR Levels 1, 2 and 3. Thus, this chapter will also discuss this design life-cycle and the different expectations for the SFRs as the design develops.

The intent in defining SFRs in this chapter is to demonstrate a logical process that combines the design stages with the specification and evolution of the SFRs. This chapter aims to give a simple broad introduction to the subject. Individual licensees will develop their own methodologies for SFR development and they may do it in different ways to that presented here. Not all licensees formally develop SFRs in this manner.

It is important to stress that it is at the design stage that there is a unique ability to effectively utilise the safety hierarchy to design out hazards as far as reasonably practicable. The specification and implementation of SFRs can help in the designing out of hazards. Where SFRs have not been applied in a structured manner it can lead to problems developing in the latter stages of the design process. Robust safety

Table 9.1: Example structures, systems and components.

SSC	Examples
Structures	Building foundations
	Structural steelwork
	Cell bulk structures
	Shield walls
Systems	Gamma door interlock system
	Ventilation extract system
	High-temperature trip system
	Leak detection and alarm system
Components	Ventilation fan
	Gamma detector
	Alarm unit
	Contactor

arguments and the demonstration of ALARP can become difficult to make due to insufficient early design thought being given to the safety hierarchy.

Generically, once we have a detailed design or operational plant, we refer to the detailed engineered plant items delivering the safety functions as the sscs. Each ssc should align with a safety function. Table 9.1 provides examples of sscs, i.e. the structures or the systems or the components.

sscs can deliver their relevant safety functions during normal operations, fault conditions and accident conditions. It is important not to overlook the sscs associated with normal operations as these are important in ensuring a safe plant. After all, we seek, through good design and operation, to minimise the initiation of faults and subsequent reliance on safety measures. This chapter will therefore describe what is meant by normal and fault condition safety functions and how they might be written.

Safety functions are often written in a 'goal setting' way. The detailed specifics of the parameters that the safety function must deliver may not be included in the wording of the safety function. This becomes of importance when we have reached the latter stages of the design when we are clear on what the sscs delivering the safety function are and must do. Therefore, accompanying the safety function of an ssc is a *performance requirement*. The performance requirement will specify the detailed parameters associated with the safety function, such as trip levels, alarm points and assumptions on outage and reliability. The performance requirement may also describe the environmental properties in which the ssc will be required to operate, such as the humidity levels or magnitude of the seismic event.

An important part of defining the safety functions is their *categorisation* to determine how important they are. The safety functions will ultimately be delivered by sscs in one form or another and it must be determined how important these SSCs are in the delivery of the safety functions. This gives rise to the concept of the *classification* of the SSCs, which is discussed in this chapter.

9.1 Development of the Safety Functional Requirements

Section 3.2 described the basic broad design stages that a plant design will evolve through, noting that individual licensees may refer to different terminology and may include different or additional design stages. To recap, we may start with an early proposal for a plant for which an early high-level HAZOP 0 may be undertaken on the concept design. Following acceptance of this design, the securing of funding and the assembling of a project design team, a preliminary design will be progressed. HAZOP 1 may be undertaken on the preliminary design. This preliminary design should establish the broad outline of the plant and be sufficiently detailed that the principal plant items and layout are understood. Following the preliminary design, the detailed design will progress and this will enable the project to move forward to construction and manufacture of components. Again, we may expect HAZOP 2 to be undertaken on the detailed design before concluding that the design is complete.

We can equate three levels of SFR against these three broad levels of design, which we will call Levels 1, 2 and 3.

Level 1 SFR: High-level safety objectives of the plant that will be derived very early in the concept design phase. The Level 1 SFRs will help in the development of the early HMS.

Level 2 SFR: These are developed from the Level 1 SFRs and can be linked to preliminary fault groups developed from the HAZOP 1 studies of the PFDs for instance. They are, therefore, commensurate with a level of design detail that is available at the PSR stage.

Level 3 SFR: These specify the detailed safety functions for the SSCs that deliver the Level 2 SFRs. They would be developed from, for example, a HAZOP 2 study of the P+IDs. They are, therefore, commensurate with a level of design detail that is available at the PCSR stage. The detailed SSCs that deliver the Level 3 SFRs should be identified.

The level 1 SFRs will be set at a high level and these may seem to be intuitively obvious. However, as with most things in the nuclear industry, it is always advantageous to write things down. Writing things down provides evidence of thought process. If for no other reason, this will support the seeking of approval of whatever safety case is eventually produced. Nuclear safety committees and regulators are always keen to see that safety has been demonstrably considered from the start of the project.

During the development of the Level 2 SFRs, the safety assessor should be working closely with the designers and future operators. The safety solutions should seek to provide the optimum balance between operational flexibility and safety with the eventual chosen solution as high in the safety hierarchy as reasonably practicable. The Level 2 SFRs will focus on areas where a safety solution must be found.

By the time we get to the development of the Level 3 SFRs, we should know what the chosen design solution is. In particular, we will know the type of safety-related solution, e.g. a specific type of interlock or alarm. At this stage, the safety case will essentially be written in sufficient detail to support operations. The safety case is more than likely to designate the safety-related equipment as the licensee's naming convention requires. For example, SM is often used for important safety-related equipment.

The Level 3 SFRs would be expected to have a detailed set of performance requirements for the SSCs that deliver the safety functions. These may require input from the engineers and will include quantitative parameters associated with the operation of the SSCs. Performance requirements may include the numerical trip values, reliability values together with the conditions in which the SSCs operate.

By having a structured and organised development of the SFRs, there is a clear demonstration of the thought processes that have been undertaken through the design evolution. There should be a linkage between the SFR levels such that it is possible to follow the development of the design through the SFRs. As we've discussed, a modern approach to safety cases involves the use of CAE. In many respects, the hierarchy of SFRs facilitates the use of CAE, as the Level 3 SFRs and the SSCs will ultimately provide part of the supporting evidence that the Level 1 and 2 SFRs have been finally implemented within the design and ultimately within the plant.

It cannot be stressed enough through LFE that safety assessors must resist constraining early stages of the design by being overly prescriptive to the design solution. It may seem to be helpful specifying as a Level 2 SFR that the plant will require gamma interlocks with a pfd of 0.001 at the preliminary design stage. However, if this solution is carried forward, it may inhibit solutions that are higher in the safety hierarchy. The design may well end up with gamma interlocks, but we may also be able to design out the requirement for interlocks altogether or we may find different technology is more suitable. We should limit technological specifications at SFR Level 2.

Additionally, by seemingly being very prescriptive and detailed early on, we can give a false impression that the design is more mature than it actually is. There may still be many unknowns in how areas of the process will work. Their eventual solution may eventually render our detailed prescriptive solutions as being wasted effort. Give the designers the opportunity to design the plant as best they see fit with sufficient guidance from safety assessors.

As always, the best way to help describe the evolution of SFRs is via a worked example, which we will now proceed to do.

Example: Design of a Plant Handling High-Level Waste
A site wishes to design and build a new plant that will handle encapsulated solid high-active waste in containers. The nature of the *high-level waste* (HLW) is that it emits high levels of gamma radiation, but it does not contain fissile material and does not pose a criticality hazard. With the material being solid and encapsulated, there

is no significant hazard from the release of aerosol. Thus, the principal radiological hazard posed is solely due to external radiation.

Example Development of Level 1 sfrs

At the concept design stage, the HAZOP 0 may have been undertaken. This should identify external radiation as a significant hazard. Therefore, we would quickly establish the following Level 1 SFR:

Level 1 SFR: All waste containers must be behind shielding.

Again, it may be self-evident that shielding will be required, but the early HMS will be formally recording the need for shielding. The HMS will form an auditable 'hook' for the subsequent designers to consider shielding as the design progresses. The HMS may also record the need for some form of cooling of the containers. This is due to the large radiogenic heat that will be generated by the radiation and if the heat is not able to be dissipated, it could damage the container and give rise to a release. Thus, we specify:

Level 1 SFR: Sufficient cooling must be provided to ensure the integrity of the waste containers.

It may well be subsequently found that due to the encapsulated nature of the HLW, even if cooling was not provided, there may not be mechanisms for a loss of container integrity and/or significant/any release of activity. Operationally, however, it would be desirable to ensure containers are at an appropriate temperature. We might find that a forced cooling system is needed, but ideally a natural ventilation system would be used that does not require fans, electrical supplies and so on.

At this early stage, it is also important to record our basis of assessment of the nature of the waste within the containers, again as an SFR. Indeed, this is arguably the most important SFR as the passive nature of waste in the container eliminates a whole range of hazards. A plant that handles HLW in a liquid form is a significantly different plant to one that handles only solid material. It will have range of different hazards due to the mobile nature of the liquid and it will be required to have vessels and pipework connected to a vessel ventilation system with its abatement systems to clean-up discharges to the atmosphere. The most obvious fault associated with handling liquid material is a loss of primary containment through the failure of pipes or vessels. Thus, for our solid encapsulated plant, we can write:

Level 1 SFR: All waste received in the plant must be solid and encapsulated within containers.

There may be a number of other important SFRs that the initial hazard analysis will identify, but we will leave our example with the three above.

Example Development of Level 2 sfrs

Time passes and the project design evolves. We have moved on to the preliminary design phase, where we have now developed, in outline, the principal plant and process areas. The plant may consist of container-handling areas, storage areas, maintenance areas, transfer areas, contamination and surveying areas and so on. The containers will also be imported and exported from the plant in shielded flasks. At this stage, there may still be fluidity in design aspects.

Some aspects of the plant design may even be 'boxed off' with the design work occurring in the next design phase, perhaps due to the need for outstanding R+D to be included.

For this example, we will solely focus on developing the SFRs for the shielding and we will leave it as an exercise to the reader to develop SFRs for the cooling SFR. Keeping to the spirit of the Level 1 SFR for shielding, the waste containers will need to be behind shielding at all times. Thus, with the increased detail available, we can specify all process areas where containers will be present:

Level 2 SFR: Storage Area bulk shielding

Level 2 SFR: Contamination and Survey Area bulk shielding

Level 2 SFR: Maintenance Cell bulk shielding

Level 2 SFR: Et cetera.

We have now also conducted HAZOP 1s at this project stage and we now know that there are potential hazards associated with the movement of containers and the potential for a loss of the bulk shielding. This is because there are operational requirements to import and export the containers. Additionally, periodic maintenance of the mechanical handling systems will be required. The unfortunate effect of these necessary operational and maintenance activities is to put 'holes' into the bulk shielding or require parts of the shielding to be periodically moved from position. Therefore, instead of a passive set of walls, there are walls and doors and hatches and so on.

The design must find a way of ensuring that operators cannot be exposed to radiation shine paths, for instance when a container is initially imported into the plant. Thus, overall shielding must be maintained even when one part of the shielding is moved aside or opened. Typical solutions involve the use of shielding labyrinth entry arrangements or the use of inner/outer shield doors or gamma gates.

Let us look at the import of a container into the process plant via the Posting Cell. The container will enter into the plant in a shielded flask. The flask will mate with the cell's posting port (a gamma gate) to enable the container to be withdrawn from the flask to the Posting Cell. Export of containers will follow the reverse of this route.

The mating arrangement is such that the container will be shielded at all times by the combination of the flask, the posting port and the Posting Cell's bulk shielding. The HAZOP has subsequently identified radiation hazards associated with the posting operation that could lead to a loss of shielding and exposure of operators to high radiation levels, specifically:

1. On export, the loaded flask is withdrawn without its shielded lid being closed, or

2. The full or empty flask is withdrawn without the Posting Cell posting port shield door being closed.

Should item 1 above occur, an operator could be exposed to an unshielded waste container due to the flask's integral shielded lid being open. Should item 2 occur, an operator could be exposed to the contents of the Posting Cell, which could contain a number of waste containers awaiting export or movement through the process. We clearly need to protect against these faults and we write:

Level 2 SFR: Sufficient means must be provided to prevent the movement of a flask from the Posting Cell posting port without the flask lid being closed.

Level 2 SFR: Sufficient means must be provided to prevent the movement of a flask from the Posting Cell posting port without the posting port being closed.

At this stage we have not defined interlock arrangements nor pfds. The designers will work with the safety assessors to produce the optimum solution.

There are also operational and maintenance reasons for operators to periodically enter the Maintenance Cell. The Maintenance Cell will feature an outer shield door and an inner shield door to form a shielding 'airlock'-type arrangement. Entry into the cell can be undertaken with the outer door open when the inner door is closed and the cell is free from containers. The inner shield door can only be opened when the outer door is closed (and hence operators no longer present in the cell).

The HAZOP has subsequently identified radiation hazards associated with the cell entry operation that could lead to a loss of shielding and exposure of operators to high radiation levels, specifically:

1. The outer shield door being opened when a container is in the cell, or

2. The outer shield door being opened when the inner shield door is open, or

3. The inner shield door being opened when the outer shield door is open, or

4. The operator is trapped in the cell when the inner door opens (the outer door being closed).

We clearly need to protect against these and we write:

Level 2 SFR: Sufficient means must be provided to prevent the opening of the outer shield door into the Maintenance Cell when a container is in the Maintenance Cell.

Level 2 SFR: Sufficient means must be provided to prevent the opening of the outer shield door into the Maintenance Cell if the inner shield door is open.

Level 2 SFR: Sufficient means must be provided to prevent the opening of the inner shield door to the Maintenance Cell if the outer shield door is open.

Level 2 SFR: Sufficient means must be provided to prevent the operator being trapped in the Maintenance Cell with the outer door closed.

Let us remember, whilst we are confident that shielding will be provided around the Maintenance Cell, we may not be clear on the technology that will be used to prevent the opening of the shield door or introduction of a container once the shield door is open. At this stage of the design, we know something must be provided to protect the workers and we specify this. Also, at this relatively early stage of the design, we do not need to know how reliable the equipment will be in delivering the SFRs as we are not expecting to formally demonstrate compliance with risk targets and so on.

Example Development of Level 3 SFRs

The design has now moved on from the preliminary design phase into the detailed design phase. Again, we have conducted HAZOP 2 and have established a wide range of detailed faults that may compromise the integrity of the shielding such as maloperation of the shield door opening sequence or errors in tracking or detecting containers. We now know the technology that will be used to prevent entry into the Maintenance Cell when a container is present and some of this technology may have been presented on the P+IDs that were subject to HAZOP.

We have established the appropriate technology through discussion with the engineers and the operators. We will assume that at this stage of the safety case, the site licensee has chosen to refer to important safety-related system equipment as *Safety Mechanism*:

SM:	Outer Maintenance Cell shield door gamma interlock system 1
Safety function:	To prevent access to the Maintenance Cell when there are high radiation levels in the Maintenance Cell.

We have now also undertaken DBA and PSA and concluded that a second independent interlock system is required.

SM:	Outer Maintenance Cell shield door gamma interlock system 2
Safety function:	To prevent access to the Maintenance Cell when there are high radiation levels in the Maintenance Cell.

Alternative technology was discussed in the design process, but was deemed to be unsuitable for the interlock systems (this should be documented to support the ALARP justification). An interlock based upon a load cell on the crane was considered, but rejected. This would have isolated the outer shield door if a container was held by the crane. However, there were situations whereby the container was not always held by the crane. Thus, the gamma interlock was the only system that could always detect the presence of the container. Moreover, should the inner shield door be open, for which other containers would then be exposed, the crane interlock would not provide protection, but the gamma interlock system would provide protection.

On the last point, we note that it is preferable to utilise a safety measure that can protect against multiple combinations of scenarios, rather than having to use lots of different safety measures to cover the different scenarios. In our example, the gamma interlock will provide protection irrespective of where the container is situated. The load cell interlock on the crane would have to be supplemented by another protection system to cover the time periods when a container is not suspended by the crane or when the inner shield door is open. Thus, this could require an additional two or three different protection systems. This will increase the maintenance requirements and cost and dose burden to the operators. Each maintenance event may require entry to the same cell, thus posing additional risk should a fault arise. Thus, it is advantageous to consolidate the protection claimed.

Conversely, relying on two gamma interlock systems does present problems in demonstrating independence and the potential for CCF. The two systems can be fully independent and have entirely separate detection, logic and termination points. They can also be physically segregated in the cell as far as practicable with logic cabinets situated in different rooms for instance. Their proof testing can be staggered and undertaken by different maintenance teams. These factors will all help to reduce, but not eliminate the potential for CCF.

When the outer shield door is successfully opened, operators may enter the Maintenance Cell. Following HAZOP 2, we now know that the only way for radiation levels to suddenly increase is if the inner shield door is erroneously opened enabling exposure to an unshielded area beyond, or the introduction of a container. The gamma interlock systems will now not protect us. Thus, to provide protection, an option is for the inner shield door's drive motor to be isolated on the opening of the outer shield door. Again, DBA and PSA lead to the requirement for two independent interlocks, i.e.

SM:	Inner Maintenance Cell inner and outer shield door interlock system 1
Safety function:	To prevent the opening of the inner shield door when the outer shield door is open.
SM:	Inner Maintenance Cell inner and outer shield door interlock system 2
Safety function:	To prevent the opening of the inner shield door when the outer shield door is open.

Again, alternative technology may have been discussed in the design process. Indeed, it would obviously be preferable if the design could do away with the need for entry into the Maintenance Cell. However, designing lifting equipment that would not require periodic maintenance may not be reasonably practicable. It was also found that designs that could deterministically remove the potential for containers and operators to be simultaneously in the cell at the same time were not feasible.

The design will also incorporate systems to prevent operators from becoming trapped in a cell. This may involve the use of key exchange systems, windows to enable operators to see what is going on in the cell, crash-out doors or a combination of all of these. In summary:

- The gamma interlock systems will prevent the outer shield door from being opened if there is a high radiation level in the Maintenance Cell, which could be due to either a container being present or the inner shield door being open.

The design incorporates two of these interlocks that are independent, but there is a need to consider CCF;

- The inner and outer shield door interlock system will prevent the inner shield door from opening if the outer shield door is open. Again, there are two of these interlocks that are independent with a need to consider CCF;

- Systems will be incorporated to prevent operators from being trapped in the cell between the shield doors.

If we map the SFRs, we may find that we have missed something. We started with the Level 1 SFR requiring containers to be shielded. The Level 2 SFRs specify the bulk shielding and the means to prevent a loss of bulk shielding occurring during entry to the cell. The Level 3 SFRs, so far, have only specified the shield door interlock systems. We seem to have lost the *bulk shielding aspect* itself, which normally provides the shielding day-to-day, minute-to-minute, and so on.

Additionally, safety measures should ideally operate in low-demand mode; i.e. they should provide protection in the background and rarely, if ever, be used for real. The normal means of access to the cell, *the control system*, should also be considered and it is the failure of this that initiates the fault. We therefore need to understand how these aspects relate to the Level 3 SFRs.

Thus, we need to be clear in distinguishing between:

1. The SSCs that routinely and normally deliver safety through their correct operation on a continuous basis;

2. The SSCs that provide normal control; and

3. The SSCs that solely provide protection following an initiating fault.

We state here that the SSCs that deliver functions 1 and 2 above have normal safety functions and may be considered to be *duty systems*. The SSCs that deliver function 3 are the safety measures and have a safety function associated with a fault condition. If we take a duty control system away, the process will not work. If we take a safety system away, the process will work, but there will be no protection should a fault arise. For our example, we identify the following bulk shielding SFs.

SF:	Maintenance Cell bulk shielding
Safety function:	To minimise external radiation levels in out-cell areas.
SF:	Maintenance Cell outer shield door
Safety function:	To minimise external radiation levels in out-cell areas.
SF:	Maintenance Cell inner shield door
Safety function:	To minimise external radiation levels in out-cell areas and in the Maintenance Cell.

For the control system that we call a DUTY system we have:

DUTY:	Maintenance Cell access control system
Safety function:	To operate reliably and minimise the potential for spurious operation.

9.2 Critical safety functions

The worked example above shows the development of the SFRs for an HLW plant. Essentially, the example SFRs refer to the provision of:

- Shielding;

- Temperature control;

- Containment.

The SFRs were worded in a tailored manner for the type of HLW plant considered. Fundamentally, however, the SFRs broadly align with three of the four *critical safety functions* (CSFs) often utilised in the global nuclear industry, particularly for reactors. The CSFs refer to:

CSF-1:   Control of reactivity (i.e. fission reactions);

CSF-2:   Removal of heat from the core;

CSF-3:   Control of direct radiation;

CSF-4:   Confinement of radioactive material.

Some licensees will take the CSFs as defined above without further development and assign them as the default Level 1 SFRs. From these Level 1 SFRs will develop the lower level SFRs. When constructing a safety case, it is always necessary to defer to the licensee's particular approach to the development of the SFRs and whether or not their starting point is the CSFs as defined above.

9.3 Categorisation and classification

In developing a safety case, the safety functions will be defined. Broadly, the safety functions will fill a particular gap whereby 'something' must be provided to ensure that there is no compromise in the four CSFs as discussed above. However, some safety functions are more important than others and this may be true in considering the difference between reactor plants and plants handling LLW. Therefore, a fault might progress to give rise to a significant consequence and the safety function that protects against this fault will be very important. The converse of this is also true.

It is necessary for a safety case to understand which safety functions are more important than others as this will ensure that a proportionate safety case is constructed and subject to appropriate due process. Ultimately, the safety functions will be delivered by SSCs within the plant. The importance attached to each SSC and its delivery of the safety function is important, as this will determine how much effort is required in terms of design justification and substantiation (see Section 10), maintenance, testing and inspection. The importance may also help to define the outage requirements, i.e. whether the plant can or cannot continue to run in the absence of the SSC (see Section 7.2).

The importance of the safety function, or the contribution that it makes to safety, is rated with a categorisation scheme, i.e. the *categorisation of the safety function*. A related exercise is the *classification of the ssc* that delivers the categorised safety function. The categorisation and classification processes are sometimes confused.

A licensee may define their safety function categories in any manner that they wish to within the bounds of relevant industry practice and regulator expectation. Three categories are often used, which are defined along the lines of:

Category A: A safety function that plays a principal role;

Category B: A safety function that plays a significant role;

Category C: A safety function that play a minor role.

The definition of 'principal', 'significant' and 'minor' will be up to the site licensee and they may be based upon the range of unmitigated consequences from their relevant site's hazards. Therefore, what may be defined as providing a 'principal' role on one site may barely be classed as a 'minor' role on another. There is scope for a considerable degree of interpretation between different sites in the schemes defining the categorisation of the safety functions. There is nothing wrong with this providing there is always a proportionate approach.

Similarly, the classification of the sscs delivering the safety function is based upon schemes derived by the site licensees. An illustrative approach is given below.

Class 1   sscs that provide a principal means of fulfilling a Category A safety function;

Class 2   sscs that provide a significant contribution to fulfilling a Category A safety function or the principal means of fulling a Category B safety function;

Class 3   sscs that contribute to a Category C safety function.

On reactor sites the faults are generally significant and if unmitigated, may give rise to societal consequences. The reactor protection systems may therefore be Class 1 sscs to protect against a range of reactor-based faults. However, on non-reactor sites, the unmitigated consequences may be less severe (certainly for the public) and Class 1 sscs are often only attributed to sscs that provide significant normal safety functions for which great credit must be taken in their integrity. A failure of such an ssc may give rise to an immediate significant consequence for which there is no practicable protection. Consequently, the likelihood of their failure to deliver the safety function must be shown to be not credible or at least of negligible frequency. Examples of sscs and their classification delivering safety functions are given in Table 9.2.

Table 9.2: Example sscs and their classification delivering Category A safety functions. For the shield wall and glovebox, a single failure of these sscs will lead to significant consequences in a very short time. For the vessel containing fissile liquor, the principal claim is on the safe-by-shape nature of the vessel. The neutron poison insert must also fail and this provides a significant, independent, diverse but supplemental role in delivering the overall safety function to ensure that the liquor is sub-critical. Some licensee methodologies may enable the classification of the vessel to be reduced to 2 because no single failure will give rise to a criticality.

Safety function	SSC	Class.
To shield HLW containers	Shield wall	1
To contain plutonium activity	Glovebox	1
To prevent criticality	Safe-by-shape vessel	1 / 2
	Neutron poison insert	2

Example: Reactor Protection
A reactor will have a control system but there are a range of faults that can give rise to a significant release of activity. These faults may be failures of the control system or they may be due to mechanical failures of the cooling systems, for instance. The unmitigated consequences from a reactor failure are significant and may give rise to societal consequences, i.e. consequences that may affect hundreds or thousands of people and lead to the evacuation of large areas of land.

To protect against the faults, a Category A safety function is required to be delivered. The reactor protection system provides this protection and is the principal means of achieving the Category A safety function. It is, therefore, defined as a Class 1 ssc. In order to satisfy DBA and to achieve the risk targets, a second safety system is required. This will be independent of the first safety system and will be diverse. It will also implement the Category A safety function, but being the secondary protection system, it is defined as a Class 2 ssc.

Example: Waste Management Plant
Highly radioactive containers are stored in a cell that comprises robust concrete walls to provide shielding. Without the shielding, the dose rates in the accessible areas would be $\gg$Sv h^{-1}. Therefore, the shield wall provides a normal safety function and 'in the absence of the wall' operator doses over a working year would be $\gg$1 Sv or even > 1 Sv in a few minutes. There is, therefore, a Category A safety function to ensure operational doses are <20 mSv (the BSL(LL)). In this example, the wall is the principal (and only) means of delivering this safety function and is a Class 1 ssc.

Chapter 10

Engineering Substantiation

We have examined how the safety case considers the hazards and faults and determines the risk posed to the public and workforce. The risk is mitigated by the design and mode of operation of the plant and the mixture of engineered features, safety measures and operational practices. Thus, to achieve an adequate level of safety, the safety case will rely upon engineering to deliver specified safety functions as we have already defined in Section 9. Collectively, these engineering aspects are known as the SSCs.

The SSCs may deliver a combination of normal, fault and accident condition safety functions. As we also note, operational practices are important to safety and the 'human factors' aspect is discussed in Section 11. These operational practices that contribute to safety may also require engineering to provide indicators or alarms to inform the operators that something safety-related has to be performed. There may then be a piece of equipment that the operator has to utilise to terminate the fault. The equipment used by the operator will have its own safety function.

When a safety case is constructed, it will be fruitless to make claims on SSCs if they are not capable of delivering the safety functions demanded of them. It may be that with the current state of the plant, the engineering cannot deliver the demanded safety functions, but with modification or repair it could. If these are identified, recommendations for improvement may be made. It may also be identified that the engineering simply cannot conceivably deliver the specified safety function. In this case, the safety assessment has incorrectly specified the safety functions, and it is the safety assessment that should change and not the engineering. Ideally, the safety assessors work with the engineers to ensure that the appropriate engineering is claimed, but this is not always practicable.

In addition to the safety functions, the engineering must deliver the required reliability. There must be sufficient confidence that the engineering will deliver the safety function when a safety claim is made upon it. The substantiation of the reliability may directly underpin the frequency calculations described in Section 8 and it becomes the role of engineering substantiation to provide the confidence. *Engineering substantiation* is the process by which the delivery of safety functions, at an appropriate reliability, can be assured. Once an ssc has successfully been through substantiation, the ssc is *substantiated*. Substantiation must be undertaken in a proportionate manner in which the most significant safety claims (such as in terms of integrity or reliability and risk mitigation) require the greatest degree and robustness of argument and evidence. The ssc's importance to safety can be ascertained from its classification. CAE is increasingly used explicitly in formulating safety case documents including engineering substantiation. In this context, CAE may be formulated along the lines:

Claim: The safety function, performance requirement and classification;

Argument: The written rationale of why the ssc will do as required, including its mode of operation, operating environment, challenge posed by the fault, etc.;

Evidence: The detailed calculations, design codes and standards utilised in the ssc's fabrication and installation, maintenance history and so on.

The sscs and their safety functions are collated and included in a bridging document known as the *engineering schedule* and this forms the link between the safety analysis and the engineering. The engineering schedule is discussed in this chapter. This chapter will introduce the terms *desktop*, *reconciliation* and *walkdown*, which are all important components of undertaking substantiation. Engineering substantiation also goes together with a *comparison with modern standards* and RGP and this is discussed in this chapter. Engineering substantiation may lead to the identification of *shortfalls* or *observations* and recommendations for improvement may be made.

We start this chapter with a brief discussion of the *engineering safety principles* (ESPs), as these should guide all aspects of engineering substantiation.

10.1   Engineering safety principles

It is not uncommon for licensees to write their own suite of ESPs. The ESPs should aim to distil the key principles, RGP and approach to design and safety that the licensee wishes to promote to the engineering and safety disciplines. Sometimes the ESP term is amalgamated with the word 'design' and/or 'safety' to give different combinations along the lines of *design safety principles* or *engineering design and safety principles*. Generally, the development of the ESPs is the preserve of the design side of an organisation rather than the safety case side.

As an example, the ESPs may outline how equipment is expected to behave, such as to fail-safe rather than to fail to danger. This may seem obvious, but can be forgotten, particularly if there are multiple modifications over time and the original design team has long since departed—the original design intent can become quickly forgotten. Additionally, the ESPs may specify how inherently safe processes should be developed that do not require active management to ensure safety and negates the need for safety measures to be used to deliver safety. This is an ideal that cannot always be met, but it should be a guiding principle especially in any design process. In a document, the ESPs may be written in a manner that may look like the following (the numbers used are arbitrary):

ESP 15:   **Fail to safety**—The plant with the potential to affect safety should be designed to be inherently safe or to fail in a safe manner.

ESP 23:   **Minimise claims on human actions**—Reliance on humans to ensure the safety of the plant should be minimised by design.

ESP 36:   **Testing and commissioning**—Appropriate testing and commissioning will be undertaken to confirm that the plant and equipment within it can deliver its safety functions.

The ESPs can be used as a guide for those involved in the design of new plant, process and equipment. The ESPs should ideally be met as far as reasonably practicable for new plant, process and equipment. The ESPs can also be used as a benchmark for the review of existing equipment during a periodic review of a safety case and the substantiation of the SSCs. The use of the ESPs is particularly useful if there are no modern standards design codes to refer to, i.e. if the equipment is novel or unique to a particular plant or process.

10.2   The substantiation process: an overview

Safety cases are written for the full life-cycle of nuclear plants, e.g. from early concept through to detailed design, inactive and active commissioning, operation and eventually decommissioning (these stages were discussed in Section 3). An appropriate level of substantiation should be undertaken for each life-cycle stage. Strictly, we may refer to *engineering justification* for the substantiation undertaken at the design stages before the SSC is installed. This is to justify to ourselves that when installed, the SSCs' designs will be adequate. A *design justification report* (DJR) will often be the vehicle for providing the demonstration or justification.

For an existing plant, the SSCs already exist and engineers may have the luxury of seeing the item in action with a full operational and maintenance history. An *engineering substantiation report* (ESR) is produced to provide this demonstration or substantiation. In this chapter we will discuss how DJRs and ESRs may be constructed. Whether we use the term *justification* or *substantiation* is really semantics.

Substantiation of existing equipment is undertaken in conjunction with a comparison of the design with modern standards and RGP. Substantiation and the comparison with modern standards are occasionally mistakenly confused. An SSC on a plant should not fail substantiation simply because it does not align to modern standards. It is normally the expectation that new equipment would be installed onto a plant that aligns with modern standards. The DJR will be required to demonstrate that the standards chosen for the design of the SSC are relevant and represent modern standards and if not, the good reason for not adopting these. This is a key component in the demonstration of ALARP.

Substantiation is undertaken by engineers as opposed to safety assessors. The substantiation process will be led by a lead engineer who will call upon individual discipline engineers with the specific knowledge of the types of engineered systems to be substantiated. For example, claims on the building structure will be substantiated by civil engineers and claims on gamma interlocks by c+i engineers. Process engineers may be required to support the c+i engineers by determining the relevant process parameters and instrumentation associated with the system.

The use of discipline engineers is important because substantiation must be undertaken by personnel who are demonstrably *suitably qualified and experienced persons* (sqeps). More often than not this requires education in the discipline and working experience of the particular engineering discipline. In contrast, safety assessors generally come from a more mixed background, typically from physics, environmental studies, mathematics as well as engineering (process and mechanical). Therefore, generally, safety assessors often know little formal engineering, but should be able to defer to expert engineers.

There are a number of similarities between engineering substantiation (of existing plant) and engineering justification (of new plant), but there are a number of crucial differences. The most significant and obvious is that an existing plant exists, has operational and maintenance history and can be inspected, whilst a new plant will initially exist only on paper. We will consider the substantiation of an existing plant before moving onto the design process. However, before we can consider the substantiation process, we must know what we need to substantiate, i.e. what claims have been made on the engineering. Claims on engineering are collated from the safety assessments into an engineering schedule and the development of this schedule is the next item to be discussed in this chapter.

Each ssc and its safety function developed from the safety analysis must be agreed upon with the engineers. This is an important step in the safety case process and is known as *engineering reconciliation*. In simple terms, reconciliation involves the engineers agreeing to the wording of the sscs, their safety functions and performance requirements such that they understand what is being asked of the engineering and that the wording allows them to substantiate it (or at least attempt to). We can state that engineering substantiation essentially consists of a multi-step process:

1. Develop the engineering schedule by producing the underpinning safety (and potentially other discipline) assessments;

2. Commence engineering reconciliation of the claims in the engineering schedule with the engineers who will do the substantiation;

3. Substantiate the engineering claims and complete reconciliation by taking on board the output of the substantiation process;

4. Make and agree recommendations for improvement and any additional safety analysis or substantiation.

10.3   Development of the engineering schedule

The engineering schedule is an important document that links the hazard analysis part of a safety case to the engineering substantiation part. It is the bridge between the two components. Fundamentally, it is one of the principal outputs of the hazard analysis, as it provides the details of the sscs that are important to safety. From an engineering perspective, it is the list of sscs that requires substantiation. To a large degree, the quality of the engineering substantiation and its completeness is dependent upon the quality and completeness of the engineering schedule.

The engineering schedule may also take input from environmental assessments. In this case the sscs are those that are required to ensure the minimisation of discharges (and resultant doses) off-site. Environmental assessment is beyond the scope of this book, but we note that sscs may share common radiological and environmental functions. This occurs in ventilation systems, where the abatement components have joint radiological and environmental functions to minimise the release of activity through the extract system to the atmosphere. This abatement role may occur in both normal conditions and fault conditions.

The development of the engineering schedule is a key milestone in the delivery of a safety case project. In practice, the engineering schedule is an evolving document that is populated and updated as the supporting hazard analysis develops and is finalised. In addition, the schedule takes input from the substantiation process and can provide the reference links to where each of the sscs has been substantiated. The engineering schedule is required for both an operational safety case and also the later stages of the design phase such as for a pcsr.

We should note at this point that it is entirely possible that the sscs cannot be substantiated, which is sometimes a feature of safety case assessments of older plants (and regrettably even of modern ones). Where an ssc cannot be substantiated, an engineering shortfall may be raised. The engineering schedule can note this shortfall against the appropriate ssc entry. This will then provide a consolidated listing of all of the plant's sscs and their substantiation status. How this shortfall is resolved is discussed later in this chapter.

10.3.1 Format of an engineering schedule

A site licensee can decide exactly what is wanted in the schedule for their plants, but there should be common elements in all engineering schedules. A tabular format is used, which is compiled into a formal issue document. The document as a whole may contain information on why the engineering schedule has been produced. For example, the engineering schedule could be for the whole of the plant and may be generated at the design stage or during a safety case review. A more limited engineering schedule may also be produced for a discrete project that is to introduce new equipment onto the plant. In this case, at a determined time, the project engineering schedule may be amalgamated with the overall plant engineering schedule.

The engineering schedule should provide a clear list of references to the source documents (e.g. the hazard analysis), including revision status. Thus, there is an auditable link between where the safety functions have been derived, their listing in the engineering schedule and ultimately a link to the relevant substantiation document.

The engineering schedule, being a formal referenceable document, should have a document reference number and revision status, title and be subject to an appropriate level of qa and approval. The qa process should check that all of the relevant source documents have been used and the sscs have been correctly extracted and included on the schedule. If suitable quality control is not used, it is possible that entries may be missed and that the sscs not be substantiated, or be substantiated to an incorrect classification.

By consolidating all of the sscs into one engineering schedule, the process of producing the PMS is simplified. The PMS is concerned with ensuring that all sscs that are claimed in the safety case are adequately maintained and proof tested in line with the claims made in the safety case (e.g. annual functional proof tests).

> LFE: *Engineering Schedule Resource*
>
> In producing the engineering schedule, we can make an important LFE observation. The collation of the engineering schedule can be a significant undertaking for a large project with potentially hundreds of sscs. The collation and upkeep of the schedule requires an active involvement of dedicated resource and can be a full-time role for a period of time during the project's lifetime. It is a good role for a more junior member of a project team as it will give them exposure to both hazard analysis and engineering substantiation reports. A suitable level of senior oversight and checking must, of course, be provided.

An extract from an example engineering schedule is given in Table 10.1. In our example, we have placed the safety function first with its performance requirement and the safety function category. The ssc that delivers the safety function is then given with its classification.

> *Example: Usefulness of the Engineering Schedule*
>
> By its very nature, the engineering schedule becomes a central repository for all of the sscs, their safety functions and performance requirements. For larger plants, there may be common types of ssc in a number of areas of the plant, such as shield walls or alarm systems or interlocks.
>
> In a safety case, there may be numerous underpinning hazard analysis documents written by a number of assessors, not necessarily co-located or working for the same company. They may make claims on either the exact same ssc or a common type of ssc. Without good communication, it is inevitable that the common names of sscs and the description of the safety functions derived by different assessors will be written differently.
>
> For example, let us consider an area gamma alarm. We might find that:
>
> **Assessor 1 writes:**   Gamma monitor and alarm. *Safety function: To mitigate the dose to operators.*
>
> **Assessor 2 writes:**   Area gamma alarm. *Safety function: To alert operators to high gamma radiation levels.*
>
> **Assessor 3 writes:**   Activity-in-air alarm. *Safety function: To alert operators to high radiation levels.*
>
> Here we do not concern ourselves with which is the better name or the better safety

function. We do concern ourselves that Assessor 3 has, either through carelessness or ignorance, not understood the difference between an *area gamma alarm* monitoring radiation levels and an *activity-in-air alarm* monitoring for suspended radioactive particles in the air. What we concern ourselves with is, wherever practicable, common names and safety functions should be used for the same type of equipment on the same plant (and possibly across a whole multi-plant site). Why should we do this?

- Firstly, it will reduce the size of the engineering schedule, because we will not have different entries of safety functions against the same ssc that all essentially mean the same thing. We can simply list the item once and give multiple sources for where it was claimed.

- Secondly, the subsequent substantiation reports will just need to refer to a single common entry. Again, this will simplify these documents and reduce the error potential.

- Thirdly, it will give a positive impression to stakeholders that the safety case is being managed and someone is taking an interest in ensuring the totality of the case hangs together. (It is always advisable to give a positive impression to the stakeholders.)

- Finally, the safety function is likely to be transcribed onto plant documentation (including the PMS) that will be used by operators. Simplification of their documentation is crucial and unnecessary duplication or differences should be avoided.

Whatever be the chosen name for the ssc and its safety function, it will be required to be reconciled with the requirements of the plant operators and the engineers. Plant operators may have their own way of how they like sscs to be described. They are the user of the safety case documents and also the ultimate customer of the work produced by the chosen contractor. It is usually wise to accommodate their preferences. In our example above we will consolidate the name of the gamma alarm in the engineering schedule and cascade it to all of the safety assessors working on the project. Thus, we will use the wording as written by Assessor 2:

Chosen Wording: Area gamma alarm. *Safety function: To alert operators to high gamma radiation levels.*

(Remembering that in our definitions, it is the performance requirement that will specify the alarm level and how and where the alarm annunciates and not the safety function.)

Table 10.1: Example entries on an engineering schedule. The entries within a schedule can be ordered to ensure that all mechanical or civil structure sscs, for example, are grouped for ease of use. Additional information typically included in an engineering schedule would be the relevant hazard assessment reference, equipment identifiers, ssc reference, substantiation reference and engineering discipline responsible for the ssc's substantiation.

Safety function	Cat.	Performance requirement	SSC	Class.
To maintain primary containment	A	Tank to have a volume of 100 m^3 Liquor contained to be nitric acid based	Feed stock tank	1
To prevent access to the Maintenance Cell when there are high gamma radiation levels in the cell	A	Gamma detector trip level at 0.5 mSv h^{-1} To have a pfd of 0.001 or better	Gamma interlock system 1	1
		Gamma detector trip level at 0.5 mSv h^{-1} To have a pfd of 0.01 or better	Gamma interlock system 2	2
To alert operators to high airborne alpha activity	C	To provide visual and audible local alarm and relay alarm to the control room Alarm levels and alarm location to be in accordance with the requirements of the RPA	Activity-in-air alarm	3
To minimise external radiation levels in the areas where operators have access	A	Maximum dose rate in the corridor of 7.5 μSv h^{-1} To withstand the design basis earthquake of 0.25 g To provide five hours' fire-resistance	Maintenance Cell bulk cell structure	1

10.3.2 Systemisation

Let us remind ourselves that ssc stands for structure, system or component, but to what level should we populate the engineering schedule? By way of an example, a gamma interlock system can be broken down into a number of components, i.e.

- A radiation detector;

- Wires from the detector to a logic circuit;

- Relays in the logic circuit;

- Wires from the logic circuit to the locking arrangement;

- The locking arrangement.

Indeed, each of the mentioned above could be broken down into smaller components and then broken down even further. If we take this approach and are not careful, it will uncontrollably expand the size of the engineering schedule and make the assigning of safety functions to individual components difficult or even meaningless. What exactly is the safety function of a wire? We should, as far as practicable, assign entries onto the engineering schedule at a system level, a process sometimes known as *systemisation* and this process works well for safety measures where we have the three components of detection, logic and termination and we can conduct end-to-end testing of the safety function. Correspondingly, we should assign the gamma interlock system to the engineering schedule rather than the breakdown of the above components.

This systemisation approach does not work well for all systems where there may be different safety functions assigned to individual components within the system. This is notable for ventilation systems, which may have the following principal components:

- Ductwork;

- Extract fan(s);

- Filter(s);

- Stack.

Overall, the role of the ventilation system may be to ensure a cascade of airflow from low contamination potential areas to ones of high contamination potential and also to provide a filtered discharge to the environment. Therefore, we can see several different components in the overall system that we can realistically assign different safety functions to. The mechanical components (fans and filters) can also be tested individually. For instance:

- Ductwork is there to 'direct and contain' the extract flow;

- Extract fans are there 'to provide the motive force';

- Filters are there 'to minimise the discharge of activity to the atmosphere';

- Stacks are there 'to provide authorised discharge points'.

Consultation with the engineers and plant operators/maintainers who will be responsible for managing the implementation of the safety case can be invaluable to the degree of systemisation to be adopted.

It may also be found that in order to substantiate a system, more than one discipline of engineer will be required. The process discipline has an input into alarm and trip levels and supports c+i engineers. This may lead to the production of *system* ESRs rather than solely mechanical or c+i ESRs.

LFE: *Making Life Simple*

There have been many attempts to simplify the transfer of information from one document to another in the industry. Electronic databases have been tried in some areas with hyperlinking and so on, and in principle, this ensures that consistent terms are used for the same ssc. Any changes to the name of an ssc or safety function can be instantly cascaded to all affected parts.

If unconnected documents are produced, it is essential to facilitate the easy transfer of information. This transfer will include the documents that originate the claims on the engineering (be it safety or environmental, etc.), to the engineering schedule and then to the substantiation reports. There is nothing quite as frustrating as having to trawl through an original safety document to try and pick out the engineering claims, their safety functions and performance requirements. It may be found that these are not defined very well or at all.

To minimise these difficulties, make life simple and minimise the risk of transcription errors, the source documents should tabulate all of the engineering claims so that they can be lifted verbatim to the engineering schedule. The safety function, performance requirement, safety classification and any other pertinent information should be clearly defined. The compilation of the engineering schedule should then be no more difficult than lifting out the text from one document to another.

10.4   Desktop

The establishment of which sscs are important to safety and the development of the engineering schedule has so far been described as primarily stemming from the hazard analysis. Traditionally, a complementary approach to the identification of sscs has also been undertaken by engineers in a process known as the *desktop*.

The desktop is a structured meeting involving, engineering, safety and operations personnel to identify sscs that they collectively deem are important to safety. Safety functions can be attached to these sscs together with their performance requirements and classifications. The source documentation underpinning the desktop meeting could be layout drawings or the P+IDs to establish which items contribute to safety. It

would not be a HAZOP using HAZOP keywords, but the desktop would look, in particular, for passive structures such as walls, gloveboxes in addition to indicators, alarms
and interlocks, and so on.

The output from the desktop has historically been a voluminous number of SSCs.
In principle, these would be included on the engineering schedule for substantiation
together with those SSCs identified from the hazard analysis. From experience, the
desktop process has often taken a conservative approach to the identification of these
SSCs of which many end up with low safety classification and provide only a minor
contribution to safety. A proportionate hazard analysis undertaken in parallel may
subsequently only require a fraction of the SSCs identified by the desktop to be claimed
in the safety case. Therefore, this can lead to a mis-match and differences in classification between that claimed in the hazard analysis and that specified at the desktop.

The size of the engineering schedule will drive the cost of the safety case and in the
real world there is only a finite pot of money. The more the SSCs, the more the work for
plant personnel to review engineering documents and potentially maintain and test
equipment on the plant. If they are swamped with low safety significant equipment,
this may distract them from what is really important; i.e. they may not see the wood
for the trees.

If a desktop is undertaken, deference should be given to the hazard analysis (provided it has been done correctly). This is because the hazard analysis will have assessed
the consequences of the faults and utilising the tools of DBA and PSA, designated sufficient safety measures, at the appropriate level to ensure the risk is ALARP or make
recommendations for improvement. Thus, the output of the desktop and its inclusion in the engineering schedule should be managed to ensure what is included is
sufficiently proportionate.

The desktop can provide a valuable role in the identification of the passive features
that provide normal safety functions. These passive features can be overlooked in
hazard analysis. Their importance to the contribution to safety cannot be overstated.

Example: Gloveboxes
A hazard analysis may focus on faults in a glovebox that can give rise to a loss of extract, pressurisation, fire or a damaged glove. It must be recognised that if the support
structure underneath the glovebox corrodes and collapses there will be a significant
breach of glovebox containment. If the hazard analysis identifies the need to identity
and designate the support structure (as well as the glovebox) then fine, but otherwise
the desktop will be as important as the hazard analysis to ensure everything is captured
and substantiated.

10.5   Engineering reconciliation

We have described above the process by which an engineering schedule is compiled.
There will ideally have been dialogue between the safety assessors and the engineers
to ensure that the specified safety functions are clearly worded, unambiguous and can
be delivered. However, we do not live in an ideal world and it is more likely than not

that the safety analysis may have been written in some degree of isolation from the engineers. This is because:

- The safety assessors are in a different organisation and location to the engineers and it is not straightforward to talk to them;

- The engineers have not been appointed to the project yet.

To overcome the above difficulties, *engineering reconciliation* is a formal process that brings the safety assessors together with the engineers and plant operators. Engineering reconciliation can be considered to be a two-stage process. The first stage occurs prior to the commencement of engineering substantiation proper and the second stage occurs when the results of the substantiation are available.

The starting point of the reconciliation process is the collation of the engineering schedule as we have described. This should occur when the underpinning hazard analysis is adequately developed such that the hazards and faults are well understood to the extent that the engineering sscs have been defined with their safety functions and performance requirements. The hazard analysis does not need to be fully completed and ideally should not be completed until this process has been undertaken. Then the output of this stage of the reconciliation process can be fed back into the hazard analysis.

The formal engineering reconciliation process may involve a systematic review of the engineering schedule taking each ssc and its safety function and performance requirement in turn. The meeting will be chaired and will have attendees from plant operations, the safety assessors and relevant lead engineers from the disciplines required to substantiate the sscs. The intent of the engineering reconciliation process is to:

- Ensure that the engineers understand what has been asked of them to substantiate;

- Provide feedback to the safety assessors that the claims are reasonable. If they are not, seek changes to the safety argument if it is envisaged that an ssc simply cannot be substantiated or only by a significant and disproportionate degree of effort;

- Refine the wording of the sscs and their safety functions to simplify the substantiation process and maximise the potential for success;

- Ensure that plant operators and maintainers understand the claims that are being made and that they can live with the implications on their plant operations and maintenance.

The engineering reconciliation process will inevitably involve changes to the wording of the sscs and their safety functions on the engineering schedule. Any changes should then be fed back into the hazard analysis before its completion. With the process successfully undertaken and managed, there should be a clear tie-up between the hazard analysis and the engineering substantiation reports. The time taken to do this stage of the reconciliation process should be proportionate to the number of sscs and their classification—it could last an hour or many days.

The second phase of engineering reconciliation occurs following the completion of the substantiation process. At this stage it will be known whether the safety functions can be substantiated or not. In an ideal world all safety functions will be substantiated and the claims made in the hazard analysis are capable of being delivered. In reality, there will be a mixture of safety functions that are substantiated and some that are not and there will potentially be shortfalls in the engineering. This stage involves reconciling the output of the substantiation with the hazard analysis and determining what to do to address these shortfalls. There is no one right way to resolve the engineering shortfalls and if safety function claims are not substantiated then there are broadly two options:

Option 1:   The engineering substantiation document simply raises a shortfall and an accompanying recommendation to fix the deficiency—generally this deficiency should be fixed before the new safety case is adopted if it relates to an important ssc;

Option 2:   Revise the safety argument and make a safety claim on something else.

If **Option 1** is adopted, there is no further safety assessment work to be done other than that to support the implementation of the recommendation. This option is viable if the shortfall does not pose an immediate and significant safety risk.

If **Option 2** is adopted, then there will be more work to revise the hazard analysis (with all the checking and peer review processes, etc.), potentially leading to more substantiation work as new sscs or refined safety functions are called upon. Clearly, the second approach could require weeks or months of work depending on the severity of the shortfall and the nature of the plant and availability of resources (potentially towards the end of the project when personnel have drifted away). Examples of both approaches are given in the text boxes.

Example: Liquor Containment

A safety assessment has called upon a slab tank to maintain liquor containment and the tank and its containment function must be seismically qualified to a 10^{-4} y^{-1} event. Should a loss of containment event occur, there may be an accumulation of fissile liquor in the bund under the tank. In the most onerous configuration or concentration of fissile liquor, the liquor spill may give rise to a criticality.

For whatever reason, the tank cannot be substantiated to the 10^{-4} y^{-1} event (but it can to 10^{-2} y^{-1}). The safety function (or more accurately the performance requirement) cannot be substantiated. Nominally, the substantiation report would raise a shortfall and this is likely to be safety significant, as a criticality event, unless shielded, is expected to lead to a worker fatality. There would be a recommendation to improve the seismic withstand of the tank which may possibly extend to all of the structures above the tank to prevent them falling onto the tank and failing it. It may be determined that this may not be a practicable solution given the nature of the building and so on. Therefore, the recommendation is likely to get nowhere and as assessed in the hazard analysis, there is potentially a significant and non-tolerable risk.

The second option may be to revise the safety analysis and remove excess pessimisms and relax the claims on the withstand of the tank. It may also be more reasonably practicable to make changes to the geometry of the bund or provide for fixed neutron poisons in the bund (or in the liquor itself). The tank may even be embargoed from future use and emptied of liquor entirely removing the hazard. Thus, the best approach to the reconciliation process is to revise the safety assessment in this instance.

Example: High-Level Trip System
A high-level trip is claimed on a vessel to terminate incoming liquor flow to prevent overflow. Although the safety assessment modelled the configuration that the high-level trip is independent of the control system, engineering substantiation has found this to be incorrect. It may be that there is a shared contactor or valve or even that the logic for the protection system is processed by the plant control system. The ESR will report a shortfall and would make a recommendation for improvement.

Whilst the safety analysis is clearly wrong and the DBA and risk calculations undermined, changing the safety analysis may not be desirable or possible to do. There may be no alternative safety arguments to make (there is normally not a plethora of alternative safety systems to call upon). It is also preferable to be high in the safety hierarchy and to call upon an automated trip system rather than reliance on evacuation following a spill and activation of an activity-in-air alarm.

In this example, it should be straightforward to engineer out the shortfall by ensuring that the safety measure is fully independent of the control system. The relevant recommendation to do this would be made in the substantiation report. The safety assessment would then stand as it is because implementation of the recommendation before safety case adoption would align the plant to the configuration modelled in the DBA and risk calculations.

It is worth noting that a short safety assessment may subsequently be required to formally define the safety function for the new fully independent safety measure and the associated risk reduction it is required to achieve.

Fundamentally, the best approach to the reconciliation process is to proceed with the engineering shortfall and progress with the recommendation.

10.6   Conducting engineering substantiation

Early-generation safety cases did not formally undergo engineering substantiation to the same degree as safety cases produced in the last few decades. There was a much greater reliance on probabilistic assessment, which in many ways can be considered to be 'safety by numbers'. Whether the actual equipment being called upon to deliver those numbers could do what was asked was not always demonstrated. Engineering substantiation enables the safety case to show why the plant is safe by using good engineering principles with the probabilistic numbers providing an important but supporting role. Indeed, if the engineering delivers sufficient fault tolerance and robustness, the numbers will generally take care of themselves without too much worry.

Engineering substantiation also enables the life-limiting aspects of the engineering to be defined, i.e. how the safety envelope may degrade with time. This may be due to corrosion, fatigue, wear and tear, and so on. The substantiation may define what checks must be done and what the *end-of-life* criteria may be. So far, we have discussed the collation of the engineering schedule and the reconciliation process, but have yet to explain how engineering substantiation is undertaken and we will now proceed to do this. There are three principal phases:

- Plant familiarisation and obtaining information;

- Plant walkdown;

- Detailed substantiation.

The degree of effort to substantiate each ssc is dependent upon the safety importance attached to the ssc, i.e. its classification. The classification of sscs has been discussed in Section 9.3.

10.6.1   Plant familiarisation and obtaining information

A project team of engineers will be assembled that will be led by the lead engineer. The team of engineers will need to become familiar with the plant and the safety case that is being produced. For an operational plant, there will be the ability to visit the plant and see how it operates. Collation of the original design documents, drawings and substantiation documents will be undertaken and reviewed. The previous safety case generation of the plant's substantiation documents should be obtained as a matter of priority. Maintenance and inspection records are also useful documents for substantiation engineers and should be sought together with incident reports, records of plant observations or accidents. These can all give a clue that sscs are not working as intended.

The securing of the information can often take a significant amount of time for older and more complex plants. Therefore, the earlier it is started the better. Older reference material may be of poor physical quality, physically distributed across multiple sites and there may be the issue of out-of-date computer file formats or poor-quality scanned images and text files. The audit trail of documentation from one safety case stage to the next may not have been as thorough as it should have been. All of these issues can lead to gaps in the retrieved design and substantiation documentation. It should not be like this, but the real world does have these problems.

The safety and engineering teams will start to go through the information to ascertain what will be useful for their safety case stage. Older safety cases often tended to be more conservative in their approach to the identification of sscs and a modern safety case may well be slimmer, more focused and proportionate which all lead to fewer claims on the sscs. Therefore, not all of the information obtained may be required. It should not, however, be discarded because licensees are required to keep their records and information and besides, one never knows when something may be required (normally after it is been thrown away!).

Another complication in the information retrieval process is that plants are rarely static. Modifications will have been made that will have changed the sscs. The modifications may have introduced new sscs (with their own substantiation documents) and the modifications may have removed sscs. The production of an up-to-date *plant and process description document* is an essential component of every safety case life-cycle stage and this will be invaluable for the substantiation engineers.

It is worth stressing the point that the engineers will be required to substantiate what is on the engineering schedule and nothing else. Thus, by the time the engineering schedule has been produced by the safety assessors, the actual sscs on the plant that are required to be substantiated at this life-cycle stage will have been determined.

10.6.2   Plant walkdown

The *plant walkdown* is generally the commencement of the actual substantiation process and it is a structured event. For each of the sscs listed on the engineering schedule that can be visually inspected, the relevant engineers walk the plant to look at each of the sscs. For a walkdown there is normally a set of standard substantiation questions to be asked when every ssc is visually inspected. For ease, the questions may be on a proforma check sheet.

The substantiation questions are firstly to determine that the sscs exist as utilised in the hazard analysis. The questions then determine the physical condition of the sscs and whether there are any threats to the sscs that could compromise the ability of the sscs to deliver their safety functions now or in the future (the future is a defined period of time for which the safety case will be valid for). Threats to the sscs may be due to their position leading to vulnerability to impacts, chronic vibration, rainwater, and so on. All of these threats can affect sscs in different ways. Other items considered on the walkdown may include:

- Alarm or trip levels, standing alarms, re-sets and over-rides;

- Ergonomic issues such as difficulties in reading safety-related information or timely responding to alarm instructions, such as operating manual valves;

- The reliance on services to operate the ssc or connections with other safety systems.

Any identified deficiencies in the sscs, or differences to modern standards, may be noted as observations with ALARP recommendations for improvement. If there are significant deficiencies such that the safety functions may be compromised, shortfalls and *safety significant recommendations* may be made particularly for the most important sscs. During the walkdown process, it is not unknown for an ssc to have been claimed in the hazard analysis only for it to not be found on the plant. This obviously leads to an incorrect hazard analysis leading to an engineering shortfall and recommendation. This should really be resolved through a correction to the erroneous safety analysis.

Not all sscs can be visually inspected. For example, sscs may be partially enclosed in walls, such as pipes or may be completely within process cells or a reactor core to which there can be no physical access due to high radiation or contamination levels. Alternative technology may then be required to gauge the physical state of the sscs as far as reasonably practicable.

As an example, for a pipe immersed in a wall, the physical state of the wall and the entry and exit points of the pipe may give a reasonable best engineering 'guess' as to the physical state of the section of the pipe in the wall. However, should a significant safety claim be made on the integrity of the pipe, internal camera inspection may be used as a means to determine the state of the pipe by looking for evidence of internal corrosion or fatigue.

For sscs of low safety classification, the walkdown process and the completion of the question sheets may be sufficient to conclude the engineering substantiation process at an adequate and proportionate level of confidence. The sheets may then be compiled into an overall ESR that gives an overview of the process undertaken and key findings. However, for higher safety classification sscs, it may be necessary to provide for a more in-depth substantiation process. The walkdown would support the in-depth substantiation process, as it would record the condition of the ssc and any threats to it. The more detailed substantiation process is now described.

10.6.3   Detailed substantiation

Higher safety classification sscs provide, by definition, a significant contribution to safety. A proportionate and more detailed level of confidence must be obtained that the sscs will deliver their safety functions now and into the future. The walkdown process (where practicable) will be an important aspect of the substantiation of all sscs including those of the most safety significance, as it will provide insight into its physical state and operating environment, but a more in-depth analysis will generally be required.

If a walkdown process is not practicable for the inspection of the sscs then other inspection techniques will be required to be used. These may include physical or chemical sampling, remote cameras, X-ray equipment and other non-destructive techniques.

The in-depth analysis will include a detailed review of the design of the ssc and whether the design is compatible with what is being asked of it in the safety case. Typical questions to be asked and answered are given in Table 10.2. All of the information obtained would be expected to be collated and documented either in the ESR or in a suite of documentation and then summarised in the ESR.

Table 10.2: Typical questions asked in detailed substantiation of higher category SSCs. The list is not exhaustive, but gives an indication of what may be required to be ascertained. Strictly, **16.** does not need to be conducted to substantiate the SSC, but is an important component in the demonstration of ALARP.

1. What is the background to the SSC and where is it claimed in the safety case (with its safety function and performance requirement)?	**9.** Can we substantiate the SSC in its current condition and if not, what is required for it to be substantiated?
2. How was the SSC designed, constructed and installed and to what standards including QA?	**10.** What is the SSC's operational life, including environment, maintenance issues, known failures, modifications made and their cumulative effect?
3. Do the fault conditions compromise the ability of the SSC to deliver its safety function?	**11.** What are the failure modes of the SSC (revealed or unrevealed), i.e. does it fail-safe?
4. Is the SSC operating comfortably in its design envelope or at the margins?	**12.** Can reliability claims be achieved and by what margin?
5. What is the impact of aging, corrosion, loss of tolerances and fatigue?	**13.** Is the SSC fit-for-purpose in the role that it is performing?
6. Can we substantiate the SSC going forward and for how long?	**14.** What are the predicted changes in the SSC's operating regime or environment?
7. Known future modifications to the SSC; are they accommodated by this substantiation?	**15.** Is ageing a concern and the associated need for increased maintenance, inspection and outage?
8. How is end of life defined and how do we know when that is reached?	**16.** How does the SSC's design, operation and maintenance compare with modern standards?

Drawings are invaluable in providing substantiation evidence, particularly if they are as-built, rather than simply design drawings. The former should reflect what was installed and checked as installed on the plant and the latter only reflect what was intended to be installed, but does not necessarily mean that it was. If there is any doubt about the validity of plant drawings and their as-built status, then there may be a costly and timely exercise to be undertaken to ensure that the plant drawings are up to date and reflect the actual as-built plant configuration. This happens – be warned.

10.6.4 Comparison with modern standards

Nuclear plants were designed and built at a certain point in time. Some nuclear plants date to the earliest days of the industry and they fundamentally reflect the technology, methods of working, standards and codes present at the time of their construction and the installation of their process and safety equipment, i.e. the RGP. We may be lucky and find that there have been many improvements to the plant to improve the safety. For instance, new technology may have been installed to monitor unsafe situations and take automatic corrective action or new modern cranes may have been installed that significantly reduce the potential for the drop of items onto delicate structures. However, there are always limitations to the magnitude and number of changes that can reasonably practicably be made to an existing and older plant.

If we compare the older plant to an equivalent modern plant, we would expect to see other differences. A modern plant may have a greater degree of automation, either due to a computer-based control system or due to the greater use of automated systems. Older plants generally require higher levels of maintenance and this may be in higher dose rate areas. Thus, the normal operational dose accrued by operators and maintainers may be higher on an older plant. The spectrum of hazards and faults may also be greater on older plants to their equivalent modern ones giving rise to a higher total fault risk.

We cannot just condemn old plants because they are old. Brand new reactor plants will be old in a few years' time. Technology, standards and codes evolve due to learning from experience (good and bad) and the forward march of technology. We all generally expect things to get better and safer with time and as technology improves. This does not always occur, but the general thrust (we hope) is to an improvement in safety.

It is right that during the substantiation process, comparison is made with modern standards. Fundamentally, the question that is asked is 'If we were to design it now, or define the operating and maintenance regime now, would we do it this way?' If the answer is 'no' and there is a new way, we will have a gap and the significance of this gap should be reviewed. This may lead to an observation being noted in the ESR and what the implications may be. Correspondingly, this may lead to an ALARP recommendation to bring the SSC, or its operation, or its maintenance up to modern standards. The management of ALARP recommendations is discussed further in Section 13.

We should be very clear that just because we have made an observation that the SSC does not align with modern standards does not mean that it has failed to be substantiated. The SSC may work perfectly well and it may work reliably, but it does so with older technology. It is often found that the SSC was designed perfectly correctly in accordance with previous standards that have since been superseded. It is not possible to 'back date' a modern standard to an SSC that was designed or built to an older standard because the standards involve the full design and build life-cycle. Let's give a real-world non-nuclear example.

Example: Modern Standards and Cars

Let us suppose we wish to substantiate our motor car to make repeated trips from Manchester to London. It is a 1950s' vintage Rolls Royce. It was the best and most expensive car in the world when it was designed and built and it may even have been the safest at the time. It came with seat belts as standard. Can we substantiate the car to do the trip from Manchester to London? Yes, we can. We know from operational history it has been done many times and with regular maintenance, it can do the journey. The car is fit-for-purpose to drive from Manchester to London.

But

Does the car meet modern standards? We know that a vintage Rolls Royce, whilst very grand inside, will not have antilock brakes, crumple zones, airbags, lane departure warning systems, and so on.

Observation:	The car is fitted with old technology and does not align with modern standards (or even standards that were considered to be good practice many years ago).
ALARP Recommendation:	Consider alternative means of transport for getting from Manchester to London.

We should note that if we asked ourselves whether we could *reliably* undertake the trip, say with a probability of breaking down per trip of less than 1 in 50, we would probably fail to substantiate the performance requirement. An old vintage car will require a lot of maintenance and even then, it is unlikely to be able to do repeated high-mileage journeys without something going wrong. In this instance, we would have a shortfall and a recommendation would be made with a subtle change in wording from that given above for the observation.

Shortfall:	The car is required to reliably travel from Manchester to London with a probability of breakdown of less than 1 in 50, but even with routine maintenance the breakdown records cannot support this requirement.
Recommendation:	Alternative means of transport for getting from Manchester to London must be provided.

It is expected that a licensee will have knowledge of which codes and standards reflect modern standards that are relevant to their site. Obtaining this knowledge can involve significant time, effort and cost. Working with relevant specialists in the industry and the use of cross nuclear industry forums can help to mitigate these costs and ensure that they are kept abreast of changes and proposed future changes.

It is important to note that a licensee will contain significant inertia and it may not be reasonably practicable to instantly change to every new code and standard that is developed and utilised in the industry. Some may actually be in conflict with the need to maintain nuclear safety and would not be adopted. The collaborative approach with industry and other experts should help to mitigate the effect of future changes, but where there is divergence there may need to be an action plan to bring alignment as soon as reasonably practicable.

10.7   Design justification

New plants will undergo a design process as described in Section 3.2 and this will result in the identification of sscs that will contribute to safety. In addition, an existing plant may require the installation of new equipment that may also include safety equipment and sscs that will contribute to safety. These sscs will be required to be substantiated to ensure that safety claims upon them can be delivered. As we have initially pointed out, the term *design justification* may be used for new equipment rather than substantiation, but this is really semantics and the important point is that the substantiation reports form an important component of the safety case.

For a new plant, or a significant modification to an existing plant, it is likely to be the PCSR that will contain the majority of the safety assessment and design justification. The PCSR will define the Level 3 SFRs (for the actual sscs) and these will be incorporated within the engineering schedule.

Are there any differences between engineering substantiation and design justification? The biggest difference, of course, is that the design justification is not based upon sscs installed on the plant, but on sscs only 'on paper'. Design justification can only provide confidence that the ssc will deliver the safety function at the correct reliability. However, even at the detailed design stage we may not have chosen the equipment manufacturers of the systems. Therefore, the design justification within the PCSR may only utilise the best engineering knowledge of the design engineers. The design engineers should be SQEP and have knowledge of how such systems work to give confidence that the system will work. The substantiation will eventually be updated during commissioning to reflect the as-built status.

Example: Gamma Interlock System
Let us recall the design safety case stages that we discussed in Section 3.2. The PCSR is the safety case stage when we define the Level 3 SFRs; i.e. we will know what the sscs will be with their safety functions. For example, at the PCSR stage we may well know that a duty/standby compressor system will be required and we will know that a gamma interlock system will be required on an access door.

Let us consider the gamma interlock system. This is required to prevent entry if there is a high gamma dose rate behind the door. At the PCSR stage, the manufacturers of the detector and the locking arrangement may not be known. The C+I engineers will know how to configure the C+I system in terms of detector, logic and termination.

The safety assessors will also have included on the engineering schedule the risk reduction required, i.e. what reliability the system will need to deliver. With this information and knowledge of component reliability, the configuration of the system can be determined that will show the detectors, logic and termination. With a high-reliability system required, it may be necessary to include two gamma detectors and/or two locking mechanisms on the door.

Following the installation of equipment onto the plant and ahead of inactive/active commissioning, the SSC will be physically available for inspection. Therefore, there is an opportunity, at the commissioning stage of the project, to take into account the details of the actual manufactured and installed SSCs. Thus, it may be expected that there would be an update to the design justification documents.

Design justification will take account of the LFE gained on similar plants. This LFE will help to provide confidence that the SSCs will deliver their safety functions. The LFE and possibly R+D, may also be required to justify differences in the design of the SSCs from previous generations of the SSCs on different plants. The use of LFE and R+D may be particularly crucial in defining the end-of-life criteria for structures. Let us utilise another example to illustrate this issue.

Example: Water Cooling System
A water-cooling coil circuit is required in a new vessel that will handle radioactive liquors that contain fission products. The liquors are heat generating and are essentially nitric acid within which the radioactive fission products are dissolved. The coiling coils are identified as an SSC with a safety function 'to direct and contain the cooling water' and 'to prevent the ingress of activity into the cooling water'.

In the intense radioactive and acid environment of the vessel, corrosion of the coils will occur. It is known that corrosion can eventually give rise to pin hole failures in the coils leading to activity transfer to the cooling circuit and potentially a significant radiological dose. Corrosion and activity migration have occurred on the earlier generation plants, but fortunately, the events had not led to significant dose.

LFE has been brought to bear in the design of the new water-cooling circuit from the life history of the equivalent coils on the earlier generation plants. The LFE is used to understand the coil thickness required, the operating temperature that the liquor should be held at, the composition of the water in the cooling circuit (demineralised water rather than standard water to minimise water-side corrosion) and the grade of steelwork to use for the cooling water coils that is capable of resisting the nitric acid attack and so on.

All of the above knowledge is used in the engineering justification of the new coils. The LFE will be used to justify differences in its design and mode of operation. The latest R+D on corrosion may be utilised that is based upon experiment and theoretical work. We may note that if we move too far from our operational knowledge in the design of the new coils, we may invalidate the LFE gained. If we were to use a different metal or alloy entirely for the coil composition, our relevant operational history would be reduced. This would make engineering justification much more difficult and this may require a greater degree of R+D to provide the confidence in the new metal.

Based upon known rates of coil thinning from our LFE, the design justification will be able to define the end-of-life criteria, i.e. a certain corrosion allowance. Once this corrosion allowance is reached the likelihood of coil failure has reached a point that it is deemed to be unacceptable. This point of uncertainty would have an input from the safety assessors, as it is likely to define the IEF for the FSG of activity ingress into the cooling water circuit.

During operation, it may be necessary for there to be a schedule of inspection of the coils to determine their thickness. The substantiation documents should set out these requirements and the advised rates of inspection.

Finally, as a new SSC, it would be expected that modern standards codes and standards would be utilised in the design and future operation and maintenance of the proposed SSC unless there is adequate justification to utilise an earlier standard. This can cause difficulties when a new system is installed to replace an existing SSC and the perception of 'ratcheting up' safety. We should be prepared to robustly defend the use of modern standards where appropriate. Let us give an example.

Example: Sample System
A sampling system heats up bulk (>1000 kg) quantities of uranium hexafluoride held in a container. The container is placed, via an access door, within an integrated oven-type system that heats the container's contents, takes the sample and provides secondary containment should there be a release of the uranium hexafluoride. Overheating of the container can give rise to operator consequences should there be a loss of primary containment and subsequent opening of the access door. Interlocks on the heating process and door opening sequence were claimed in the safety assessment for an operational safety case and the SSCs were included on the engineering schedule. However, during substantiation it was determined that the interlocks could not be substantiated. The reason for failure does not matter here, but in our example, a project was instigated to design and install new interlocks.

The new interlocks would result in a modification to the plant and a modification process was instigated that would encompass a PCSR. The PCSR would include a safety assessment and design justification for the new systems. The safety assessment would formally define the safety functions and the risk reduction required[a] to achieve an ALARP level of safety. It was initially perceived by 'the project' that this would be a simple 'one-out, one-in' modification.

Firstly, we should state that despite the project being simply a change of an interlock system for a new system, the hazard analysis to support the modification was required to be undertaken to the current standards employed by the licensee. It was also determined that the original safety assessment was undertaken many years ago before modern safety assessment techniques were developed (e.g. DBA). It would not be right to undertake safety assessment to old methodologies.

Utilising modern safety case approaches may require two interlocks to be installed instead of one to satisfy DBA, effectively a doubling of the protection. Moreover, modern approaches require the segregation of safety systems to protect against CCF (e.g. fire) and fire-resisting cabling, segregated logic cabinets and terminators may be required. The design engineers will also design the new interlocks to the standards associated with modern safety interlocks.

We no longer have a 'one-out, one-in' modification. A challenge to the analysis of the safety assessor may be put in by those that hold the money. However, provided the safety analysis has been undertaken appropriately and proportionately and has been reasonably accommodating in seeking alternatives, a robust defence should be made.

---

[a]The required risk reduction can be taken to be the factor to take the IEF to 10% of the risk or relevant accident frequency BSO.

Chapter 11

Human Factors

Human factors is a term that encompasses the role of the human in a plant. The human may be an operator who has day-to-day responsibility for ensuring the operation of the plant, or it may be the managers and supervisors, or the maintainers and support staff (e.g. health physics). This chapter gives a brief introduction to the topic of human factors. The Health and Safety Executive (HSE) provides guidance on human factors (e.g. see [26]) and there is also a human factors section within the SAPS [1].

The term *ergonomics* is used interchangeably with 'human factors'. The former term may be used in relation to the physical aspects of the environment, such as layout, and the nature of the control panels. The latter term may also be considered to encompass the cultural and behavioural aspects of human behaviour.

There is no denying that humans have an important role in ensuring the safe operation of a nuclear plant. Even though the role of the operator in providing protection is towards the bottom of the safety hierarchy, this does not mean that operators are not important. The safety hierarchy is there to try and ensure that sound engineering is used to remove or manage hazards. Mechanisms to reduce the rate of error in control or duty systems are fundamental in good and robust design. Humans are often integral to the control process.

A safety case team should always include those with human factors knowledge and experience. This is especially true in design projects. They will bring their knowledge to the project to provide the assessment of the human factors issues and provide guidance.

One of the principal aims of human factors is to demonstrate the adequacy of task and system designs to enable effective and error free human performance, as far as reasonably practicable. It is, in many respects, the equivalent activity to that associated with engineering substantiation of the SSCs. An objective of any human factors assessment is to seek improvements to reduce the potential for human error.

There is clearly a role for human factors assessments throughout the design life-cycle of a project for a new plant. Ideally, human factors assessments should be integrated into the design stages of a plant. For existing plants, human factors assessments must be applied retrospectively and the existing plant is compared against modern ergonomic standards and human factors good practice.

The more 'hands-on' the plant, the more likely it is for extensive human factors involvement. Poor decisions made at the design stage, without due regard for how humans will behave, can have a negative effect on the future operation of the plant throughout its life. A *human factors integration plan* (HFIP) is an early design document that explains the role of human factors through the project design life-cycle and this chapter will describe how a HFIP may be written. The majority of human factors support during design will be in the detailed design stage that will culminate in the delivery of the PCSR. This is when detailed safety arguments are made and a true understanding of the interface between humans and engineering is established.

For existing plants, there is still an important role for human factors during modifications and during safety case reviews. During a safety case review, the emphasis is likely to be on seeking improvements in recognition that standards and expectations of RGP may change with time. Human factors have a role in supporting changes with respect to regulator improvement notices, or where near misses or human errors have occurred.

Human factors may also be involved in supporting quantitative determination of the HEPs and *human performance limiting values* (HPLVs) used in safety case frequency assessment and PSA. This chapter describes these terms and how human factors assessors support their quantification and reference is made to *task analysis*. When undertaking quantitative human error analysis, a safety assessor should always consult human factors assessors to underpin any values utilised.

11.1 Background

So what exactly are human factors and what role do they have to play in a modern safety case? A definition of human factors can be found in [26], which is as good as any:

> 'environmental, organisational and job factors, and human and individual characteristics which influence behaviour at work in a way which affects health and safety'.

Human factors involve many science disciplines that include aspects of psychology and biomechanics. For instance, it considers how people behave and how they react to things, but also how they can physically do things. As examples, an assessment of human factors will consider whether operators:

- Will respond to an alarm in a timely and correct manner;

- Understand the written instructions because there is no ambiguity in the wording and intent;

- Can efficiently and safely operate in the physical environment;

- Can clearly distinguish the manual valve that is required to be opened (e.g. for normal operations or in response to a fault) and can actually open the valve given location and the conditions to be experienced.

Therefore, we can state that the role of human factors is to ensure that the systems within a plant reflect the psychological and physical capabilities of the users of the system. The users may include the operators (the workers that undertake the process work on the plant), maintainers (the workers that repair and test plant items including the sscs), supervisors, plant managers and emergency workers, and so on.

Human factors will play an important role in the substantiation of claims made on operator behaviour and they will demonstrate that the reliability claims on them are reasonable. Any operational safety measures must be clear and capable of being undertaken by those required to implement them and human factors play a role in ensuring this. To achieve this, it may be a simple task for human factors assessors to read the written instructions and ensure that the language used is appropriate, simple and clear, enabling its adherence with the minimum of confusion or error potential. Human factors can subsequently support the training of personnel in both operational tasks and those that are safety-related.

Human factors take a role in ensuring that operational tasks within a plant and the levels of supervision and management are adequately determined. Thus, they may help to ensure that the *minimum staffing levels* are appropriate for the range of tasks to be undertaken. The minimum staffing levels relate to the core personnel that must be available to support the safe operation of the plant. Even if a plant is shut down without day-to-day operations, there may be a requirement for a minimum staffing level to ensure the shutdown state is adequately monitored. There may still be faults that can lead to a release of activity in a shutdown plant, perhaps due to pipework failure or pump or fan failure. Operators must be available to ensure that faults are appropriately responded to. Emergency responses should be written within the *emergency instructions* (EIs), which should be reviewed by human factors assessors.

11.2   Human factors integration plan

The role of human factors within a project is detailed in a document known as an HFIP. An HFIP is of particular use within design projects where there will be an increasing role for human factors as the design matures, but consideration of human factors is required right from the project start. The HFIP details the scope of the required human factors activities during its individual design stages (see Section 3.2) and the document may identify the dependent stakeholders. The principal aims of a HFIP are to:

- Ensure that human factors are given consideration during all project design stages and decision-making (such as optioneering);

- Ensure adequate focus on the role of the operator, maintainer and so on is recognised in the design process;

- Identify specific human factors deliverables and their interface with the project design engineers;

- Identify the necessary support to safety justifications, which may involve the substantiation of qualitative and quantitative claims made upon human behaviour;

- Show that there is a process for the integration of human factors with the other design disciplines and suppliers.

As an output, the HFIP may identify the need for an HMI *style guide* to be produced. This can be a useful document in a design project where there may be a number of suppliers providing designs of different components of the new plant. Each of these components may have HMI issues and a common approach across the project is required, which should reflect the practices adopted by the actual licensee. Thus, the style guide will describe what is required, what standards and procedures should be adopted, the approach to alarm handling and so on. The document would be shared with all of the suppliers and may even form a part of the contractual arrangements.

Another output that the HFIP may identify is the production of a *target audience description* (TAD). When designing equipment that is to be operated or maintained by humans, it is important that the designers have an understanding of those that will interact with the equipment. This ensures that the design is based on the requirements of the user, i.e. 'user-centred'. Failure to take into account the user can result in a mismatch between the final design and the actual capabilities of the user. The TAD will inform the designers of the relevant characteristics of the user, which may reflect physical, psychological and even sociological aspects of the user and the organisation. An obvious example is when designing a system that has a display; if it utilises SI units, it may be problematic in countries where the user is more familiar with imperial units.

11.3   Reliance on operators

There is a general desire to design plants that minimise the safety demand placed upon operators. Referring back to the safety hierarchy in Section 2.5.1, passive features are preferred followed by active safety measures before reliance on operators. Let us stress that operators are still important and will have an overview of the plant and their actions are likely to be embedded in aspects of the control system. Nevertheless, plants may need to make claims on operator action. This could be to operate reliably and minimise the demand on safety measures, or to implement operational safety measures or to act in response to an accident and implement the EIS.

If an operator is required to act to implement an operational safety measure, there must be sufficient time available to do this safely. For instance, if an operator is required to add cooling water to a system and this cannot be reasonably practicably automated, there must be sufficient time for:

1. The alarm to be raised (perhaps automatically) and registered by the operator;

2. The operator to process the implication of the alarm, which may be one of many;

3. Reference to be made to an alarm response instruction and/or a supervisor (who may not be immediately to hand);

4. Implementation of the alarm response and instigation of alternative cooling water.

It would not be reasonable to expect all of the above to normally be achieved within a few seconds or even potentially a few minutes. There is something known as the *30-minute rule*, such that no safety-related action should be required to be implemented within 30 minutes. In our above example, the alarm level would need to be set at a level that allows for a minimum of a 30 minutes (if not longer) of *grace time* until the unsafe condition occurs. The operator's action should ensure that the plant conditions remain comfortably within the SOE with a good margin before the safe envelope could be breached.

There must be a balance in the setting of any alarm level—too low and we risk spurious alarms that degrade the safety significance of the alarm (crying wolf). Whatever the required time in which an operator has to implement a safety measure, human factors assessors should confirm that the time is adequate and take into account the likely conditions at the time of the fault.

One exception to the 30-minute rule is often associated with operator response to activity-in-air and area gamma alarms. If these go into alarm, the radiation levels may in fact be very high as there may have been a catastrophic failure of containment or shielding. Thus, it is not possible to engineer the alarm levels to give the operators 30 minutes to withdraw.[1] Operators are expected to withdraw promptly on their activation.

Within a safety case, defined operational safety measures will have a specified instruction for the operators. For example:

Instruction: **Following annunciation of the evaporator high temperature alarm, operators must isolate the steam heating supply to the evaporator within two hours.**

The above is an obvious candidate for automation, but leaving that aside, the safety case demand on the operator is clear. However, it does not explain exactly what an operator must do and what the individual steps to implement it are. The OIs will detail all of these requirements and will, for example, identify which steam valve is required to be closed, how it is to be closed and so on and any particular precautions that may be needed to be taken. Human factors would be expected to review and confirm the adequacy of the wording of the safety case requirement *and* the detailed working levels instructions where they are important to nuclear safety.

11.4 Human errors an analysis

Safety cases will involve the analysis of a wide range of faults where human error plays a role. This may be either in the initiation of a fault or in the failure to correctly implement an operational safety measure. It is important that these identified failures are reviewed by human factors assessors to support claims made in the safety case and to seek improvements to minimise the potential for such errors.

---

[1] The term *withdraw* is sometimes preferred to 'evacuate' as the latter term has more negative connotations.

Numerical reliability claims on humans are given in terms of an HEP, which is akin to the pfd for engineered safety measures. Where an HEP is used, it must be substantiated by a human factors assessor. Such quantitative human error analysis can become quite mathematically involved with the selection and manipulation of a number of factors that are utilised together to derive a probability. A full description of the subject is beyond the scope of this book. We can only provide the briefest overview to give to the general safety assessor a working knowledge of some of the terms and likely human error values that may be used.

To really understand a human error the task leading to the failure must be understood with all of the *performance influencing factors* that may shape or influence how the operator, supervisor, and so on will respond. This necessitates a supporting qualitative assessment and justification of the error numbers utilised. This is supported by undertaking a *task analysis*, which is described below. The approach adopted for the quantification of human errors is then discussed. Finally, this section introduces the concept of a *violation*, where there is a wilful disregard for procedure.

11.4.1   Task analysis

Task analysis must be undertaken before any attempt to substantiate numerical claims on operator reliability. How well the performance influencing factors are understood and managed against each task will determine the potential for human error. The task analysis determines what the individual is required to achieve, and how it is undertaken together with the working environment. The working environment will include the physical environment, peer and supervisor oversight and the safety culture within the plant/overall organisation. The safety culture will influence whether errors, incidents and near misses are covered up or admitted to with lessons learnt.

Focusing on key nuclear errors, the fault listing or fault schedule may be a starting point for human factors assessment. These documents will identify the faults that have a human error component, either as part of the initiating event or as part of an operational safety measure. Quantification of human errors is likely to only be necessary for the most significant faults and this will help to ensure that the human factors resource is focused in a proportionate manner.

The human factors assessor will review the fault entries, and any descriptions of the faults in other documents, liaise with the safety assessor and gain an understanding of the exact claims being made. The human factors assessor will then need to turn attention to the actual plant and understand how the particular task is performed. Ideally, this will involve a plant visit, perhaps to witness the operation, interview the relevant personnel, check incident/near miss records and read through the OIs or *maintenance instructions* (MIs) that describe the task. The human factors assessor may then begin to break down the task into a series of sub-tasks to better understand the process. From this understanding, it can be determined whether the error is an act of *omission* or *commission* for which examples are given in Table 11.1.

The nature of the error will influence how the quantification of the HEP is undertaken as there are different methodologies in the industry. The task analysis may also

Table 11.1: Example types of human error.

Error	Example
Omission	Forget to do a task
	Forget to do a step in a task
Commission	Perform tasks in the wrong sequence
	Perform tasks at the wrong time
	Perform tasks in the wrong place
	Do too much/little
	Engage the wrong control
	Issue the wrong command

offer sufficient insight that recommendations for improvement could be identified, which if adopted may have a role in improving safety.

11.4.2 Human error probability

If an operator makes an error, we may need to know the probability that this occurs. This could feed into an initiating event to determine the IEF. Alternatively, if the operator or supervisor has to implement a safety measure, a probability will need to be determined that reflects the chance that it is not correctly performed. Therefore, we need to determine the HEP associated with this fault. The different types of human error that may be encountered are described as errors of commission or errors of omission. The HEP is analogous to the pfd for physical components. There are established methodologies for determining HEP values such as *Technique for Human Error Rate Prediction* (THERP) and *Human Error Assessment and Reduction Technique* (HEART) [27].

Typical HEP values used in safety cases to reflect operator failures can be within the range of $10^{-1} - 10^{-3}$ (Table 11.2). There are some tasks or responses to events that are impossible to be undertaken by an operator or are very difficult and these would have an HEP of 1 or very close to it. It is pointless to claim these responses as operational safety measures as they cannot be substantiated to be delivered with any reasonable confidence.

11.4.3 Dependent failures

We have described a process to quantify human errors. If we have multiple independent human failures in a fault sequence, we could mathematically arrive at a very low

Table 11.2: Example HEP values. Data taken from [28].

Error type	Value
Simple, frequently performed task, no stress	10^{-3}
More complex task, less time available, some care needed	10^{-2}
Complex, unfamiliar task, with little feedback and some distractions	10^{-1}
Highly complex task, considerable stress, little time to perform it	3×10^{-1}
Extreme stress, rarely performed task	1

probability of failure. For instance, a fault sequence may require the following to all occur before there is a radiological consequence:

1. An initial operator error; then

2. Failure of the supervisor to check the operator's action and detect and correct the error; then

3. Subsequent failure of the same operator or even another operator to correctly respond to an alarm and terminate the fault sequence.

Applying individual HEP values of 10^{-2} to each of these will see a total combined HEP of 10^{-6}. This is a very small probability, but is it realistic? Combining all of the errors in this manner is only correct if there are no dependent failures between them. In reality, if an operator fails to do something, then there is a reasonable chance that the supervisor will also fail, which could be because:

1. They are both equally incompetent (harsh, but could be true);

2. They both have had a bad day and want to finish early;

3. The operator normally gets it right and the supervisor only gives a cursory check;

4. There may be systematic failings in training or equipment that is beyond their control or knowledge;

5. Any other reason...

Thus, the safety culture on the plant may affect the overall reliability a system of humans can deliver. There may be obvious dependent failures between the tasks and these should be accounted for explicitly. THERP, as mentioned above, can account for these dependencies and human factors assessors should be well versed in dealing with these issues. In our list above, the supervisor check may be classed as a dependent failure as there are reasons why the supervisor may get it wrong if the operator also gets it wrong.

An HPLV is also used to truncate the overall reliability of personnel, be it an individual or a team. The HPLV is used to account for indirect dependencies and it is applied even when dependencies are identified and accounted for. Essentially, the HPLV will capture the dependent factors that have not been explicitly thought about. HPLV can be thought to be the maximum reliability that can be expected from a task and it is analogous to the CCF for physical components.

Where individual human errors are independent and therefore multiplied together in a fault tree (through AND gates), each human error term is combined with the common HPLV value through an OR gate. The Boolean algebra within the fault tree logic will ensure that the very low total human errors from the AND gates are truncated at the HPLV value. As an example, for three individual independent operator errors, the errors in the fault tree will effectively give

$$\text{Overall human reliability} = (\text{HEP}_1 \times \text{HEP}_2 \times \text{HEP}_3) + \text{HPLV}$$
$$\approx \text{HPLV},$$

when the product of the individual HEP values is small compared to HPLV. Typical HPLV values are given in Table 11.3.

It can be tempting to simply defer to the HPLV in a safety assessment to account for multiple human errors, as this can give a quick ready estimate of a frequency if it is HPLV limited. However, individual human errors should always be explicitly identified and the associated HEPs determined.

11.4.4 Violations

Good design with robust engineered safeguards should preferably ensure the safety of a plant. Even a well-engineered plant will rely on operators to some extent and their need to 'follow the rules'. The plant design should be tolerant to operators making casual errors, but a wilful disregard for the rules may invalidate important assumptions

Table 11.3: Example of HPLV values. Data taken from [28]. The HPLVs should be applied in conjunction with individual HEPs.

Personnel	Value
Single operator	10^{-3}
Operators	10^{-4}
Control room-based team (operator, plus supervisor and shift manager)	10^{-5}

in the safety case and invalidate safety systems. For instance, deliberately disabling safety systems to force an entry will render the protection ineffective. Disregarding the rules may lead to unsafe plant states developing that were not originally foreseen in the design process.

If an operator wants to do something, deliberately and with full knowledge that this is against the rules, then there is little that can be done to prevent this. Peers and supervisors may form a barrier, but they may be collaborating, for whatever reason, in the undertaking. We refer to this process as a *violation*. We must distinguish two things:

1. A violation is not a malevolent event such as sabotage, terrorism, theft or other crime—these are aspects of security and beyond the scope of this book and safety cases in general;

2. A violation is a *deliberate and wilful* undertaking and is not simply an error either of omission or commission.

Taking the above two points together, it may be that the intent of the violation is to short-cut a process for convenience, but not to develop an unsafe condition. An unsafe condition may materialise, but it is not the express purpose of the violation. A violation may involve the disregard of established working practices and procedures that are written down in OIs or MIs. Violations may occur as a one-off event or they may be routine events. The Chernobyl disaster is one infamous example where violations occurred. The violations, when coupled with the poor reactor design and lack of operator understanding of the reactor's shortcomings, resulted in the unsafe reactor state escalating into an explosion.

Safety cases cannot generally numerically model violations. Where these are identified, human factors assessors should be involved to try and eliminate the potential for violations. Should it be determined that violations occur or are likely to occur, the root cause should be investigated and changes made. It may be that the procedures require tasks to be done that have no perceived benefit or the task may be repetitive and boring. Changes to the procedures or work environment may remove any incentive to deliberately cut the corners. Working in conjunction with the operators and plant managers will be essential in doing this and gaining the buy-in.

Example: Why Violations Will Eventually Catch You Out
An operator has to check the liquor level in a vessel at the end of the shift. For whatever reason, this is a cumbersome operation and leads to a delay in clocking off and going home. One particular operator decides to not bother most of the time and records the usual level in the log. This is a wilful violation of procedure as it is deliberate and it occurs most days. The operator has never known the level to be wrong and feels confident it never will be (or is perceived to be very unlikely). The operator is not seeking to develop an unsafe state and simply wants convenience.

One day the liquor level is wrong, but is not recorded. The wrong liquor level may then give rise to a product quality issue or even a safety issue. It does not matter what the progression is, the wrong level will not be detected if it is never measured. The final undesired event will occur with almost certainty when a violation routinely occurs and there is a reasonable chance that the first error in the chain will happen over the plant's lifetime.

Let us contrast this with an error of omission; i.e. an operator forgets to undertake the check. Assuming that this has a low probability, it is more than likely that this will not occur when there is an erroneous liquor level as two independent and unlikely events must occur together. It is probable and even overwhelmingly probable that the undesirable event will not manifest itself.

In this simple example, it does not take a specialist to see that changes could be made to remove the error potential. For example:

- The measurement could be automated;
- The timing of the manual measurement could be made easier and undertaken earlier in the shift;
- Better training of the importance of the check could be made.

Chapter 12

Services

Nuclear plants will require an electrical supply to operate the lighting, ventilation systems, computers, pumps, process equipment, and so on. The plants may also need compressed air, steam and other gas supplies to operate. Collectively, these supplies are known as *services*. In addition to operational needs, the services may also be needed to maintain nuclear safety by managing hazards and terminating faults. This chapter will discuss services in relation to nuclear safety and it cannot be overstated that service provision is essential in maintaining nuclear safety. In these circumstances, a safety case is required to demonstrate that robust arrangements are in place to ensure that services can be provided through a wide range of hazards. In particular, faults arising from flooding, fire or seismic events can affect multiple systems at once and disable normal service providers and any back-up supplies. Thus, tolerance to the events may be required to be assured.

The requirement for services to maintain safety is not ideal; the preference is always that the plant can be 'switched off' and left in a safe state without the continuous supply of services. A plant that needs a continuous supply of services to maintain safety effectively needs to continue running to some degree (e.g. valves to be held open or pumps to continue running). The need to actively run the plant in this manner to maintain safety is low in the safety hierarchy. This will significantly complicate the design and add cost to the plant. However, the nature of much of the nuclear material within plants leads to the requirement for service provision to maintain safety and it is unavoidable. This chapter will discuss this.

All safety cases should provide an assessment of the effect of a loss of services. It may simply be stated, with evidence, that services are not required to maintain nuclear safety. However, some plants (such as reactors) will require extensive assessment of service provision. The importance of service provision was illustrated in Fukushima where the loss of duty and back-up electrical supplies from the common seismic event and flooding gave rise to a loss of cooling water.

An assessment of services may also need to consider the interrelationship between different services. For example, should safety claims be made on ejectors to empty vessels or bunds, the ejectors will not only require steam, but also compressed air to actuate valves in the steam line and electrical power to provide signals to the valve actuators. Compressed air is often an overlooked service that can find its way into operating a wide range of safety systems on plants.

12.1   Identification of service requirements

During the early stages of the design process, the requirement for service provision should be established. How the plant operates (the process) will be one of the principal inputs in defining what services are required. For example, an operation may require a constant supply of air to dilute hydrogen gas that is released to prevent a flammable atmosphere from forming. Another example is that cooling water may be required to remove decay heat from the reactor or liquor tanks. Conversely, a supply of helium gas may be needed for leak testing or carbon dioxide for a chemical reaction in a glovebox experiment. In our examples, a failure to supply either the helium or carbon dioxide may simply lead to a production delay and not a safety issue. It should be distinguished early in any design process whether services will be required solely to enable the process operation to occur or whether services will also be required to ensure safety.

We should note that even if a plant is fail-safe on loss of service, there may be an expectation for a minimum electrical supply for a period of time. This may be to support evacuation through the provision of emergency lights, an alarm system and potentially the monitoring of key conditions within the plant.

12.1.1   Electrical supply

Like our homes, offices, shops and factories, plants require electrical power to operate. This will be to enable the lights to function, heating and cooling systems to provide a comfortable operating environment, and computer systems to operate. In addition, the electrical power will be used by pumps, motors, cranes, ventilation systems and safety equipment.

The electrical power to the plant will be received from one or more local site substations. The sub-stations will receive power from the incoming national electrical grid infrastructure. Even nuclear power stations will utilise incoming electrical supplies from the national grid network, as the plant will still require electrical power when it is not generating its own electricity. The service originating outside the site is known as an *external service* rather than an *internal service* that is generated internally to the site.

We can define the incoming electrical supply as the *normal electrical supply*. Normal in the sense that it is from where day-to-day electrical supply is sourced, which is usually a public generator connected to the national grid. The risk from a loss of electrical supply can be reduced by utilising two parallel feeds; i.e. the plant can be fed with an 'A' supply and a 'B' supply. This increases the tolerance of the plant, but would not protect against a total loss of incoming supply to the site from a national grid failure.

From time-to-time, as at home, the incoming externally generated electrical supply will be lost, i.e. a national grid failure. Hopefully, this is infrequent, but we know from our own home experience that this does occasionally happen and nuclear sites are no exception. Normally, the loss of supply is only for a few minutes, but it is not unknown for electrical supplies to be occasionally lost for a number of hours. We may generally expect that the longer the loss of supply duration the less likely it is to occur. After all, we will all likely to have experienced interruptions in the electrical supply of a few minutes, but rarely, if ever, for more than one day. This may occur if there has been a significant country-wide event such as a storm or an earthquake.

Standby systems

To protect against a failure of the incoming national grid supply, standby electrical supplies can be provided. This is traditionally supplied by one or more back-up generators that may utilise diesel as a fuel source (or as battery technology improves this could become the default provision in the future). These generators may auto-start on loss of incoming supply or may require manual initiation to start. Thus, with generators we can now guarantee an electrical supply to the plant, but there may be a brief interruption to the overall supply. This can be defined as a *guaranteed interruptible* (GI) electrical supply.

The electrical supply provided by a generator will clearly last for as long as the diesel supply lasts. A week's diesel supply or more may be defined to cater for the most significant events such as a seismic event where the plant may not have immediate access to external support. A diesel-backed electrical supply system is able to provide relatively significant levels of power to the plant. In principle, depending on electrical loading calculations, it may be able to provide sufficient power to enable a range of operational or safety process equipment to continue to function. Cooling circuit pumps and air compressors may be amongst the most important process equipment to require this power. Compressed air is an important service as it is used to actuate valves, which may be needed to be moved to respond to plant conditions.

It may also be necessary to provide an electrical supply to sensitive process equipment that cannot tolerate interruption in supply, such as a computer-based plant control system or calibrated non-destructive assay equipment. Safety systems may also require a continuous supply of power before the GI supply is initiated, as it is likely to be desirable for alarms and emergency lights to have a continuous supply of power. Thus, it may be necessary to provide a continuous electrical supply, i.e. a *guaranteed non-interuptible* (GNI) power supply. This GNI power supply is provided by a battery system and is also known as an *uninterruptible power supply* (UPS). Typically, an UPS will only last for a couple of hours or so, but the batteries can normally be recharged by either the emergency diesel generator or the normal electrical supply if that is restored.

The design of the electrical supply system is undertaken by electrical engineers. The electrical engineers will be guided by the safety assessors and other engineers to determine which systems will require connection to the GI and the GNI supplies. The electrical engineers will have an important role in ensuring the safe design of the electrical supply systems due to the large electrical loads carried by the systems and the associated high voltages, which may range from 10 kV or more to the normal household level of 240 V or lower. One aspect that will require careful thought by the electrical engineers is the mechanism for the safe isolation of the plant fed by the diesel generator from the main supply.

Fail-safe position

As we have stated, our preference is always for a fail-safe plant that does not require electrical power to maintain nuclear safety. A loss of electrical supply will lead to a loss of operations. Indeed, should electrical supply be lost the general expectation is that the operators within a plant will withdraw from the active areas. This is because the ventilation systems will be lost and prolonged residency in a plant without a cascade of air flow may lead to activity levels in operational areas increasing with time (note that physical containment barriers should still be in place to ensure that activity levels do not rapidly increase following a loss of ventilation).

On a loss of electrical supply, safety systems should fail to their defined *safe state*. Interlocks and trips should normally fail to the position commensurate with a trip signal being generated. This is simply achieved by noting that the systems are designed so that power is required to 'hold off' the interlock or trip. For instance, the brakes on a crane hoist are power off, so that should power be lost, the brakes automatically engage. Trip valves in a fluid circuit will be automated valves that have a spring return. Thus, electrical power (or more often compressed air) is required to keep the valve open against the spring return. Thus, on loss of electrical supply (or compressed air), the valve returns to its defined safe state of closed.

The defining of the safe state of safety systems is deeply embedded in the design process that engineers utilise. Thus, it is a reasonable expectation that engineers working to the ESPs will get it right without input from safety assessors. The safety assessor's role is to confirm that the defined safe state has been correctly determined. The P+IDs should show the failure position of valves, for instance, which will include the normal process valves and the automated safety valves.

For plants that are fundamentally fail-safe and do not require services to run to maintain safety, the above approach should be relatively straightforward. Generally, on loss of electrical and/or air supply all of the trip valves will close. However, for plants that need to run to maintain safety, this could be disastrous in certain areas as there may be competing and conflicting safety demands. This is far from an ideal situation, but it occurs. Let us again illustrate this by way of an example.

Example: Balance of Risk
Consider a cooling system that uses pumped water through a tank to remove decay heat. The water will pass through a heat exchanger and then pass back through the tank on a continuous basis. There will be redundant cooling circuits so that if one were to fail, the second should remain operational. The heat exchanger will then

be cooled by a secondary cooling circuit that will also be pumped with the heat eventually being discharged to the atmosphere via cooling towers.

It is envisaged that it is possible for corrosion to lead to activity ingress into the primary cooling water circuit. Consequently, should activity enter the primary cooling circuit, contamination of the whole primary circuit will occur. If sufficiently large, the contamination may give rise to a radiological dose to the operators. Through careful selection of material, thickness, and operating conditions we seek to minimise this potential, but cannot deterministically dismiss it. Thus, to provide protection, the design includes activity detectors that would close isolation valves in the cooling circuit to prevent the activity from being transferred around the whole circuit and to plant areas where personnel may be located. This activity ingress isolation system is clearly a safety system. What is the fail-safe mode for this safety system?

The normal design practice would see that the isolation valves should fail closed on loss of electrical power and indeed from my experience this is how the trip valves were initially shown on the P+IDs. However, an interruption of electrical power to the valve has now given rise to a closed route for cooling water flow, which itself is a hazard. There may be a redundant circuit, but this too could be affected by the same loss of electrical power event. A global loss of power would disable the cooling water pumps, but as they are important to safety they are connected to a GI supply.

For our design it may be preferable, on a balance of risk, to utilise valves that 'stay put' on loss of electrical power. By doing this we can remove the potential for a local loss of electrical supply to restrict the route for cooling water flow. With a local loss of power supply, fail-close valves will initiate a loss of cooling fault. Conversely, stay-put valves will not initiate a loss of cooling fault; there is no mechanism by which a loss of electrical supply will lead to activity ingress into the cooling circuit. With the valves staying open it will ensure that:

1. The interlock does not need to be reset on the restoration of power with the valves then closed. This is one less thing for the operators to do and is one less thing to go wrong;

2. If electrical power were to not be reinstated from the GI supply, the use of fire hoses for a once-through cooling system could be used. The once through system would not function if the isolation valves were fail closed.

The ALARP consensus was for stay-put valves. Finally, we should consider the potential for corrosion to lead to activity migrating into the primary circuit and then into the secondary circuit should there be a leak path in the heat exchanger. Again, through appropriate selection of materials, thicknesses and operating conditions, this should be a very remote possibility. Indeed, it may well be more likely that because the secondary circuit is open to the atmosphere (via the cooling towers) activity enters the secondary circuit due to a release from an accident on another plant even from another nuclear site (consider that the activity released by Chernobyl was detected at nuclear sites across Europe). The use of automated isolation valves in the secondary circuit should be considered carefully.

12.1.2   Compressed air

Many plants utilise compressed air for operational reasons and the management of hazards. Operational examples of compressed air use are:

- As a process gas;

- To agitate liquors and ensure solids are maintained in suspension;

- To measure liquor level (pneumercators[1]);

- As a motive force to actuate automated process valves or pumps;

- As a motive force to actuate lifting equipment.

Compressed air is also used as breathing air for air-fed pressurised suits. These suits are used when making entry into potentially highly contaminated areas where the sole use of respirators is not sufficient. In terms of maintaining safety, examples of compressed air use include:

- The dilution of radiolytic hydrogen gas;

- As a motive force to actuate safety valves;

- To provide a flow of air through activity-in-air monitors to facilitate airborne activity reaching the filters for detection by the radiation probe.

Large nuclear sites often have a site ring main from which individual plants tap off an allocation of compressed air. The fed plant may then have its own ring main from which individual pieces of equipment take their feed from spur lines attached to the ring main. Conversely, a plant may also generate its own compressed air supply, which may feed into the plant's own ring main. In this instance, the air supply is still a service, but is not classed as an external site service.

The site or plant main will be pressurised by the use of one or more duty air compressors with one or more generators on standby. The number of compressors in the duty/standby system will be determined by operational need and safety and availability requirements. At any one time, it can normally be assumed that in a multi-compressor system, at least one compressor may be unavailable due to EMIT or breakdown. The standby compressor would automatically take-over the duty role should there be a failure of the duty compressor with the standby compressor now becoming the duty compressor. The failed compressor would then be repaired, which may take a few hours, days or even weeks to repair depending on the severity of the failure.

---

[1]A pneumercator is an instrument that is used to measure liquor level in a vessel. It consists of a dip pipe into the base of the vessel into which a flow of compressed air is directed that will then bubble into the liquor and from there rise into the vessel ullage. The back-pressure of the compressed air is related to the weight of the liquor at the base of the dip pipe and from knowledge of the liquor density, the depth of the liquor can be determined.

A pneumercator contains no moving or maintainable parts in the liquor and is therefore an ideal instrument for use in radioactive liquors, though there may be the potential for blockage to occur should there be solids in the liquor and a loss of compressed air.

A duty/standby pair of compressors would periodically change the allocation of which compressor is the duty compressor. This ensures that both compressors get runtime and helps to maximise the likelihood that the standby compressor will operate if a demand is placed upon it. It may be advantageous for reliability if the ratio of runtime between the compressors is 2:1 rather than 1:1. This approach helps to ensure that if there are failure modes that are runtime dependent, then both compressors would not fail at the same time.

The use of an air accumulator after the compressor will help to ensure a constant flow of air to the plant should there be a short-term interruption of compressor service. Therefore, from a safety perspective, it will also provide a buffer of air should all of the compressors fail. The decay time of this reservoir will be dependent upon system use and leakage. Fifteen minutes or more of an air buffer for pressurised suit work is often required. Should the compressor systems fail, this would give time for the personnel wearing the suit to safely withdraw from the contaminated area.

Given the extent of compressed air lines within a plant, there is always the potential for a breach of the line to occur. This could be due to impact with a vehicle, collapse of another structure onto the line or even maintenance personnel inadvertently cutting through the line should it be misidentified. A breach would be revealed to control room operators through an impact on operations, e.g. as pneumercator level measurements are lost. There may also be alarms that indicate a loss of pressure or flow through instrumentation or equipment.

Throughout the ring main will be located isolation valves and these can be closed either side of the breach site. This will then enable the non-isolated pipework to re-pressurise and restore operations and so on. During normal operations, the isolation valves will be locked in position to prevent inadvertent closure.

An important role of the safety assessor is to understand and assess how the loss of air may affect safety. We must note that until the breach in the damaged pipework is repaired and the isolation valves reopened, the ring main is no longer a ring. Further damage to the pipework would lead to the inability to supply some of the users, which could have safety implications. Whilst it may be expected that two damaging events occurring is unlikely, the likelihood of it occurring should be considered. It may be necessary for the safety analysis to specify how long the plant can be justified running in this compromised configuration. Additionally, a breach in the pipework and loss of supply is a potential CCF that may initiate failure of duty systems and safety systems if both rely on the supply of the air. The isolation valves should be sited so that it is possible to restore air to the duty and/or safety systems. This consideration is important when considering the supply of compressed air to purge radiolytic hydrogen from vessels. The purge air will be supplied by multiple air lines delivering air into the vessel. It is important that sufficient air can still be delivered should a section of the ring main be isolated.

12.1.3 Specialist gases

Many plants require the use of specialist gases and these may be used directly as process gases to enable chemical reactions to occur. Specialist gases may also be used in inert gloveboxes or other process areas to prevent oxidation and reduce the risk of fire. The use of the gases and their supply mechanisms should be considered in the safety analysis.

The gases may be supplied from a bottled source, which may be local to the point of use or it may be supplied from a bottle store outside of the plant. Some gases may also be supplied by a ring main.

The safety analysis will consider the effects of loss of supply of the gases. Ideally, the operational processes should fail-safe on loss of supply of the specialist gases, but this cannot always be guaranteed. There may be an inter-relationship with the electrical supply and compressed air supply; valves to supply specialist gases may need compressed air to remain open.

Due to their high internal pressure, gas bottles are a source of stored energy. They can pose a hazard to nuclear plants due to their failure potentially leading to damage to primary and secondary containment layers and safety systems. The use of gas bottles should be considered carefully and if possible, their use avoided or arrangements put in place to protect sensitive nuclear plant, e.g. by the use of dedicated bottle storage racks outside of the building. The correct use of bottle transporters, bottle caps and securely storing the bottles should reduce the chance of the bottle being significantly damaged to the extent that it either ruptures or acts as a projectile. Ensuring that combustible inventory is not co-located with the bottles will reduce the potential for over-pressure due to fire.

A release of compressed gas into a confined space can give rise to asphyxiation. This is an industrial hazard for which there should be arrangements to eliminate or minimise this risk. However, there can be a nuclear context as the presence of the gas may lead to operator disorientation that could either initiate a fault or compromise the ability of the operator to respond to the fault.

We should of course note that most of us will be familiar with seeing gas bottles in hospitals and old peoples' homes to supply oxygen. They can be used safely with a low risk of failure if used, handled and stored properly. However, there are no practicable alternatives to their use to supply oxygen to these patients. Conversely, there may be reasonably practicable alternatives to the use of gas bottles in nuclear plants. Hence, it is reasonable to seek, as far as practicable, alternatives to ensure that the risk is ALARP.

Example: Argon Use

On a particular plant, there was a requirement to take packages containing nuclear material and over-pack them into additional package layers. It was known that radiolytic hydrogen could be produced that would pose a hydrogen explosion hazard, though the likelihood of this occurring was more theoretical than real. To further minimise the remote risk of explosion in the packages, a design change was instigated to inject argon gas into the packages to purge atmospheric air from the layers. The argon would displace oxygen and minimise the theoretical hydrogen hazard. The use of the argon purge would provide defence-in-depth, but it was not the principal means of providing for safety.

The change was close to proceeding until a concern was raised that argon has a lower thermal conductivity than air (it is used between the glass panes in double glazing). The use of argon would affect the thermal modelling that had been undertaken to justify the packages and their storage arrangements.

Whilst a HAZOP had been undertaken, for whatever reason, the HAZOP had missed the issue. Indeed, on re-running the thermal model with argon the packages were predicted to have a higher temperature, but fortunately, this was found to be within acceptable limits. The question raised regarding argon was a valid one. The lesson learned is that one must always be aware of unintended consequences and that the right team members must be involved in a project right from the start.

12.1.4 A final note on service inter-relationship

As we have alluded to, there can be a complex relationship between services with one service being dependent on one or more other services. For plants that are required to be run to maintain safety, it is essential that this inter-relationship is understood. If emergency provision of a service is required following failure of the duty supply, failure to understand the inter-relationship can lead to problems in delivering the necessary safety functions to assure safety on failure of the duty supply. We will illustrate this with a simple example.

Example: Emergency Pumping
A new waste retrieval plant is being designed to remove waste from an underground waste storage vault. The vault is not impervious to groundwater and this must be periodically removed to prevent the migration of activity to the wider environment. Loss of incoming electrical supply is identified as a CCF that would disable the duty and standby pumps. Therefore, the pumps are designed to be connected to a standby diesel generator. With these alternative power arrangements, the plant is initially considered to be tolerant to loss of incoming power.

But, has the design process thought through to where the water is being pumped? Is the destination tolerant to a loss of incoming power? Additionally, an inspection of the P+IDs for the new design shows a number of safety valves in the discharge pipework. These are initially identified as air-actuated valves and are fail-closed. Therefore, on loss of incoming power supply, the air compressor will also fail and the valves will close preventing the transfer of the groundwater.

Leaving aside the question of where the water is being pumped to, the design must ensure that the valves in the line can be actuated to open to enable the water flow. This could be achieved by ensuring the air compressor is connected to the generator, but this has now increased the capacity and cost of this system. Manual over-rides to the valves could be provided as a simple cost-effective solution, but the valves are found to be within a shielded cell to protect against the radiation hazard from activity in the water. Operator entry should only be after the pipes and vessels have been emptied and flushed. This cannot be done without even more valves being actuated and a water supply being available (or at least sufficient buffer tank capacity). The design is potentially becoming more complex and costly.

We will not labour on this design any more nor comment on its eventual design solution. The important learning here is that it is not sufficient to simply and naively provide a standby generator system and be done with it. The full relationship of the services required to achieve the safety function must be understood and the full end-to-end system reviewed and confirmed to function as intended.

Chapter 13

Recommendations and Achieving ALARP

Within the UK, the licensees have a legal duty to ensure that the risks from their operations are ALARP. This stems from the Health and Safety at Work Act and this was discussed in Section 2. Achieving ALARP is not a static condition; standards change and what constitutes RGP will evolve with time. Remember, it was only a few decades ago that RGP for cars was for them only to be fitted with front seatbelts and it was not standard practice to wear them. Seatbelts were not automatically equipped in the back of the car.

In addition to changes in RGP, the physical condition of a plant will deteriorate with both use and time even if it is routinely maintained. Thus, one-off and potentially significant maintenance tasks may need to be performed that may be outside of the usual maintenance programmes. These may have significant impacts on the plant and process.

We have discussed how the periodic review of safety cases, together with engineering substantiation, may identify shortfalls and observations with their associated recommendations for improvement. As definitions:

- A shortfall is where there is a deficiency in meeting safety case criteria or there is an inability to substantiate an SSC;

- An observation is when improvements to procedures or engineering have been identified that can further reduce the risks.

We might initially expect that if a recommendation to reduce risks has been identified from a shortfall or observation, we should simply accept it and implement it. This would surely ensure risks are reduced to ALARP? No—to achieve an ALARP status on a plant it is not necessary to implement all of the identified recommendations. It may be acceptable to implement only some of them or even none of them, *if* adequate justification can be made; i.e. they are not reasonably practicable to do. A balance must always be struck between the benefit from the improvement and the time, trouble and cost of implementing the recommendation. In the real world, time and effort and even money spent somewhere cannot be spent somewhere else and the somewhere else may provide more safety benefit. Of course, saying we cannot *afford* to do something is not a reason to not do it—an adequate ALARP justification must be made. This justification should focus on other sound engineering aspects rather than cost. So how do we determine which recommendations should be implemented and which should be rejected? The ALARP process lets us do this. The ALARP process can be considered to be a three-step process that involves:

1. Identification and collation of the recommendations;

2. Sentencing of the recommendations for implementation and over what timescale, or their rejection with justification;

3. Implementing the recommendations.

We have essentially discussed Step 1 in the previous chapters as the safety case production process, notably from the design process or from an LC 15 review. The collation of the recommendations simply involves bringing together all of the recommendations from the source documents so that they can be considered holistically. This chapter will discuss Step 2 and Step 3 and how they may be implemented within a plant. This process may involve an ALARP *committee* to make informed decisions as to the reasonable practicality of implementing the recommendations.

This chapter will discuss the use of *optioneering studies* to help make ALARP decisions. There are sophisticated optioneering methodologies available on the market and we will only provide a brief high-level outline of the process. Another tool used in the decision-making process is the use of *cost benefit analysis* (CBA) and this is also discussed. A CBA focuses on the numerical aspects of risk reduction against financial cost and should only be used in conjunction with other processes for making ALARP decisions.

It is worth noting that we have made reference here to the UK's Health and Safety at Work Act, which we have stated covers all industries. Therefore, this ALARP process should not be considered to be unique to the nuclear industry. The steps outlined here could essentially be adopted by any industry or organisation to an appropriate degree. The nuclear industry is experienced in undertaking formal ALARP reviews and the nuclear regulator takes a keen interest in the achievement of ALARP.

13.1 Generating options

A shortfall or observation may be identified, but without an obvious route for improvement, i.e. a specific recommendation. There may be deficiency in terms of risk, safety hierarchy, number and quality of safety measures or that the normal operational dose was 'high' and not demonstrably ALARP. Indeed, this may also be the situation in a design project where the detailed analysis has identified gaps in the design and improvements are required to enable the relevant safety criteria to be satisfied and the risk demonstrably reduced to ALARP.

Clearly, if there is no obvious way forward there will need to be some research to identify solutions. In contrast, there may also be a spectrum of options and it is not clear which to choose. One option may be easy to do but have limited risk reduction or improvement to the position in the safety hierarchy. Another option may involve a complex system that will be difficult to engineer and costly to design and install, but may have significant safety benefit. There needs to be a mechanism to help make these decisions and a structured approach can help to do this and provide evidence that the chosen solution is the ALARP solution. The ALARP solution does not have to be the most complex and costly solution if it can be shown that this is not reasonably practicable. The process that identifies and selects an option is known as *optioneering*.

The optioneering process is undertaken in an optioneering study. This is a desktop exercise that may require pre-work to identify options, etc., and that will systematically review each option, compare and contrast and determine the optimal solution that meets the goal of the study. Optioneering should be forward looking and not seek to 'rubber stamp' a previously made decision. This is an error that is too often made and calls into question the validity of the chosen ALARP decision.

13.1.1   Optioneering

A chosen solution cannot be identified if there are no options available to choose between. There is always the base option of doing nothing and leaving the situation as it is. Indeed, in the end, this may be found to be the chosen solution, but if there is a deficiency in safety provision this is unlikely to be ALARP for a new design. Therefore, a team of relevant engineers, safety assessors, RPAs, plant operators and so on should be involved in identifying options. Nothing should be discounted at this initial stage.

Once there is a list of options, it is perfectly acceptable to weed out any obvious non-starters. This could be because they rely on unavailable technology, or they would not be commensurate with RGP or that they fundamentally compromise the function of the plant. Additionally, options could be justified as not being reasonable at this stage on the basis that the cost is clearly grossly disproportionate to the benefit gained if this is unambiguous and beyond reasonable debate.

A chosen solution will need to be determined and to do this each option will need to be compared against a common set of selection criteria. Examples of the criteria are given in Table 13.1. Taking each option in turn, a score (say between 1 and 5) may be assigned to each of the selected criteria with the 'winning' option the one that scores

Table 13.1: Example selection criteria that may be used in optioneering.

Selection criteria	
Normal operational dose	Programme
Nuclear safety (faults)	Cost
Industrial safety and fire	Impact on environment
Novelty (unknown risks)	Reliance on-site infrastructure
Operator flexibility	Efficiency

the highest. It may be felt that not all of the criteria in Table 13.1 may be as important as others. Therefore, a weighting system can be used to introduce bias into the scoring process. The development of the selection criteria and any weighting will need to be discussed and agreed with the participants of the optioneering study.

13.1.2   Cost benefit analysis

The use of CBA can be helpful in the formulation of ALARP decisions. For many in the wider non-nuclear industry, the use of CBA has been seen as the first choice in making an ALARP decision. However, this approach is not always successful. Sound, engineering and logic-based reasons that are supported by CBA are preferable. The regulators and if it comes to it, the courts, are not likely to be swayed by arguments solely based upon cost. Indeed, the court of public opinion is not convinced by CBA arguments; 'My son's life was not worth spending...'.

At the heart of CBA is a numerical attempt to compare the cost of something against the quantum of risk reduction. It determines whether the associated cost of the reduction is grossly disproportionate or not. The rationale is that if it is grossly disproportionate then it is not necessary to make the postulated improvement, which should be backed up by a sound argument in terms of time and trouble as well as cost. The trouble can relate to factors such as dose, environmental impact, waste, RGP, industrial safety, safety hierarchy, uncertainty, novelty, and so on. The use of CBA cannot be used to provide an ALARP case on its own and it cannot be used to justify intolerable risks or a failure to perform a legal duty.

If we are observant, we will note that CBA focuses on risk reduction—this is a numerical term. It is simply the difference in the risk before the change compared to after the change. The risk may be due to normal operations (e.g. due to the radiation exposure from a normal discharge to the atmosphere) or from a fault condition. Although we often pride ourselves on our numerical risk analysis and the use of (sometimes) complex risk models, they are just that, models. They are subject to input errors, estimations that may or may not come be correct and aspects that have not been thought about and accounted for. Hence, risk models can only provide confidence that the risks are low or even negligible, but the actual numerical value is only as good as the input data and model algorithm. These facts help to explain the desire to make ALARP decisions based upon sound argument and not solely on the manipulation of numbers. Moreover, there are other intangible aspects that we have mentioned, such as the safety hierarchy, that are not directly reflected in a risk number.

Once we have established the risk reduction, we compare that to the cost of implementing the change. This cost is the actual cost in performing the modification, including design and installation, equipment costs and potentially also costs associated with the lost production time of the plant. The cost will be reasonable if it passes the following test:

$$\text{cost} < rvd, \tag{13.1}$$

where r is the risk avoided, v is the monetary value attributed to a unit of risk and d is the disproportionate factor. The monetary value of a life lost due to cancer is given by

Table 13.2: Disproportionate factors for consideration in CBA. The values have been taken from a review of [29] noting that there are no *mandated* values for use. If there are high risks or consequences then a disproportionate factor of 10 may not be sufficient. There is no clearly defined value of what constitutes 'low risk', but it could be taken to be a value close to the BSO, as this is 'broadly acceptable.'

	Workers	Public
Risk in the vicinity of the BSL	10	10
Low risk	3	2

the HSE as £2.7 million as of 2003, which can be adjusted for the current year. Therefore, we can equate £2.70 for every 10^{-6} of risk that we can save (remember we can equate a dose to a chance of fatal cancer via 0.05 Sv^{-1}, as described in Section 5.2.5).

There are suggested values for the disproportionate factors for the workers and the public, but there are no mandated values. Suggested values for use are given in Table 13.2.

13.2 Sentencing of recommendations

A safety case may generate anything from a handful of recommendations to many hundreds depending on the size of the plant, its age and operational and physical state. If all of the recommendations were to be adopted then this could have a significant detriment to the plant's ability to operate. The vast majority of recommendations may require modifications to improve safety and make the plant safer, but they do not necessarily mean that the plant is currently unsafe.

It may be determined that recommendations could have a detrimental effect on safety when considered in the round or holistically. For example, increasing the proof testing of a safety measure may sound like a sensible idea to improve its reliability (see Section 8). However, this may involve additional work in a high-dose environment that may be significantly detrimental—a real hazard from radiation that is experienced every time there is a proof test compared to a theoretical hazard from a fault's consequence that may be very unlikely to occur.

An approach often adopted in carrying out the ALARP process is to establish an *ALARP committee* to undertake a *desktop review* of all of the recommendations. The committee would ideally consist of a number of experienced and relevant individuals from the plant and the wider site. Individuals from the wider site can bring their experiences to the ALARP committee. Table 13.3 lists the individuals that may be on an ALARP committee. Table 13.3 includes safety case members from both the plant and the project. This represents the fact that the plant will have its own personnel who are responsible for safety case and engineering functions on that plant. A new safety case, including that resulting from a LC 15 review, is likely to be undertaken by a project team, possibly using external organisation resource. It is the external

Table 13.3: Example members of an ALARP committee.

Committee attendees	
Chair/secretary	Plant manager
Plant maintenance	Plant operations
Plant safety case	Plant engineering
Project safety case	Project engineering
RPA	Environment
Human factors	Independent
Originator of the recommendation—*optional*	

organisation that is likely to have made the majority of the recommendations. It may be helpful for the originator of the recommendation, which may be from the external organisation, to also be present to put it into perspective and to offer ideas of how it was envisaged to be adopted and the risk benefit it would bring. Finally, individual specialists could be utilised for relevant issues to help with the ALARP discussion.

The ALARP committee should systematically review all of the recommendations and formulate an ALARP opinion on each and every recommendation. It may be necessary to group some of the recommendations because they are related or that because implementing one recommendation may negate others. Therefore, there should be some planning for the meeting before it starts. What is often adopted at an ALARP review is to sentence each recommendation to a specific category, which will then define what, if anything, should be done. An example category system is presented in Table 13.4.

For complex issues there may need to be information gathering and research into the viability of implementing the recommendations. This may necessitate a package of work that may take time to complete. Formal optioneering processes may also be required to be undertaken and this will form the audit trail of how an ALARP decision was made.

For some recommendations there may be no clear way forward and the balance of risk may be hard to establish, e.g. an improvement in nuclear safety at the expense of industrial safety. It is good practice to clearly record this difficulty and a decision will have to be made one way or another. Advice from a wider pool of resources can be sought if needed. Ultimately, the ALARP process and key findings should be documented in the top tier safety report. This gives an opportunity to discuss some of the difficult ALARP decisions and gain assurance from other senior members of the safety community that the correct decision has been made.

13.3   Implementing recommendations

An LC 15 review of a safety case is one of the principal vehicles by which recommendations are made to improve the safety of a plant. Once the recommendations have been sentenced for implementation, packages of work must be initiated to make the necessary changes on the plant. However, recommendations cannot all be implemented at once, as this is not practicable with realistic levels of resources that will be finite. There must be a phased programme of adopting the recommendations.

Table 13.4 describes the most important recommendations that must be adopted in a relatively short period of time, which for an lc 15 review normally means before the plant transitions to the revised safety case. There will be an *implementation plan* to adopt these recommendations. The less significant recommendations can be adopted over a longer timescale and there will be an *improvement programme*.

The recommendations may require external organisations to design, install and commission new systems, such as interlocks. Some of the recommendations, irrespective of their safety significance, may be able to be implemented quickly (quick wins), but some could take many months to complete (long lead). If a recommendation can be adopted quickly without undue influence on more safety significant recommendations, there may be no good reason to delay the changes being made.

Example: Quick Win

An interlock has a 12-month proof test. The safety analysis has concluded that a six-month proof test is required to reduce the risk to below the bso. The proof testing is not required to be undertaken in a high-risk area and the alarp committee agreed that decreasing the pti was acceptable. It was categorised as a safety significant recommendation and it could be implemented quickly on the plant requiring little change to safety documentation.

Example: Long Lead

There is an identified deficiency in the number of safety measures on a plant to protect against inadvertent opening of a shielded container. A new interlock system was recommended to be installed and this was accepted by the alarp committee. The interlock requires a design that involves process, c+i and mechanical disciplines together with safety. The interlock must be defined, its safety function and performance requirements specified and level of risk reduction determined.

Once designed, a djr may be required to confirm that the safety functions and performance requirements have been delivered. The interlock will then need to be installed on the plant and commissioned and these activities may require consideration of the relevant hazards associated with installation and commissioning. There are clearly packages of work that will require co-ordinating including the provision of workers on the plant that will need to interface with the day-to-day operations. Even for a simple interlock this is going to take a period of time to undertake.

Table 13.4: Example ALARP categorisation scheme.

Category	Description	Adoption
i	A high consequence fault has no safety measures; or Imminent failure of a principal SSC (Class 1); or An intolerable risk is calculated	Immediate action
ii	An important SSC (Class 2) does not exist or cannot be substantiated; or Credit is taken for an important SSC (Class 2) in the safety assessment that does not currently exist, but is intended to be installed; or Risk is currently tolerable, but can be reduced to below the BSO	Implementation Plan if reasonably practicable to adopt
iii	A less significant SSC (Class 3) does not exist or cannot be substantiated; or Credit is taken for a less significant SSC (Class 3) in the safety assessment that does not currently exist, but is intended to be installed; or Risk is below the BSO, but could be further reduced	ALARP Improvement Programme if reasonably practicable to adopt
iv	The recommendation does not provide a safety improvement, but may offer other benefits such as efficiency savings	Alternative arrangements if accepted
v	The recommendation is not reasonably practicable to implement	Not applicable

Appendix A

Bits and Pieces

This appendix is intended to provide a few helpful bits and pieces of information.

A.1 Adequate

The term *adequate* is a common term in safety cases. It may be used in the concept of 'An adequate safety case has been made' or 'The safety measure is adequate to mitigate the dose'. The term *adequate* means good enough or fit-for-purpose and that we are happy with the outcome. Safety cases will always refrain from using excitable claims on performance. This contrasts somewhat with normal everyday experience where the term *adequate* is taken to mean that something is only just about acceptable with a slight negative connotation.

A.2 Checking, reviewing and approving

Organisations producing safety cases and licensees have a *quality management system* (QMS). The QMS will define a set of policies, processes and procedures required for planning and execution of the organisation's core business. Of interest to us is the production, checking, reviewing and approving of safety case documents. A QMS will normally require a *quality plan* to be produced and this should set out the roles and responsibilities of those involved in document production, checking, reviewing and approving (for a document, we can also place drawing, calculation, model, and so on.).

Once drafted, documents should start with a self-check by the author. It is the author's responsibility to get the document right and not that of the checker or reviewer. However, even the best safety assessors may not get everything right and they may not know of certain facts. Therefore, the checking and review cycle ensures documents are correct and complete.

It is important to distinguish what we mean between a check and a review. Firstly, a check of a document should be a systematic confirmation that everything in the document is correct and it will include:

- Plant and process details;

- Scope;

- Logic and methodology;

- Calculations;

- References;

- Formatting, layout and self-consistency.

The checking of a document is usually a big ask and it is often necessary to allocate some aspects to different checkers. If this occurs, then the responsibilities should be clearly specified. As an example, another senior safety assessor can check the safety arguments and provide a technical check, a more junior member could provide a calculation and consistency check whilst a plant representative would check the plant details and the impact of the safety case on the operation of the plant.

During checking, a positive check is as important as a negative check. By this we mean that every number, calculation and reference should be confirmed as being correct and if so, a tick applied on a mark-up. This mark-up of the document can then be scanned and stored in the project directory as evidence that checking has been undertaken and that there is evidence of what was checked. This is more reassuring than solely identifying where things are wrong. Significant comments that should be written out on a checking sheet that has a response and close-out column. Comments should be factual and avoid making personal remarks as to the competence of the author.[1]

The review of a document is different from a detailed check. There are different types of review, and it is expected that a review does not check all of the calculations and references and so on. A review would normally happen after a detailed check, but the review may include a sample check to provide confidence that the checking process has been done adequately.

The document review may be during a committee stage or it may be as part of an IPR. A review may focus on the specialism of the reviewer, such as human factors, radiation protection or engineering. A tabular review sheet may be used to feed-back comments and any inevitable typos marked up. A review is intended to gauge whether the document feels correct with the methods and calculations used are appropriate. The review will also focus on whether anything has been missed.

When updating the document, the draft or issue number should be increased and a means of identifying the changes provided in the document as this really helps the checker or the reviewer. The author should engage positively and constructively with the checker or reviewer.

Following writing, checking and reviewing a document will generally be *approved* for an issue. Approval is normally given by a senior project person or a senior member of the licensee. The approver's role is to ensure that the document has been through

---

[1]Other than pure politeness, the safety case community is a small one and very often the tables are turned.

appropriate due process. There may be a read through of the document, but more often than not the approver simply requires evidence that the checking and review cycle is complete and that the paperwork has been correctly produced and signed. They would not do a detailed check. However, if on a sample read through the approver spots something that is wrong it can bring into question the whole authoring, checking and reviewing cycle.

A.3   Document control

A safety case will comprise many documents and many of these will be obviously associated with the safety case, such as the top-tier report and supporting hazard analysis. In addition, there will be a whole host of drawings, configuration diagrams, calculations and so on that describe the design of the plant and are important as they form the basis of the safety case. These documents must all be retrievable and easily identifiable. Many hours are lost on projects looking for information that may be lost or hidden on a local drive rather than a network drive. It is essential that a good quality document control system is utilised. In addition, the licensees are required to maintain their records even after the plant has been decommissioned.

Safety case authors and engineers must utilise the document control system and ensure that their documents are correctly stored. Each should have a unique reference number and be available for those that need it. This will enable work to continue if the author leaves the project. Version control needs to be applied with the document history sheet reflecting where the document is up to in the checking/review cycle. Each licensee will have their own preference for the numbering/lettering of the document draft, issue and revision status. One may expect a document to be in draft until it has at least passed through checking and then it may become a formal issue for peer review or committee approval.

A reference quoted in a report should always be to a 'proper' document that can be identified and retrieved. Reference to a personal communication or to an email is useless as these will more often than not be lost and never found again once the author has disappeared. The way round this is to either put a copy of the relevant text in the document itself (such as in an appendix) or to create a new document, give it a reference number and place the communication or email within this document. This document will then be able to be stored in the project directory/archive system and will be retrievable.

A.3.1   Ensuring success

A safety case may be a standalone package of work or it may be one part of an overall design and build project. A design and build contract may have an overall budget of hundreds of millions of pounds and the safety case cost may be a small fraction of the overall price. The whole project will depend upon the successful delivery and acceptance of the safety case. The production of the safety case will need an appropriate level of planning and project management for successful delivery.

Ownership

There needs to be a sense of ownership of the safety case by the project and crucially, the operators and plant managers. Too many safety cases have historically been written by the 'Safety Department' and imposed on the plant. The plant manager and operators need be engaged in all aspects to ensure that it delivers what they need in order to safely operate the plant, within the necessary constraints that the safety case process will identify. With ownership comes a desire to improve documentation and provide information in a timely manner.

Resource

A safety case needs sufficient and adequate resource to produce it. As with all projects, individuals will differ in their ability and their style of presentation of argument. It is accepted that not every safety case project will have access to the 'A' team of resource. Provided that there are sufficient checks and balances and that there are some 'A' team member somewhere on the project, adequate documentation should be able to be produced.

Resource does not only relate to the safety assessors, but also engineers, approvers, peer reviewers and so on. These must be available when required and have sufficient qualifications and experience to undertake the tasks. Good programming is essential to ensure that work loads are balanced and resource is available when required. Timescales for resourcing requirements must be realistic—too often the back-end tasks (such as peer review) are squeezed because the project is running behind programme.

Communication

Interactions between safety assessors, engineers and plant operators is essential. Ensuring access to information is invaluable, which includes the ability to visit the plant as often as practicable. Engaging with stakeholders early, including with written documents, can help to prevent late challenges that may undermine safety case arguments. Plant visits and discussions with the operators are essential to understand how the plant works.

A.4   Proportionality

A safety case should be *proportionate* to the harm potential or the magnitude of the nuclear hazard. This is subtly different from being proportionate to the magnitude of the risk. In principle, a high-hazard plant can still present a very low quantified risk in comparison to a less hazardous plant if the latter does not have the same degree of defence-in-depth. For the high-hazard plant, we would naturally seek more information and confidence in the systems that provide this defence-in-depth. After all, if things can go very badly, we would seek a lot of confidence in the systems that are there to protect us. Even in providing confidence, a high-hazard safety case should be written concisely and provide an appropriate level of detail that is commensurate with the complexity of the argument in the relevant document. Reading through long, complex discussion only to find trivial consequences is frustrating and distracts from the focus on the more important sections.

The top-tier safety case report should be focused and utilise supporting references for the detail rather than seeking to add every available fact that may be of interest to anyone that reads it. The more (unnecessary) information added to the top-tier document (or any document) the greater the cost to produce it (and then check it). The more the information is given, the more opportunity is given for comment to be raised through the due process. All of the comments add up and if many are raised on unnecessary text it can be distracting to the delivery of the overall safety message.

A.5   Fit-for-purpose/pragmatic

The terms *fit-for-purpose* and *pragmatic* are used in the safety case community. They are often used in bids for work as 'buzz' words. It is, however, less clear what they mean. There are even industry conferences associated with defining what it means to be *fit-for-purpose*. One person's pragmatic view is often considered to be someone else's short-cut or 'cowboy' attitude. There is a difficult balance to achieve the correct level of pragmatism.

On a personal reflection, I can sum up that a fit-for-purpose safety case should:

- Deliver the specification required for the safety case life-cycle stage;

- Be proportionate (see above);

- Be delivered on time;[2]

- Adequately assess the hazards;

- Include input from the operators;

- Satisfy a wide range of stakeholders often with competing requirements, as far as reasonably practicable;

- Deliver an adequate level of safety whilst also enabling operations to be conducted efficiently;

- Identify sensible recommendations for improvement.

---

[2]In the world of project management, there is a thing called the time, cost and quality triangle with each of these terms in a vertex of the triangle. It is difficult to deliver all three corners to their maximum potential, i.e. minimum time, minimum cost and maximum quality.

As an example, if we do something more quickly, it is likely that it will also be cheaper (as much safety case work is performed on a rated basis), but we will likely deliver a less polished product. Conversely, if we spend more money and take more time, we would expect a better-quality product (such as a Rolls Royce). Safety cases require a quality product (good enough for sure) and on time (e.g. to meet the LC 15 timescale), and as a result, the control of cost may be sub-optimum.

A.6   Proprietary names

A safety case should avoid, where possible, the use of proprietary names when describing equipment. For example, a compressor should be referred to the type and perhaps its duty capability. The fact that it was manufactured by *Ace Compressors* is not really essential information to include in the safety case. Moreover, should a new compressor be provided it may require a safety case modification to change the source manufacturer even if essentially the same compressor is being sourced. This is not an efficient use of resource.

Appendix B

Useful Physical Information

Property	Value
Constants	
Acceleration due to gravity g	9.81 m s^{-2}
Standard temperature and pressure (STP)	$273.15 \text{ K} = 0 \text{ °C}$ and 1 bar(a) = 101.3 kPa
Avogadro's number N_A	$6.022 \times 10^{23} \text{ mol}^{-1}$
Molar gas volume at STP	22.4 l mol^{-1}
Universal gas constant R	$8.31 \text{ J mol}^{-1} \text{ K}^{-1}$
Water properties at STP	
Enthalpy of vaporisation L	$2.501 \times 10^6 \text{ J K}^{-1}$
Specific heat at constant pressure (liquid) C_{pl}	$4218 \text{ J kg}^{-1} \text{ K}^{-1}$
Conversion factors	
Number of seconds in five minutes	300 s
Number of seconds in two hours	7200 s
Number of seconds in one year	$3.15 \times 10^7 \text{ s} \ (\approx \pi \times 10^7 \text{ s})$
Cross section 1 barn (b)	$10^{-28} \text{ m}^2 = 10^{-24} \text{ cm}^2$
Activity 1 curie (Ci)	$3.7 \times 10^{10} \text{ Bq}$

Ideal gas equation:
$$PV = nRT, \tag{B.1}$$

where P is the pressure of the gas, V is its volume, n is the number of moles, R is the universal gas constant and T is the absolute temperature.

Appendix C

Nuclear Properties

This appendix provides basic nuclear properties of common nuclides found in the nuclear industry. Unless noted, data has been taken from [30]. Main decay mode and half-life listed for each nuclide. There may also be accompanying gamma emission for the transitions. For example, the ^{60}Co will β decay to an excited state of ^{60}Ni, which

Nuclide	Principal decay mode	Half-life
neutron (free)	β^-	615 s*
^{3}H tritium	β^-	12.32 y
^{60}Co cobalt	β^-	5.27 y
^{90}Sr strontium	β^-	28.79 y
^{90}Y yttrium	β^-	64.10 h
^{95}Zr zirconium	β^-	64.03 d
^{103}Ru ruthenium	β^-	39.26 d
^{106}Ru -	β^-	373.59 d
^{131}I iodine	β^-	8.02 d
^{134}Cs caesium	β^-	2.06 y
^{137}Cs -	β^-	30.17 y
^{141}Ce cerium	β^-	32.51 d
^{154}Eu europium	β^-	8.59 y
^{233}U uranium	α	159.2 ky
^{234}U -	α	246 ky
^{235}U -	α	704 My
^{238}U -	α	4.47 Gy
^{238}Pu plutonium	α	87.7 y
^{239}Pu -	α	24.11 ky
^{240}Pu -	α	6.56 ky
^{241}Pu -	β^-	14.35 y
^{242}Pu -	α	375 ky

* from [4]

269

will then emit two gamma rays. Other than the emission of the gamma rays, ^{60}Ni is stable. It is often stated that ^{60}Co is a $\beta\gamma$ emitter, but strictly, it is the ^{60}Ni that emits the gamma rays.

Bibliography

[1] ONR (2020) *Safety Assessment Principles for Nuclear Facilities*.

[2] HSE (1992) *The Tolerability of Risk from Nuclear Power Stations*, Her Majesty's Stationery Office, London.

[3] HSE (2001) *Reducing Risks, Protecting People*, Her Majesty's Stationery Office, London.

[4] Lilley, J. S. (2001) *Nuclear Physics Principles and Applications*, Wiley, Chichester.

[5] Krane, K. S. (1987) *Introductory Nuclear Physics*, Wiley, New York.

[6] Bounds, A. (2020) *Implementation of Nuclear Safety Cases*, Safety and Reliability, DOI: 10.1080/09617353.2020.1800977.

[7] Bureau International des Poids et Mesures (2019) *The International System of Units*.

[8] Marshall, R. (2018) *Three Centuries of Manchester Physics*, Vol. III, Champagne Cat.

[9] ICRP (2012) *Compendium of Dose Coefficients based on ICRP Publication 60*, ICRP Publication 119, Ann. ICRP 41(Suppl.).

[10] DOE (2011) Standard Derived Concentration Technical Standard DOE-STD-1196-2011.

[11] ICRP (2007) *The 2007 Recommendations of the International Commission on Radiological Protection*, ICRP Publication 103, Ann. ICRP 37 (2-4).

[12] McLaughlin, T. P. *et al.* (2000) *A Review of Criticality Accidents*, LA-13638, Los Alamos, New Mexico.

[13] DOE (1994) *Airborne Release Fractions/Rates and respirable Fractions for Nonreactor Nuclear Facilities*, DOE-HDBK-3010-94.

[14] Sutter, S. L. *et al.* (1981) *Aerosols Generated by Free Fall Spills of Powders and Solutions in Static Air*, NUREG/CR-2 PNL-3768.

[15] Selby, J. M. *et al.* (1975) *Considerations in the Assessment of the Consequences of Effluents from Mixed Oxide Fuel Fabrication Plants*, BNWL-1697 Rev. 1, Pacific Northwest Laboratories, Washington.

[16] NCRP (2007) *Development of a Biokinetic Model for Radionuclide-Contaminated Wounds and Procedures for Their Assessment, Dosimetry and Treatment*, NCRP Report No. 156.

[17] Veigele, Wm. J. and Head, J. H. (1978) *Derivation of the Gaussian Plume Model*, Journal of the Air Pollution Control Association, Vol. 28 No. 11.

[18] Clarke, R. H. (1979) *A Model for Short and Medium Range Dispersion of Radionuclides Released to the Atmosphere*, R-91, National Radiological Protection Board, Harwell.

[19] Simmonds, J. R. *et al.* (1995) *Methodology for Assessing the Radiological Consequences of Routine Releases of Radionuclides to the Environment*, Radiation Protection 72, European Commission, Luxembourg.

[20] HSE (2017) *Failure Rate and Event Data for use within Risk Assessments*, PCAG chp_6K Version 14.

[21] Byrne, J. P. (1997) *The Calculation of Aircraft Crash Risk in the UK*, Contract Research Report 150, HSE, Her Majesty's Stationery Office, Norwich.

[22] IAEA (2018) *Regulations for the Safe Transport of Radioactive Material*, No. SSR-6, Rev. 1.

[23] Center for Chemical Process Safety (1999) *Guidelines for Chemical Process Quantitative Risk Analysis*, 2nd Edition.

[24] Barlow, R. J. (1999) *Statistics A Guide to the Use of Statistical Methods in the Physical Sciences*, Wiley, Chichester.

[25] Dezfuli, H. *et al.* (2009) *Bayesian Inference for NASA Probabilistic Risk and Reliability Analysis*, NASA/SP-2009-569, National Aeronautics and Space Administration.

[26] HSE (1999) *Reducing Error and Influencing Behaviour*, HSG48 Second Edition.

[27] Swain, A. D. and Guttmann, H. E. (1983) *Handbook of Human Reliability Analysis with Emphasis on Nuclear Power Plant Applications Final Report*, NUREG/CR - 1278, US Nuclear Regulatory Commission.

[28] Kirwan, B. (1994) *A Guide to Practical Human Reliability Assessment*, Taylor and Francis, London.

[29] ONR (2019) *Guidance on the Demonstration of ALARP (As Low As Reasonably Practicable)*, ONR NS-TAST-GD-005.

[30] ICRP (2008) *Nuclear Decay Data for Dosimetric Calculations*, ICRP Publication 107, Ann. ICRP 38 (3).

Useful sources of information

The ONR's TAGs, which provide more guidance to inspectors of aspects of the ONR's SAPs.

The Charles Haddon–Cave QC report into the Nimrod crash in Afghanistan in 2006 in which 14 were killed. Whilst it was not a nuclear issue, the points made are just as relevant and the LFE is applicable. There are very powerful words in the report including: 'Unfortunately, the Nimrod Safety Case was a lamentable job from start to finish. It was riddled with errors. It missed the key dangers. Its production is a story of incompetence, complacency, and cynicism. The best opportunity to prevent the accident to xv230 was, tragically, lost'.

The Safety and Reliability Society, which is applicable for all hazardous industries as well as nuclear.

The NUREG series of documents are published by the United States Nuclear Regulatory Commission. They provide information on regulatory decisions, results of research and incident investigations, and technical and administrative information.

The IAEA including the TECDOC series.

The UK Nuclear Safety Directors' Forum, which provides written advice on aspects of safety case development.

The ICRP, which provides many documents associated with the impact of radioactivity on the body.

Delacroix, D. *et al.* (2002) *Radionuclide and Radiation Protection Data Handbook*, Radiation Protection Dosimetry, Vol. 98 No 1, Nuclear Technology Publishing, Ashford.

The Chartered Institute for Ergonomics and Human Factors.

Glossary

AC *Authorisation Condition.*

ACOP approved code of practice.

ALARP *as low as reasonably practicable.*

BAT *best available techniques.*

BDB *beyond the design basis.*

BOD *basis of design.*

BPM *best practicable means.*

BSL *basic safety level.*

BSO *basic safety objective.*

C+I control and instrumentation.

CAE *claims, arguments and evidence.*

CBA *cost benefit analysis.*

CCF *common cause failure.*

CFA *conditions for acceptance.*

CMF *common mode failure.*

COMAH Control of Major Accident Hazards Regulations.

COSR *continued operations safety report.*

CREAM Consequences of Releases to the Environment: Assessment Methodology.

CSF *critical safety function.*

CWS *criticality warning system.*

DBA *design basis analysis.*

DBE *design basis earthquake.*

DCN *design change notification.*

DCP *double contingency principle.*

DF *decontamination factor.*

DJR *design justification report.*

DNSR Defence Nuclear Safety Regulator.

DOE Department of Energy.

DSEAR Dangerous Substances and Explosive Atmospheres Regulations.

EA Environment Agency.

EI *emergency instruction.*

EMIT *examination, maintenance, inspection and testing.*

EPD *electronic personal dosimeter.*

ERICPD *eliminate, reduce, isolate, control, personal, discipline.*

ESP *engineering safety principle.*

ESR *engineering substantiation report.*

FSG *fault sequence group.*

GA *general arrangement.*

GI *guaranteed interruptible.*

GNI *guaranteed non-interuptible.*

HAZID *hazard identification.*

HAZOP *hazard and operability.*

HEART *Human Error Assessment and Reduction Technique.*

HEP *human error probability.*

HFIP *human factors integration plan.*

HLW *high-level waste.*

HMI *human machine interface.*

HMS *hazard management strategy.*

HPLV *human performance limiting value.*

HSE Health and Safety Executive.

HVAC heating, ventilation and air-conditioning.

IAEA International Atomic Energy Agency.

ICRP International Commission on Radiological Protection.

IEF *initiating event frequency*.

IPR *independent peer review*.

IRR17 The Ionising Radiations Regulations 2017.

ITER International Thermonuclear Experimental Reactor.

JET Joint European Torus.

LC *licence condition*.

LD *lethal dose$_{50/60}$*.

LFE *learning from experience*.

LL *legal limit*.

LLW *low-level waste*.

LOLER Lifting Operations and Lifting Equipment Regulations.

LTPR *long-term periodic review*.

MAC *malicious aircraft crash*.

MAGIC MERV mass, absorption, geometry, interaction, concentration, moderation, enrichment, reflection and volume.

ME+I mechanical, electrical and instrumentation.

MFD *mechanical flow diagram*.

MHD *mechanical handling diagram*.

MI *maintenance instruction*.

MOD Ministry of Defence.

NCRP National Council on Radiation Protection and Measurements.

NIA *Nuclear Installations Act*.

NRW Natural Resources Wales.

NSL *nuclear site licence*.

OA *operating assumption.*

OBE *operating basis earthquake.*

OI *operating instruction.*

ONR Office for Nuclear Regulation.

OR *operating rule.*

P+ID *piping and instrument diagram.*

PACSR *pre-active commissioning safety report.*

PCSR *pre-construction safety report.*

PFD *process flow diagram.*

PICSR *pre-inactive commissioning safety report.*

PMS *plant maintenance schedule.*

POCO *post-operative clean-out.*

PPE *personal protective equipment.*

PSA *probabilistic safety analysis.*

PSR *preliminary safety report.*

PTI *proof test interval.*

QA *quality assurance.*

QMS *quality management system.*

R+D *research and development.*

R2P2 Reducing Risks, Protecting People.

REPPIR Radiation (Emergency Preparedness and Public Information) Regulations.

RF *release fraction.*

RGP *relevant good practice.*

RPA *Radiation Protection Adviser.*

SAA *severe accident analysis.*

SAP Safety Assessment Principle.

SEPA Scottish Environment Protection Agency.

SF *safety feature.*

SFAIRP *so far as is reasonably practicable.*

SFR *safety function requirement.*

SI International System of Units.

SM *safety mechanism.*

SOE *safe operating envelope.*

SQEP *suitably qualified and experienced person.*

SSC *structure, system or component.*

STP standard temperature and pressure.

TAD *target audience description.*

TAG Technical Assessment Guide.

THERP *Technique for Human Error Rate Prediction.*

TNT trinitrotoluene.

TOR Tolerability of Risk.

TRA three-letter acronym.

UPS *uninterruptible power supply.*

VFD *ventilation flow diagram.*

pfd *probability of failure on demand.*

UK United Kingdom.

US United States.

Index